Drama,
Baby

By Jamie Brittain

It's the final rehearsals before the practical A-level Theatre Studies exam, and Neil wants everything to be just perfect. Two competing groups of students attempt to achieve that ever elusive 'A' grade, soon finding the competing forces of sex, alcohol and Artaud threatening to destroy their hopes of a good university place. As egos clash and new relationships are formed and broken, *Drama, Baby* goes to the heart of what it means to perform, and what it's like when the handbags and gladrags are stripped away.

Age suitability: 15+

Cast size:
8 main characters plus two choruses

Jamie Brittain was born in Edinburgh in 1985 and grew up mostly in the Lake District and Bristol. He created the teen drama series *Skins*, which he wrote for throughout its seven-year run, picking up a BAFTA along the way, and has since written for the Channel 4 show *Dates*. *Drama, Baby* is his first piece of theatre.

Characters

Neil
Kate
Dave
Emily
Mark
Amy
Lisa
Derek
A Chorus

Scene One

Darkness.

Then, thunder and lightning, impossibly loud and bright.

'O Fortuna' from Carmina Burana *plays.*

A **Chorus** *appears.*

The following to be pitched at a level of complete hysteria.

Chorus   Darkness is coming. Darkness is coming. Darkness is coming.

They continue chanting as **Neil** *steps forward.*

Neil   Do you fear the dark? Do you fear the endless night? Do you fear the coming terror?

Chorus   We fear the dark. We fear the endless night. We fear the coming terror. Darkness is coming. Darkness is coming. Darkness is coming.

Dave *steps forward.*

Dave   Do you hunger for the light? Do you despair at the emptiness? Is all hope lost?

Chorus   We hunger for the light. We despair at the emptiness. All hope is lost. Darkness is coming. Darkness is coming. Darkness is coming.

Emily *steps forward. Drops to her knees. Appeals to the* **Chorus**.

Emily   Don't you understand? It doesn't have to be this way! There is hope! There is light! There is love!

Chorus   We understand. It must be this way. There is no hope. There is no light. There is no love. Darkness is coming.

Emily (*covering her ears*)   No! It's not true!

Kate *steps forward. Points.*

Kate   She denies the darkness.

Chorus   She denies the darkness. The darkness cannot be denied.

Emily   No!

Neil   She must be cleansed. She must know fear. She must know darkness.

Emily   Please . . . please don't . . .

Neil   Cleanse!

Chorus   Cleanse! Cleanse! Cleanse! Cleanse!

The **Chorus** *produce knives and start to advance rhythmically on* **Emily***.*

Emily   Leave me alone! Please!

Chorus   Cleanse! Cleanse! Cleanse!

Neil   It must be done!

Dave   It must be done!

Kate   It must be done!

Chorus   Cleanse! Cleanse! Cleanse!

Emily   No! No! No!

They surround her. **Emily** *screams. The* **Chorus** *raise their knives. Then* **Emily** *breaks off her scream.*

Emily   I'm sorry, Neil, can we stop for a second?

Neil *looks towards the back of the room, and draws his hand across his throat. The music abruptly cuts off. He strides towards* **Emily***, looking annoyed.*

Neil   What is it now, Emily?

Emily   It's just . . . do you think it's a bit much?

Neil   What do you mean?

Emily   I mean, the opera, the thunder and lightning, the knives . . .

Neil Yes?

They're all looking at her.

Emily Well . . .

Neil Go on.

Emily It's only A-level Theatre Studies. (*Note: feel free to change exam for age / location.*)

Neil *sighs heavily.*

Neil Take five, everyone.

The **Chorus** *slowly disperse through the following, leaving* **Neil**, **Emily**, **Dave** *and* **Kate** *standing in a little group.*

Neil Now. What's really the problem here? You don't like my script?

Emily No! It's great! I love the script.

Dave It's a great script, Neil. Great script.

Neil Cheers, Dave.

Emily All I'm saying is . . . it's so intense. A murder on page one. I mean, how do you follow that?

Kate (*leaving through a script*) It's the orgy next, isn't it?

Neil Thanks, Kate. That's right. Act One, Scene Two. The orgy in the Houses of Parliament.

Kate Love it. Love the orgy.

They all look at her.

In the script, I mean. Not in general.

Emily Murder, sex. And that's just Act One.

Kate It's done in tableau though. So it's not as bad.

Dave Yeah. Tableau sex. Best kind.

Emily I'm just saying –

Neil   Look. We are performing this next Monday. You've had plenty of time to raise any objections. Now unless you're suggesting I rewrite the entire thing from scratch –

Emily   I'm not. I'm just saying –

Neil   What?

Emily   Mr Henderson said we just have to tick the boxes, and we'll get an 'A'.

Kate   That's true.

Emily   Look, I've got the examiner requirements here . . .

She produces a piece of paper and reads.

It says that 'candidates must devise a piece of theatre in a selected performance style, which demonstrates their knowledge, understanding and practical competence in incorporating features of that style into their piece'.

Neil   Yeah. So?

Emily   So what style are we? We need one.

Dave   What styles are there?

Emily *turns a page.*

Emily   There's loads: epic, docu-drama, Brechtian, Grotowski, physical theatre . . .

Neil   Oh please.

Kate   Which style are we then?

Dave   We're a bit Brecht, I think. Maybe a bit physical.

Emily   What's Brecht again?

Dave   That's where it's like, really bad, but for some reason also good.

Emily   Oh yeah. *Verfremdungseffekt.*

Kate   What does that mean?

Emily   No idea.

Dave   Is Stanislavsky a style? Or is it just a bloke?

Kate   Method acting.

Dave   What's that?

Kate   That's where you act like a dick for the entire time, then win an Oscar.

Neil   We're *our* style. We don't need to conform to some fidgety old fart's conception of what makes good theatre. We create as we go. We're original. And in my book that counts for a lot more than ticking boxes.

Emily   Okay. But . . .

Four people appear: **Mark**, **Derek**, **Amy** *and* **Lisa**. *They stand a little way off, waiting.*

Mark   Are you guys finished? We need the room.

Neil *holds a hand up, irritably.*

Neil   In a minute. Emily. You were saying?

Emily   Just . . . Maybe we could take it down a notch.

Neil (*aghast*)   'Take it down a notch'? 'Take it down a notch'?

Dave   Uh-oh.

Neil   Did Shakespeare take it down a notch? Did Beckett? Did Pinter? Well? Did they?

Emily   . . . No . . .

Amy   Could you hurry up . . . we really need to practise.

Neil (*once again aghast*)   Rehearse!

He turns to **Emily**.

Neil   It's not supposed to be comfortable. It's not supposed to be easy. If you can't handle it, then I suggest you go and work with the other group. I believe they're doing a simply charming play about homelessness or something. Do you want that?

Emily (*quietly*)   No . . .

Neil   I'm sorry? I didn't hear you.

Emily   I said no.

Neil   Good. (*Turns to* **Kate** *and* **Dave**.) You two got anything to say?

Dave   No, boss.

Kate   Nope.

Neil   Good.

Derek   Guys . . .

Neil *walks away towards the other group, holding his hands up.*

Neil   Okay okay. We're done, we're done. Have you –

He stops. **Emily** *has run to* **Mark** *and kisses him long and hard.* **Neil** *watches.*

Derek   Eeeew. Guys, can we keep the PDAs to an absolute minimum, please?

Emily   Sorry, Derek.

Mark   Yeah, sorry . . . I just can't keep my hands off her.

He tickles her. She squeals and twists in his arms.

Emily (*laughing*)   Stop it, stop it. (*Serious.*) No, seriously, get off.

She moves away from him. He lets her go. A beat of silence. **Neil** *is staring at* **Mark**.

Mark   What you looking at?

Neil   Nothing.

Derek *grabs* **Neil** *and cuddles him.*

Derek   Oh, leave Neil alone. He's a sensitive soul. Isn't that right?

Neil *struggles away from* **Derek***.*

Lisa   We really need to start.

Kate   What's your play called again?

Amy   *Private Parts.*

Dave   Sorry, 'Private' . . . ?

Amy   *Parts.*

Dave   That's some title.

Neil   Yeah, why not go the whole hog and call it 'dicks and fannies'?

Amy   It's an exploration of modern gender roles, focusing on the way we force people into strict gender roles based on performativity of homogeneous societal norms.

Neil *makes a 'hmph' noise. Everyone looks at him, but decides to ignore.*

Kate   Sounds . . . political.

Amy   It is.

Emily   What style is it?

All   Feminist.

Neil *suppresses another laugh. Everyone looks at him.*

Lisa   You got something to say, Neil?

Neil   Sorry? Oh, no, nothing. It's just that –

Amy   What?

Neil   Well, I just think your thinking is clearly disordered.

Amy   Disordered?

Neil   Performativity of gender roles? Load of nonsense. All these men you claim to be repressing you and the rest of humankind. Who brought them up? Women. Mothers, grandmothers, aunts, nannies. Women. There's no such thing as patriarchy. It's *mat*riarchy that's the problem.

A beat of stunned silence.

Amy   Wow. That is wrong is so many ways, and offensive in so many other ways.

Neil   Tell me I'm wrong. I tell you, this society has got it all wrong. Women aren't repressed, they aren't discriminated against –

Dave   Er, maybe shut up now, Neil?

Neil   – they're free to do whatever they like.

Lisa   Damn right.

She steps forward and grabs him by the bollocks. He squeals.

Lisa   And this woman is saying, 'Shut up, sod off, and let us practise.' Okay?

Neil *doesn't say anything. She squeezes harder, making him squeak again.*

Lisa   Okay?

Neil *nods. She releases him. He drops to the floor, clutching himself.*

Lisa   Now. Off you sod. All of you.

Emily *kisses* **Mark***, and exits with* **Kate***.* **Dave** *helps* **Neil** *to his feet as* **Lisa***,* **Derek***,* **Mark** *and* **Amy** *move away.*

Dave   You okay, buddy?

Neil *is looking across at* **Lisa***, talking with her group.*

Neil   I think I'm in love.

Darkness.

Scene Two

Darkness.

'100 Ways to Be a Good Girl' by Skunk Anansie starts playing.

Lights up on **Mark**, **Lisa**, **Derek** *and* **Amy** *standing in a row. As they sing, the two men change into women's clothes (dresses, hats, skirts), the women into men's clothes (jeans, T-shirts, hats).*

Lisa (*singing*)
 I caused a major war, just by talking . . .

Mark
 You flew into a rage, cos that's everything you know . . .

Derek
 Childhood of violence filled with heartache . . .

Amy
 I flew into a rage, cos that's everything I know . . .

All
 I know a hundred ways to be a good girl,
 A hundred ways, my willingness to please,
 I know one hundred ways to be a good girl,
 Still I'm alone, I'm alone, I'm alone, I'm alone,

 I'm alone, I'm alone, I'm alone, I'm alone . . .

They circle each other, then spin out, propelled by unseen forces into different corners of the stage. As the music continues, they perform a pantomime/dance drama, based on the lyrics. Maybe a spotlight could pick out each performer in turn. This should be meticulously choreographed as, in contrast to the other group's piece, it's quite good. We let this continue for a while, and soon find them rushing across the stage.

Neil *appears, frolicking and dancing across the stage, perhaps waving a scarf, Pan's People style, mocking them. He is wearing a bra over his T-shirt.*

Neil (*singing*)
I've got a lovely bunch of coconuts
There they are, all standing in a row . . .

Lisa *nearly crashes into him as she moves across the stage.*

Lisa   Ah come on, man, what are you doing?

The music cuts off. **Neil** *continues dancing and singing in the heavy silence.*

Neil
'Big ones, small ones, some as big as your head,
Give them a twist a flick of the wrist,
That's what the showman said. Oh!
I've got a lovely bunch of coconuts . . . '

They are all watching him. He trails off.

Neil   What? Oh come on, don't look at me like that.

Derek   What are you doing?

Neil   Oh you know. I was watching from the side and was moved to join in. Or, how would you put it, Amy, 'confirm my gender role in a structuralist pantomime of femininity'.

Mark   Why are you wearing a bra?

Neil   For . . . fun?

Lisa *approaches him, examines the bra.*

Lisa   Hey, that's my bra.

Neil   Is it? Are you sure?

Lisa   What the hell are you doing wearing my bra?

Neil   Oh, this is *your* bra? I just found it.

Amy   Where?

Neil   Oh, just . . . around.

Mark   He's been going through our stuff. Not cool, man. Not cool at all.

Neil Oh, chill your boots. I didn't go through your stuff. This was just on a pile of clothes when we came in to change. I saw it, thought, what the hell . . .

Lisa Take it off. Now.

Neil *looks at her. She's serious.*

Neil Take it off?

Lisa Take. It. Off.

Neil Right. Okay.

He reaches behind him and attempts to take off the bra. But he struggles with the catch, and can't get it off. The others just watch.

Hmm. I seem to be having some trouble here . . . Ugh, come on, you little . . . If one of you wouldn't mind . . . wouldn't mind . . . aaargh!

Kate, **Emily** *and* **Dave** *all enter to see* **Neil** *struggling.*

Dave What the hell is going on?

Neil *is now ridiculously contorted.*

Neil Ah, Dave, hello. I seem to be having a little trouble with . . .

Derek Oh for God's sake.

He strides forward, reaches out and undoes the bra in one swift movement.

There you go.

He tosses the bra to **Lisa***, who catches it, and stuffs it away.*

Neil Thanks, Derek. Where did you learn to do that?

Derek *smiles enigmatically*

Kate How did your practice go?

Neil Rehearsal!

Amy (*ignoring him*)   It was going fine, until Neil ruined our final run-through.

Neil   Yeah, well, we've booked the room from three, so if you lot could just . . .

He whistles, and points, indicating 'piss off'.

Lisa   Yeah, alright. I think we've done it to death anyway. Just give us a second to pack up.

They pack up their props through the following.

Derek   So you think you're ready for the exam tomorrow?

Kate   I hope so. All a bit scary!

Amy   You'll be fine.

Kate   It's just the idea of doing it with the examiner sitting right there. Gives me the willies.

Amy   You're really good.

Kate (*flustered*)   Oh. Thanks. So are you. Good, I mean. The play's good. I mean. You know what I mean.

Amy   Yeah. Thanks.

They share a smile.

Mark   You still coming tonight?

Emily   Yeah.

Mark   Should be a good one. Check it out, my brother bought it for me for finishing school

He produces a large bottle of whisky. They all take it in.

Emily   Shit, put that away. What if Mr Henderson sees?

Mark (*pocketing it*)   Chill. He'd probably be into it. I reckon he was a proper rocker back in the day.

Neil   Oh please. Nigel would never drink to excess.

Dave   'Nigel'? What's with 'Nigel'? Call him Mr Henderson, you bummer.

Derek *clears his throat.*

Dave   Oh, sorry, Derek. Forgot you were here.

Derek   No problem.

Dave   So what's going on tonight?

Lisa   Big party at Mark's. End of exams and that – there's only tomorrow left, everyone else has finished.

Dave   Oh cool.

Amy   We'll all be there.

Mark   You're welcome to come too, Dave. Kate, you too. And . . .

*He looks at **Neil**, who waits expectantly.*

Mark   . . . Yeah.

Silence.

Derek   Oh come on. Neil can come too, right, Mark?

Mark   Well . . .

*He looks at **Emily**, who gives him a pleading look.*

Mark   I suppose so.

Neil   Well, yeah, I might drop by, yeah. I've got friends coming by, but yeah, sure, maybe later.

Amy   Riiight.

Neil   Will you be there, Lisa?

She gives him a look.

Lisa   I might be.

Neil   Interesting. Interesting. Maybe you and me can get some one on one time.

Lisa   Ew. In your dreams. Right. Ready?

They finish packing up and begin to exit.

Mark   See y'all tonight.

He kisses **Emily**. *He,* **Lisa**, **Amy** *and* **Derek** *all exit, ad libbing farewells.*

Emily   We'll go and get changed.

She and **Kate** *exit, leaving* **Dave** *and* **Neil** *alone on stage.*

Dave   So you like Lisa now?

Neil   Yeah. Girl's got spirit. A feisty one she is.

Dave   Wow. Yoda talk. Must be love. But I thought you liked . . .

He lowers his voice. **Emily** *appears on the other side of the stage, pulling on a T-shirt.* **Dave** *nods at her.*

Neil   What?

Dave (*whispering*)   I thought you liked Emily.

Neil *smiles, holds his fingers up and waggles them. Then mimes inserting them into something.*

Dave   What the hell does that mean?

Neil *does it again.*

Neil   Many fingers . . . many pies . . .

Dave *stares at him.*

Dave   You're disgusting.

He walks away to talk to **Kate** *and* **Emily**. **Derek** *reappears onstage.*

Derek   Hey.

Neil   Hey. Did you forget something?

Derek   No . . . actually I wanted to talk to you.

Neil   Oh yeah?

Derek   Yeah, well. This party tonight. I thought you might . . . I'm sorry, this is a little awkward.

Neil   What?

Derek   I thought. You might want to go with me.

He trails off. **Neil** *stares at him, uncomprehending.*

Neil   Oh. Right. You mean, you and me . . . like a date? Together?

Derek   Yeah. I've been watching you from afar and have fallen deeply and desperately in love with you.

Neil   Are you having me on?

Derek   Yes, Neil. I'm having you on. Though it may surprise you to learn, not every gay man spends his nights lusting after straight boys with narcissist complexes. No, I just thought it might be nice.

Neil   Oh. Okay then.

Derek *smiles and starts to move away. But* **Neil** *stops him.*

Neil   Derek. Why did you –

Derek   What?

Neil   Why did you ask me that? Like, instead of the others?

Derek   I'm just being nice, Neil. There's no ulterior motive.

Neil   Oh. Okay.

Derek *starts to move off.*

Neil   It's just. Well. If you're not in love with me . . .

Derek   Which I'm not. Hard to believe I know.

Neil   Yeah. If you're not . . . that . . . then why ask me?

Derek   Cos. Well. I don't mean this in a bad way. But you seem a bit lonely. You don't seem to have any friends.

Neil   Oh. Well. Why would I think that would be bad?

Derek   Neil, come on. We've known each other almost all our lives. Our parents know each other. We've never been best mates, but . . . I know you. And through all that time you've never really had any friends.

Neil *hesitates, then counts them off on his fingers.*

Neil   Dave. Kate. Emily.

Derek   They're just schoolmates. When was the last time you spoke to them outside of school, outside of drama? Drama's weird. You get lost in this world, putting on a play. You get caught up in it all. But when it's over. You just go back to the way it was. It's, like, fleeting, you know. Dave. Kate. Emily. After this is done, they'll all be gone.

Silence. They stare at each other.

Neil   You know . . . ?

Derek   What?

Neil   Nothing.

Derek   No, go on.

Neil   Well. You're a nice guy, Derek. But if I were gay, and I'm not, but if I were, and I'm not, but if I were, I wouldn't be so obvious about it. It wouldn't be the most interesting thing about me. I wouldn't talk such shit all the time. And I'd be more than just a faggot.

Derek *punches him hard in the face.* **Neil** *goes straight down to the floor, clutching his nose.*

Derek   You pretentious little dick. I should fucking kill you.

He starts to kick **Neil** *in the stomach, so* **Emily**, **Dave** *and* **Kate** *rush over to pull him off.*

Dave   Enough, Derek. Enough!

Derek *pulls free of them.*

Kate   What the hell is going on?

Derek *looks down at* **Neil***, then quickly walks offstage.*

Neil   Yeah, that's right, flounce off like a little girl! Ow, my face . . . my bloody face!

Emily   What was that all about?

Kate   What did you say to him?

Neil   Nothing!

Dave   You must have said something!

Neil   Who knows? Drama, baby. Just drama.

Darkness.

Scene Three

Mark*'s house party. This should be staged as swiftly and creatively as possible, moving from scene to scene with lighting and music changes as needed.*

Loud music plays.

Mark*,* **Emily***,* **Lisa** *and* **Amy** *are sitting in a vague circle drinking from cans. Other members of the* **Chorus** *fill out the stage as partygoers. They are all watching* **Lisa** *down a can of beer.*

All   Chug chug chug chug!

Lisa *finishes one can. Then immediately opens another and starts to knock that one back too. They all cheer when she finishes. She holds the can above her head.*

Lisa   Fuck yeah!

Mark   You're a monster, girl. Okay, now you, Emily.

Emily   I'd rather not.

Lisa   Go on . . . gets you good and pissed.

She hiccups and passes **Emily** *a can.*

Emily   But the exam is tomorrow. I don't want to be hungover.

Mark *takes the can from her and opens it for her, then hands it back.*

Mark   It's not until the afternoon. You'll be alright by then. Full English and a Red Bull, you'll be fine.

Emily *looks at can. Starts to take a sip, then pauses.*

Emily   I really don't want to.

Amy   Don't make her, Mark.

Mark   Come on! We've all done it! Chug chug chug chug . . .

All join in chanting.

All   Chug chug chug . . .

Emily   Okay! Okay.

Emily *sighs, then chugs the can of beer in one, with effort. Everyone cheers.* **Emily** *burps, her hand to her mouth. Everyone laughs.*

Mark   That's my girl.

He kisses her on the cheek. She doesn't react.

The doorbell goes. **Lisa** *stands.*

Lisa   I'll get it.

Mark   Now . . . who wants a sip of my magic bottle of chuckles?

He produces the bottle of whisky. Everyone crowds round, and he pours for them all. **Amy** *and* **Emily** *abstain.*

Mark   Hey, don't crowd me, fans. Amy, don't you want some?

Amy   I'm not drinking that.

Mark   Go on. It'll loosen you up. It's not strong at all. It's only – (*Reading the label.*) Sixty-five per cent.

Amy   God, you sound like the dude at the beginning of an episode of those films they show at school.

Mark   What do you mean?

Amy   You know, the plausible nice guy out to corrupt the mind and bodies of innocent young women.

Mark   Thanks.

Amy   It's not a good thing. I'll just have a beer.

Mark   Ems? How about you?

Emily (*swallowing, slightly sickly*)   Yeah okay, beer too then.

Mark *turns away to get them a beer.* **Lisa** *appears with* **Neil** *and* **Dave** *in tow.* **Neil** *is holding a plastic bag, and has a plaster on his nose.*

Lisa   Look who I found.

Mark (*handing the girls their beers*)   Oh, great.

Neil   I brought wine.

He pulls out a bottle of wine. A random reveller snatches it out of his hand almost immediately and disappears. **Neil** *calls after him.*

Neil   Be sure you chill that, it's absolute piss at room temperature. And make sure you serve it in a large glass, helps enliven the nose.

But they're long gone.

Dave   I think they're gone, mate.

Neil   Nine bloody quid that cost me. Philistines will probably mix it with lemonade.

Lisa   Guys, get over here. We're drinking like it's the end of the universe . . .

She hands them both a beer. **Dave** *immediately opens his and takes a sip.* **Neil** *is studying the can.*

Mark   Hey what happened to your face?

Neil (*not looking up*)   I walked into a door.

Lisa   Not what we heard.

They all laugh. **Neil** *is still reading.*

Mark   You gonna drink that or review it for *The Times*?

Neil *looks at him. Then opens the can and takes a sip. Everyone cheers again.*

Lights. Music. The scene rearranges. Everyone is in the middle of the room, doing a loose, synchronised dance routine. They are all off their heads, drugged up and drunk as skunks. They keep bashing into each other. **Emily** *and* **Amy** *stand apart from them, watching.*

Emily   Jesus.

Amy   Yeah.

Emily   Look at Neil. Can and a half of lager and he thinks he's in Diversity.

Neil *is dancing like a loon, bashing into people.* **Emily** *and* **Amy** *laugh.*

Emily   Still though. That beer's gone right to my head. I feel totally messed up.

Amy   Yeah, me too.

Emily   You don't think . . .

Kate *has appeared on the other side of the stage, looking sober and alone. She clutches a bottle of wine.*

Amy   Kate's here! Woo! Hey, Kate, how you doing?

She leaves **Emily** *alone as the rushes over to* **Kate** *and hugs her.* **Kate** *responds, slightly awkwardly.*

Lights, music. The scene rearranges again. Everyone is dancing, but this time much less coherently. The music is intense, fast dance music. A drunken **Neil** *emerges, jabbering with an even drunker* **Lisa**.

Neil   I mean in your play the influence of a number of thinkers is clear. I can see Judith Butler, Eve Sedgwick, Sylvia Plath. Do you know what I mean?

Lisa   Yeah. Sylvia Plath. Got you.

Neil   Do you want to kiss me?

Lisa (*thinks*)   Okay!

She grabs him and pulls him into a kiss. Then she separates.

Wait, what am I doing? Why am I kissing you?

Neil   Off the top of my head, I can think of six, no seven main arguments for . . . One –

Lisa   Shut up.

She kisses him again. They remain in an embrace like that, together on the stage, snogging, for now, as the revellers move round them.

Lights, music. The scene rearranges again. Now everyone is singing a drunken song, some with shirts off, or over their heads. **Mark** *and* **Emily** *emerge out of the chaos.*

Emily   I can't believe you did that!

Mark   Babe, chill, it's all good, yeah.

Emily   You just . . . put whisky in my drink! I feel absolutely off my face.

Mark   Just go with it. Don't fight it.

Emily   I don't want to just go with it. I don't want to be on it at all!

Mark   Come here, kiss me.

He pulls at her.

Emily   Ugh, you're no use. You're totally out of it.

Mark   I spiked Amy's drink too. Look at her, she seems to be having a good time.

They look across the stage to where **Amy** *and* **Kate** *are dancing together.*

Emily   I'm going home.

She starts to walk away. **Mark** *pulls her back.*

Mark   No, babe, c'mon.

She shakes him off.

Emily   No, don't touch me!

She runs off and exits.

Lights, music. The scene rearranges itself. Now everyone is lying or sitting on the floor, drunk as skunks. **Kate** *and* **Amy** *sit in front,* **Amy**'s *head in* **Kate**'s *lap. The music is mellow, romantic.*

Kate   I wish I was as smart as you.

Amy   You are.

Kate   I'm not.

Amy   You're smarter if anything. I've seen you in English. You just sit there, thinking all these deep thoughts about everything.

Kate   How do you know what I'm thinking? I might be thinking about *Hollyoaks*.

Amy *sits up and turns to face* **Kate**. *They are very close.*

Amy   No, I can tell, I can tell. You're thinking all this deep shit. Like . . . My mum would say you carry the weight of the world on your shoulders. But you shouldn't. You're so smart, and pretty and . . .

Kate *kisses her.* **Amy** *pulls away. Then goes back in again. The music gets louder and louder and then suddenly cuts out. Silence.*

Music, lights. Morning. Everyone's asleep. The music is off. Dawn light floods the stage. After a moment, **Derek** *enters, gingerly stepping over bodies and empty cans.*

Derek Jesus.

He pauses at **Amy** *and* **Kate***, asleep, entwined in each other's arms.*

Derek Phew . . . didn't see that coming.

The sound of a toilet flushing. **Dave** *appears, wiping his hands on his jeans. He pauses when he sees* **Derek***.*

Dave Oh. Alright?

Derek Hi.

Dave Missed you last night.

Derek I wasn't here. Decided to stayed home, learn my lines. You know. Was it a good one?

Dave *shrugs.*

Dave Everyone was pretty out of it. I stuck to beer, so I'm alright. Had a nice sleep in his mum's bed. She has interesting taste in wall hangings. Where are his rentals anyway?

Derek Grand Canaria, I think.

Dave Nice . . . What time is it?

Derek It's past eleven.

Dave Shit. The exam is at two.

Derek I know. No one turned up for registration today. So I thought I'd pop by. Was Neil here?

Dave Yeah. Don't know where he's got to though.

Pause.

Dave Derek. It was shitty what he did.

Derek It was shitty what *I* did.

Dave Yeah . . . And, also pretty funny.

They share a smile.

Derek   You're a good guy, Dave. Now. To business.

He approaches **Mark***, asleep with his hands down his trousers. Kneels down beside him. Shakes him gently.*

Derek   Mark . . . Mark . . . Mark!

Mark *awakens with a start.*

Mark   What? What is it?

Derek   Time to wake up. You need to take a shower . . .

Mark *stands abruptly, scattering cans, invading* **Derek***'s personal space.*

Derek (*smelling him*)   Ugh, you *really* need to take a shower.

Mark *looks around, a bit deranged.*

Mark   What time is it?

Dave   Past eleven.

Mark   Oh bollocks. Everyone, wake up! Wake up!

He moves around the room frantically, waking people.

Come on! Wake up!

Throughout the following, everyone slowly pulls themselves together and exits.

Mark   Amy, wake up!

Amy *wakes up, arms still entwined with* **Kate***'s.*

Amy   Shit. Did we oversleep?

Mark   Massively. Come on, we've got to get to college.

Amy *extracts herself from the still-sleeping* **Kate***'s arms. Stands up, staggers.*

Amy   Ah fuck. I think I'm still drunk.

Mark   I spiked your drink. With the whisky. That's probably why.

Amy   What?

Mark   Emily's too. I don't know where she is. Shit, I've got to clear up. My parents are back tonight. Bin bags . . . bin bags . . .

He exits. **Amy** *stands, stunned.*

Derek   You okay?

Amy   I can't believe he did that. Spiked my . . .

Derek   Didn't make a fool out of yourself, did you?

Amy *looks down at* **Kate** *for a long moment. Then hurriedly heads for the door.*

Amy   Excuse me.

She exits. **Kate** *is waking up.*

Kate (*still asleep*)   Amy?

Dave   You just missed her.

Kate   Oh . . . okay . . .

She looks at her watch.

Oh . . . shit.

She stands up.

Mark *reappears with a bin bag, and starts clearing up all the beer cans in the now empty room.*

Mark   You all gotta make a move. I need to clear up.

Derek   I'll give you a hand.

He helps him clear up.

Dave   Okay, well . . . See you later.

Kate   Hold on, I'll come with you.

They exit, leaving **Mark** *and* **Derek** *alone, clearing up.* **Neil** *and* **Lisa** *enter the room stealthily, holding hands, but freeze when they see* **Mark** *and* **Derek***. They drop hands just as* **Derek** *and* **Mark** *turn to see them.*

Mark   Where have you two been?

Neil   I . . . er . . .

Lisa   We just . . . er . . .

Neil   The thing is . . . er . . .

A long moment of heavy silence as **Derek** *and* **Mark** *stare at the unlikely couple. Then, darkness.*

Scene Four

Backstage at the performance.

The **Chorus** *are onstage, in costume, waiting.*

Dave *and* **Kate** *are waiting in front as* **Neil** *enters, drinking a bottle of water.*

Kate   There you are! Cutting it a bit fine, don't you think? We're on in five minutes.

Neil   I know, I know. I'm sorry. I had a . . . thing.

Dave   What sort of thing?

Neil   I'll tell you about it later. Is everyone ready?

Kate   Everyone except Emily.

Neil   Where is she?

Kate   Breaking up with Mark. He spiked her drink last night.

Neil   Wow . . . that's . . .

Dave   Yeah. Heavy.

Neil   Have you had a look out there yet?

Dave   Yeah. Your mum and dad are in the front row.

Neil   Typical.

He moves to the back of the stage and looks through a pair of curtains.

Oh yes, there they are. Hello, Mummy, hello, Daddy. Which one's the examiner?

Dave   The woman who looks a bit like a chicken. Sitting next to Nigel – I mean, Mr Henderson.

Neil   Ah yes. I see her. Excellent.

He turns back to them.

Think you're ready?

Kate   It was really stupid getting drunk last night. Really really stupid. This stuff is important. And we're going to do it with a hangover.

Neil   Hangover? Pshaw!

Dave   Pshaw?

Neil   Never had one myself. I hear they're intense.

Kate *(clutching her head)*   Ugh, they are. I just threw up in the girls' loo.

Emily *enters.*

Neil   Emily. Finally.

Emily   Sorry.

Neil   You can't muck around with this stuff. This counts. Do you want to go to Cardiff University? Cos that's where you're heading if we mess this up.

Emily   What's wrong with Cardiff?

Neil   Oh please.

Kate   Are you okay?

Emily   I'm fine. No really, I'm fine. Dickhead had it coming, right?

Neil   Right. No use crying over spilt dickheads. Got to get on with it. And we're on in . . . two minutes.

He turns to the **Chorus***.*

Neil   Right. You lot. You all got your knives?

The **Chorus** *produce their knives.*

Neil   Excellent. Now. I'm not one for speeches . . .

The **Chorus** *all groan.*

Neil   But I just want to say . . . after all the hard work, after all the tears, fallings out, affairs, bust-ups, screaming tantrums – you can put your knives away now – after everything we've been through you must remember one thing, and one thing alone. That it is all worth it. Why? Because you . . . are . . . actors. You are the vanguard, existing at the very zenith between fact and fiction. You are actors. The chosen few. Now, go out there and make me proud.

The **Chorus** *nod and begin to shuffle off.*

Neil   Okay. Was expecting applause then, but . . . okay. Ready?

Dave   Yes.

Emily   I think so.

Kate *(shouting)*   I was born ready! Sorry, I'm nervous.

Neil   Good luck everyone. On we go.

They make to move off, but **Lisa** *appears on the other side of the stage.* **Neil** *glances round.*

Neil   Oh. Lisa.

Dave   You coming?

Neil   One second.

He walks across to **Lisa** *as* **Dave**, **Kate** *and* **Emily** *exit.*

Neil   So . . .

Lisa   So . . .

Neil   Last night.

Lisa   Yeah. Last night.

Neil   I'm sorry I had to leave in such a rush. There were things I wanted to say to you. Things I've been burning to say ever since I laid eyes on your . . . sweet face.

Lisa   Er, yeah, me too. Listen, Neil . . .

Neil   Thing is, I'm a *little* pressed for time right now so if they could wait a *teeny* bit longer.

Lisa   No, Neil. I need to talk to you right now.

Neil   Right now?

Lisa   Yeah.

Kate (*off*)   Neil!

Neil (*shouting to off*)   I'll be there in a minute. So. Last night.

Lisa   Yeah. Last night. It was . . .

Neil   Amazing.

Lisa (*unsure*)   Er, yeah. But I think, Neil, it'll be best if we just stay friends. And not, you know, complicate things.

Neil   Oh.

Lisa   Derek and Mark know, but they've promised to keep quiet. I don't want you to tell anyone else. You haven't told anyone, have you?

Neil   No. But why?

Lisa   Why what?

Neil   Why can't we celebrate our love?

Lisa   Love? That wasn't love. I was just really drunk.
And . . . Oh, what am I doing? I can't lie to you . . .

Neil (*hopeful*)   Oh?

Dave (*off*)   Neil! Mr Henderson wants to start!

Neil (*screaming*)   In a minute, Nigel! You were saying
something about lying.

Lisa   Yeah. I don't want to be your girlfriend. But I also
don't want to be your friend either.

Neil   Right.

Lisa   The truth is, I can't stand you. You're a moron.
A complete cretin. I don't think I've ever met someone so
insensitive, arrogant and completely up his own arse.

Neil   Right.

Lisa   And? And nothing. That's it. I hate you. And
everything you stand for. So I won't be shagging you again.
Last night was the worst mistake of my life. I will live with it
until I die. Okay?

Neil   Um. Okay. So, definitely no chance of more sex then?

Lisa *sighs.*

Lisa   Good luck with the play, Neil. You completely
talentless, waste-of-space tosser.

She walks away. Pauses.

And you're terrible at sex.

Neil *stands there, alone. A long, long silence.*

Emily (*off*)   Neil!

Neil   Yeah . . . coming . . . coming . . .

*He moves to the exit. Pauses. Then goes. After a beat, thunder and
lightning and 'O Fortuna' starts playing. We now see the front of the
stage. The cast are arranged as before.*

Chorus   Darkness is coming. Darkness is coming. Darkness is coming.

They continue chanting as **Neil** *steps forward. But this time he pauses, for a beat too long. The rest of the cast stare at him imperiously.*

Neil   Do you . . . do you . . .

He's lost the line. The rest of the cast exchange panicked glances. But then he's back in the room, delivering his line with terrible ferocity.

Do you fear the dark? Do you fear the endless night? Do you fear the coming terror?

Darkness.

Scene Five

Backstage. Later.

Derek, **Mark**, **Lisa** *and* **Amy** *are getting ready to go onstage. They speak in hushed whispers, as the show is still going on behind them.*

Mark *is peeking through the curtains.*

Derek   They still on?

Mark   Yeah. Just finishing.

Derek   Us next.

Lisa   Yeah. You guys nervous?

Amy   Petrified. And my head feels like someone's been kicking it with a pair of Doc Marten boots for five hours. Thanks for that, Mark.

Mark   Hey. I said sorry, didn't I? I'm paying for it. Emily dumped me.

Amy   I'm not surprised. It was a violation. Anything could have happened. People could have got hurt.

Mark   Alright, alright.

The sound of applause.

Derek   They've finished. Here they come.

Neil, **Dave**, **Emily** *and* **Kate** *enter.*

Lisa   How did it go?

Emily   Good, I think.

Neil   Good? We bloody killed out there. Massacred them in their sleep. Come on, let's take a curtain call.

Lisa   But they've stopped clapping. You can't go back on in silence.

Neil   I don't give a damn. I'll go back on if I want . . .

Dave   Neil, no . . .

Mark   Wow, he's really doing it . . .

Neil *exits. The rest peer through the curtains.* **Kate** *turns away.*

Kate   Oh God, I can't watch . . . What's he doing?

Derek   Just sort of . . . standing there. Oh wait, there's still some people clapping. Oh. It's his mum and dad.

A beat of silence.

Kate   What's happening now?

Dave   He's shaking hands with Mr Henderson. And . . . oh God, Neil, don't do it!

All   Noooo!

They all deflate.

Kate   What? What is it?

Neil *enters again, looking pleased with himself.*

Dave   I can't believe you did that.

Kate   What did he do?

Emily   He kissed the examiner.

Kate   On the cheek?

Emily   On the mouth. For a disturbingly long time.

Lisa   What's wrong with you?

Neil   Hey. Don't judge me. You of all people.

Emily   What does that mean?

Neil   I'll tell you what it means, slut.

Lisa   Neil!

Neil   Me and Lisa did it last night. Full sex. The whole caboodle. Intercourse . . . er. Yes. Sexual intercourse.

A long silence. Everyone looks from **Neil** *to* **Lisa**. **Lisa** *looks horrified.*

Amy   We've really got to get ready. We're on next.

Derek   Yeah. All you guys get out of here.

Dave   Okay. Come on, Romeo.

He pulls **Neil** *offstage.* **Emily** *follows.*

Mark   Hey, Emily, can we . . .

She ignores him and exits.

Shit . . . Babe!

He follows her off. **Derek** *and* **Lisa** *are fiddling with props, leaving* **Amy** *and* **Kate** *alone in the centre of the stage. They exchange an awkward glance.*

Kate   I don't remember much about last night.

Amy   Oh. Well. You didn't miss much.

Kate   But I know what happened. Between us.

Amy   Oh. Yeah. Well. Sorry about that. I was all drunk, cos Mark spiked my drink and . . .

Kate   I don't regret it.

Amy *doesn't say anything.*

Kate   Amy. I don't regret it. I want to see you again.

Amy *looks at her.*

Amy   Really?

Kate *nods.* **Amy** *smiles.*

Amy   But now . . . I've really got to go.

Kate   Okay. Break a leg.

Amy *kisses* **Kate** *briefly on the cheek, then exits.* **Kate** *pauses, smiling, and then exits in the opposite direction.*

Derek *and* **Lisa** *are left alone.*

Derek   I can't believe you slept with Neil.

Lisa   I can't believe you punched him.

Derek *smiles.*

Derek   Touché. Shall we get on?

Lisa   Good luck.

He gives her a little Regency-style bow.

Derek   And to you, my dear.

They exit, leaving an empty stage. '100 Ways to Be a Good Girl' starts playing.

Darkness.

Scene Six

Results day. A few weeks later.

Kate *and* **Amy** *are sitting. Both are holding envelopes.*

Kate   It's hard isn't it?

Amy   What?

Kate   Not opening them.

Amy   Ah, come on now. Not till everyone's here.

She smiles. **Kate** *holds the envelope up to the light, examining it.*

Kate   Maybe I can . . .

Amy *deftly snatches the envelope off her, grinning.*

Kate   Spoilsport. Give it back.

Amy   No.

Kate   Come on, give it back!

Amy   Er. No.

Kate *jumps on* **Amy**. *The two squeal and giggle as they wrestle for the envelope.*

Kate   Give it back!

Amy   No way!

Kate *kisses* **Amy**. **Mark** *appears holding an envelope. Watches them for a moment, then clears his throat.* **Amy** *and* **Kate** *climb off each other, as* **Mark** *approaches.*

Mark   Hello.

Amy   Hi, Mark.

Mark   Have an alright summer?

Kate *and* **Amy** (*exchanging a glance*)   Great.

Mark   Good for you.

Kate   What have you been up to?

Mark   Oh you know. Hanging round, mostly. Played some GTA. Not much, to be honest.

Amy   Ah. Still in love with Emily?

Mark (*pause*)   Yeah. She . . . ah . . . she doesn't forgive me.

Amy   Neither do I.

Mark   I know. I was hoping . . .

Kate   To see her today? Yeah, she'll be here any minute.

Mark   Okay. Cool.

Kate   Got your envelope?

Mark *holds it up.*

Mark   Not that it matters. My dad's already got me a job with him.

Amy   Doing what?

Mark   Dunno. Finance, or something.

Kate   You're lucky.

Mark   Maybe.

Dave *enters.*

Dave   Wazzup, bitches!

Kate   Hello! Got your results?

Dave   Got 'em right here! Three 'C's. I'm going to Cardiff!

Amy   We were supposed to open them all together!

Dave   Oh. Really? Sorry.

Kate   Who else is coming?

Lisa *and* **Derek** *hurry onstage holding their envelopes.*

Lisa   Sorry we're late, sorry we're late.

Mark   It's okay, we haven't started yet.

They all hold up their envelopes. **Lisa** *approaches* **Dave** *and kisses him.*

Mark   Whoah whoah whoah, what's this? When did this happen?

Lisa   Where have you been? The moon?

Dave   Prom. It happened at the prom. And we couldn't be happier. It's due next March.

He tenderly touches **Lisa***'s belly. Everyone goes silent.*

Dave   Um. That would be a joke.

Kate   Hilarious.

Dave   Cheers.

Emily *enters.*

Emily   Hi, everyone.

All   Hello!

Mark *moves towards her.*

Mark   Emily. Hey.

Emily   Hi, Mark. How you been?

Mark   Okay . . . Listen. I was thinking . . .

Derek   Come on, come on, no time for that! Everyone's here. Let's open them!

Amy   On three?

All   One, two, three!

They all open their envelopes. A silent moment of fervent reading. Then they all explode in cheers and screams – except **Mark***, who only has eyes for* **Emily***.*

Derek   Swap, swap!

They all swap results except **Mark***, who holds on to his.*

Amy   Wow.

Lisa   Did anyone fuck up? Did we all manage it?

Kate (*reading*)   Yep . . . we all did well. Really well.

They cheer again, except **Mark***.*

Emily   Mark, you alright?

Mark *doesn't say anything, just holds out his paper to her.* **Emily** *takes it and reads it, as the rest swap more results and congratulate each other.*

Emily   Mark . . . three 'A's. That's fantastic.

Mark *takes it back from her.*

Mark   Doesn't matter.

Emily   Your dad, right?

Mark   Yeah. Doesn't want me to go. Wants me to stay with him.

Emily   You don't have to do what he says, you know.

Mark   Yeah. I do. Emily. Listen. Do you think there's any chance . . .

Emily   No, Mark. No chance. Sorry.

Mark *nods.*

Mark   I love you, though.

Emily *shakes her head.*

Emily   Come on. Come and celebrate.

She takes his hand and leads him back to where **Derek** *has produced a bottle of champagne.*

Derek   Look what I've got!

He pops the cork. Everyone cheers. They find glasses and begin to fill them up.

On the other side of the stage, **Neil** *appears, clutching his envelope. The rest don't see him. He stands, watching them celebrate, drinking their champagne.*

Neil *opens his envelope, pulls out the paper. Reads for a moment. Doesn't react. Then puts the paper back.* **Dave** *notices him and approaches.*

Dave   Hey, Neil!

He walks across to him.

Dave   What have you been up to all summer, mate?

Neil   Oh you know. This and that.

Dave   Sorry I haven't called.

Neil   Don't worry. I get it. So, you're with Lisa now?

Dave   What?

Neil   You and Lisa. You're a thing right?

Dave   Well, yeah. I would have told you man, but you were AWOL.

Neil   Yeah. No worries.

And he walks away from him towards the crowd of people, all still celebrating and not seeing him. He stands awkwardly, with them not noticing him for a long moment. Then suddenly –

All hail, Macbeth! Hail to thee, Thane of Glamis!

They jump, startled, and turn to look at him.

All hail, Macbeth, hail to thee, Thane of Cawdor!

Emily   Neil . . .

Neil   All hail, Macbeth, thou shalt be king hereafter!

Silence.

Neil   So how you all doing? I take it the champagne means success?

Kate   Yeah. Well. We all did really well.

Derek   How did you do, Neil?

Neil   Sorry?

Derek   Your results!

Neil   Oh, yeah. Fine thanks, yeah. Got everything I needed.

*Before **Neil** can do anything about it, **Dave** snatches the results off him.*

Dave   Let's see!

Neil   No, no!

He scrabbles to get the results back, but the gang toss it between them quickly, so he can't reach.

Neil   That's private, that's private!

They end up with **Lisa**.

Lisa   Relax, what have you got to hide? You said you did fine, right?

Neil *stops struggling and deflates.*

Neil   Yeah.

Lisa *opens the results and reads.*

Lisa   So let's see . . . oh.

Neil   It's fine.

Lisa   Oh Neil . . .

Kate   What is it?

Emily   What's wrong?

Lisa   He failed Theatre Studies. Badly.

Mark (*laughing*)   Shit, really?

Dave (*to* **Mark**)   Dude. Chill.

Mark *reads the results, laughs again, then passes them on. They all look at* **Neil**. *He hangs his head.* **Emily** *is reading the results.*

Emily   Oh Neil. You really messed up.

Neil   You think I don't know that?

Emily   But –

Neil   But nothing. I'm screwed, I needed to get a 'B' to get my place.

Derek   What did you write? In the exam? What did you do?

Neil Tried to be clever. Attacked the question. Called it stupid. Stuff like that. Guess they didn't find it funny.

Derek What are – ?

Neil What am I going to do? Sod all, that's what I'm going to do. I'm not going to uni, I'm not getting a job, I'm not doing anything. I'm screwed. My life is ruined.

Emily Neil, it's not!

Neil Yes it is, Emily! Yes it is. And do you know what? Do you know what the worst thing is? I couldn't give a toss about these stupid bloody results. I was just excited to see you all today. You know. My friends. You got no idea . . .

Lisa No idea what?

Neil No idea what it's like. To be so lonely. And none of you. Not even one. When I arrived, just now, was pleased to see me. I mean. You're my friends, right?

They all look at each other.

Derek Neil. You have spent the past two years belittling us, calling us stupid, taking the piss and acting like a completely up-himself dick. Don't you see . . . don't you see that affects people?

Neil It was all just . . . banter. I didn't mean any of it.

Derek Like calling me a faggot.

Lisa Or me a slut.

Neil Just . . . banter.

Silence, for a long moment. They all look at him.

Lisa Well . . .

*She looks at **Derek**, who nods.*

Lisa We're all off to the pub, if you want to come?

Neil No, it's all right. You don't have to do that.

All ad-lib encouragement: 'No, come on', 'Please', 'It'll be fun', etc.

Derek   Neil. Results or not. We did it. We made it. We're grown-ups. And that means leaving all the childish shit behind, you know?

Neil   Yeah.

Derek   So. Come on. Come and have a pint. It's legal now!

Neil   Yeah. I might see you there later.

Derek *nods, knowing he'll never come. They all exit, chattering away, leaving* **Neil** *alone. After a beat, he exits in the opposite direction.*

Scene Seven

Neil*'s room.*

A desk and chair centre. A laptop.

Neil *sits and types As he types, he talks.*

Neil   Lights up on an empty stage. A desk and chair centre. A laptop. A boy sits typing. As he types, he talks. He is alone. There is no one with him. No one to talk to. No one to confide in. No action. Just him, sitting, typing, for the longest time. Time passes . . . and yet more time passes. But no one comes. He is alone. For ever.

As people enter, they find a space and stand, motionless, staring outward.

Enter **Mark***.*

Neil   But slowly, people start to emerge.

Enter **Kate***.*

Neil   Where there was once space, there are now people.

Enter **Dave***.*

Neil   One by one, they enter.

Enter **Amy**

Neil   Slowly filling the world around him.

Enter **Derek**.

Neil   The room is filling up with figures.

Enter **Emily**.

Neil   He is no longer alone.

Enter **Lisa**.

Neil   He is no longer alone.

Throughout the following, the **Chorus** *start to arrive onstage, filling up all available space. They start to hum, softly at first, but growing louder, '100 Ways to Be a Good Girl'.*

Neil   The boy looks up . . .

He looks up.

And sees he is surrounded. And even though it's not real. Even though he's conjured it from nowhere. Even though any minute it could end, and he would be alone again . . . he's happy. For that moment, he's happy.

He pauses. Then sings along with the humming.

> I caused a major war, just by talking . . .
> You flew into a rage, cos that's everything you know . . .
> Childhood of violence filled with heartache . . .
> I flew into a rage, cos that's everything I know . . .
>
> I know one hundred ways to . . .

He cuts off abruptly. Everyone exits leaving him alone.

Neil   But then. It's all over. And he's back where he started. A boy. On the stage. Alone.

(*His voice cracking with emotion.*) . . . Alone.

Dave *enters.*

Dave   Hey, Neil?

Neil *turns to look at him, surprised.*

Neil   Oh. Hey.

Dave   Fancy a drink?

Neil *pauses again. Then looks at his computer.*

Neil   Oh. Thanks . . . but . . . no. Sorry. I'm working.

Dave (*pauses*)   Oh. Cool. Anything good?

Neil   Just something I'm trying.

Dave   Nice. Okay. Well. Another time then.

Neil   Yeah. Another time.

Dave *nods. Then exits.* **Neil** *turns to his computer, and starts to type.*

Then the music starts. Skunk Anansie plays loud and clear. The chorus. As the music rises and crescendos, the lights go down.

Drama, Baby

BY JAMIE BRITTAIN

*Notes on rehearsal and staging drawn from a workshop
with the writer held at the National Theatre, October 2014.
Workshop led by Anthony Banks, with notes by Olly Hawes.*

The workshop was led by director Anthony Banks (AB).
Throughout the day Anthony and writer Jamie Brittain (JB)
ran a series of exercises and facilitated numerous discussions
with around thirty-five directors from schools and youth
theatres from around the country (questions asked by these
directors appear in italics).

How Jamie came to write the play

'I was born in Scotland at the Edinburgh Festival – I go back
every year – and I grew up in the Lake District, Bristol and
London. I've always been a big fan of theatre, always wanted
to write a play, and always followed Connections, so when
Anthony asked me to write a play for the programme, I
jumped at the chance.

'I had a very interesting first twenty years. My parents divorced,
I moved house a lot, I had a very *Skins*-like teenagehood – but
life was suddenly boring when I got into my twenties! So
I find myself fascinated by teenagers. I believe teens are at the
heart of the moral centre of a society. They feel more and
they experience life more vividly than older people. You have
something you slightly lose when you get older: "Your heart
dies" – that's a quote from *The Breakfast Club*, it's one of the
great lines in cinema, so I write to try to get back to that.

'I'd like the audience to be reminiscing about the mistakes
they made – and might still be making. The mistakes you
make as a teenager aren't the be-all and end-all. Things settle
into a groove as you get older, you get more comfortable.
The ultimate message of the play is that out of the chaotic
existential mess of being a teenager, sometimes a person is born.'

Approaching the play and planning your rehearsals

'How much time should we spend on each scene?'

AB 'In an ideal world, you should plan to spend, on average, two hours per page of script.'

AB arranged the script on the floor so that all the pages were lined up consecutively, side by side, then stuck them together in a long line with masking tape. This created one long roll of script that could be taped to the wall. He then put Post-it notes on the pages where a scene begins, so everyone could see how long each scene is. From this it became apparent that every scene is pretty much the same length apart from Scenes Five and Seven, which are shorter. Arranging the script on the wall like this is a useful way of understanding the way the play is structured overall, before going into more detail about various character journeys and starting to think about pacing, which in this play is crucial – without it, it won't gather comedic momentum.

AB 'If you have a room where you can leave things stuck to the wall, this is a great way of treating the script as an object which is at a distance from the rehearsal on the floor, rather than a flapping bunch of A4 paper in an actor's hands, which can perhaps labour their physical responses to it. Instead, it is a map, a set of signposts towards the live play the actors are creating. The whole company can begin to own their work on the play – if notes and scribbles surround the wall-script they can collectively refer to them from one rehearsal to the next.'

The world of the play

AB 'There are two microcosms at work in a school. The first is the students. How do each of the characters from our play fit into the rest of the school? What tensions are going on offstage that might fuel the action onstage? The second is the teachers. What are the politics of the staff room, what is the chemistry of the teachers in the school? All schools are not the same, they are different places. These lines of enquiry might help you to make choices about the design, atmosphere, energies, etc.

'It is also worth researching the following timelines before you start rehearsals: the history of theatre; the history of "the school play" (when was the first school play?); and the formal study of drama in schools, which has been debated a lot in the press recently. What would Mr Henderson be teaching his class? What posters would he put on the wall? How would this inspire what the exam pieces are? Which shows would the candidates have seen in their local theatres?'

Thinking about the kissing scenes

'What is the best way to approach the kissing scenes with young people?'

AB   'You must be sensitive to the temperature of your group and think carefully about all the stage pictures that are necessary to convey the story that Jamie Brittain has written.'

The ending

'What is the significance of the ending?'

JB   'I like to leave things on an intake of breath, an off-beat. I think it's really effective, to do a sudden click where the story finishes.'

'The play could be seen to be about the formation of a writer. When thinking about what happens in that final scene, does he have to be a playwright? Or could he be be writing a journal – perhaps on the advice of a medical/psychological professional?'

JB   'That is a valid way of looking at it – the important thing is that Neil enters a period of introspection . . . I wanted to play against the rest of the play a little bit at the end.'

'What do you think happens to the characters once the play has ended?'

JB   'I don't really have any thoughts about that. I hope the play is a complete story and I hope it finishes with a sense of hope.'

Language

'What's the phrase "Drama, Baby" about?'

JB   'I suppose now people might say something like "jokes", but it's what me and my friend used to say to denote "fatuous high jinks".'

JB noted that he has tried to make the location of the play as open as possible, to accommodate any accent and that he has 'tried to … "de-swear" the play as much as possible', because there's a misconception that teenagers swear a lot more than they actually do.

The relationships between the characters

JB began by discussing what it's like to be in a group of young people studying drama together. 'Everyone in this room has been a drama student. It seems like when you're a drama student, when you're doing a play, things happen that wouldn't usually. That's what happens with Neil's narcissism and with the girls' love. In drama the atmosphere that is created between people is magical, and I miss it a lot.'

Here are his thoughts on other characters:

NEIL

JB   'I've always been of the opinion characters should make mistakes. I do believe Neil is likeable. He is partly based on myself – I was a young narcissistic drama buff in the early 2000s, and I put into him all my worst qualities.

'In some ways the play could be seen to be about the formation of a writer – but the reason he is writing at the end is that he has learned that being a smarty pants pseudo-intellectual isn't the way to succeed. You have to be a good person. To be smart isn't enough. To be able to cut people down isn't what life is about – I was like that as a teenager, and I was hugely insecure.

'I don't think he is a horrible person. Sometimes people think the way to interact is to use their intelligence to take people down and there is nothing worse. He is so socially inept that when confronted about his behaviour at the end of the play, "It's just banter" is the only thing he can say. He thinks the other characters are his friends, but they are not.'

MARK

JB 'I wanted to offset Neil with a bit of an arsehole (as opposed to the other characters who are nice). I wanted to show some of the disappointments that happen in their lives.'

LISA

JB 'I know girls like Lisa. All my sisters and female friends seem to think they're ugly and misshapen when they're brilliant and brave and talented. It's harder when you're a teenager and it's great when someone can bust through that. That's my thinking behind all the female characters in the play.'

AMY

JB 'I created the gay relationship because it just seemed like the girls would fit well together. I have no political agenda with it. I think it's just nice when nice things happen – and sometimes they do.'

DEREK

When Derek asks Neil to go to the party with him, does he actually fancy Neil? Is he using the Eminem lyrics to cover his embarrassment?'

JB 'I don't think Derek is *in* love with him, or fancies him. He does, however, feel a true platonic love for Neil. Derek is the only person who really understands Neil – and perhaps Neil is the only one who understands Derek.'

DAVE

'On results day Dave asks Neil to come for a drink with the rest of the group. Is Dave trying to redeem himself?'

JB suggests that Dave's act reflects on the situation he finds himself in after the journey he's been on through the play. 'I think Dave feels bad. Derek defends Neil, talks him up, but doesn't invite him. Dave does.'

MR HENDERSON

JB   'When I was first working on the play, I quickly got rid of the idea of having the drama teacher in it. I think Neil is Mr Henderson's star pupil and they get on really well. He's one of those great, benign, creatively inspiring drama teachers who was probably Neil twenty years ago!'

Casting

When casting your production, it could be useful to run a workshop as well as (or even instead of) auditions in the more traditional format. This can help you discover more about the world of the play, which actor will be good for which character, and also, crucially, how different actors might work within the company as a whole, which is of particular importance in this play.

When it comes to the genders of the actors, JB noted that he would prefer companies to have girls playing boys or boys playing girls, as opposed to swapping the genders of the characters.

Staging and design

AB   'One of the most important tasks towards the end of rehearsals is evaluating all the ideas you've got spinning and deciding what to keep – "finding the pearls". When you are tight for time, working out what to keep and what to discard can be stressful. When rehearsing a comedy, leave enough time in rehearsals for plenty of run-throughs so that a strong sense of timing can be found, but get the production choices right first. It is worth it, because this final ruthless editing process can make a good production great.

The setting

JB   'I'm not strict at all on the location of the play. I've deliberately made it vague in terms of whether it's a private school or state school, what race the characters are, what region it is in, etc. I've intentionally written vague locations and sets and I know there are some quite complicated moves in it, so I'm really interested to see what happens. Remember, when you stretch yourself you become more creative!'

The school/the party

It's important that the atmosphere of the school scenes and the party scenes are different. In the school at rehearsal, the collective objective is to do well in exams; in Mark's house the collective objective is something very different. How will this impact on your directorial choices?

AB   'I encourage you to really make the play yours – to make the audience think, "Yes, that party could be just down the road, that rehearsal could be happening at our school." This is also something to think about in terms of design. One set of scenes needs to be in school, another on private property at a parents' house at night.'

JB   'Sometimes it's easy being a teenager, sometimes it's a nightmare – and parties can be both of those things. The party scene is written to be slightly incoherent, it is a series of vignettes to describe a party. The scene can be as free-flowing as you like, and as long as you are bold in your choices, you can do what you like with it. It is a messy party. I tried to write it from the viewpoint of someone who was drunk at that party. I think with parties like this it's almost like the significant moment is what happens the morning after – when one person thinks they've offended another, and people are unsure about what actually happened. My experience of kissing someone as a teenager is that the psychologically testing stuff happens later.'

The challenge for the party scene is to get that sense of a party, that sense of chaos, but also to ensure the key moments of the story are clear for the audience. For example, there are three key moments that happen quickly over only a few pages of text – Emily and Mark have an argument and two couples get together – but everything else that happens around that seems to be chaos.

AB asked a small group to rehearse a few pages and the result was a scene that was constantly moving and rhythmic, with moments that seemed to break out and catch the audience's attention. It gave a sense of one of those parties with so much going on, but also allowed the story to unfold.

JB   'I like how the moments within it were all just little moments, that is what it's like at a party – and it's only in the morning when you realise that the things that happened actually meant something.'

As with the rest of the play, pace is so important in the party scene, as is the right music.

Music

'What is behind the choice of music? Could there be live music in the piece?'

JB   'I used to be in a dance troupe in Bristol – it was awful! We used to do an improvised tableau to Skunk Anansie, so that's why '100 Ways to Be a Good Girl' is in there. I chose to play the song as the play finishes because initially Neil mocks it, but by the end it means something to him. And live music could be a great idea.'

The Chorus

The Chorus offers flexibility to the different youth theatre companies staging the play.

JB   'The Chorus are there for you to use as you want or need. Do whatever feels right for you. Be creative.'

AB was keen to highlight the creative possibilities of using a large company: 'There can be a lot of pleasure in lots of people on stage and then very few – and this is something that you can really choreograph.' In the workshop staging of the party scene it was both useful having a large group of actors in terms of creating an appropriate atmosphere, and it also presented challenges with regards to how to structure the audience's attention.

Style and technique

You might want to consider asking your company, 'What are your favourite funny shows from the world of entertainment?' (comedians, television sit-coms). Write a list of them and discuss them – this is a useful way of creating a shared understanding of comedy within your company.

AB pointed out: 'The thing is, it's *about* "the school play", but it shouldn't be *like* "the school play".'

JB   'TV and theatre are very different animals. I try not to repeat myself, I have a horror of doing that. *Drama, Baby* is less cynical and hopefully sweeter and less dark than *Skins*. Stories are a fundamental need of humans, and it's important that teen stories are told. I have found that teen drama is often led by an issue. There's nothing wrong with that (and *Skins* did that), but I want to do something a little lighter with this play. I hope it's a fun and funny experience. Teenagers playing teenagers in a comedic setting is something that – when it works – is great.'

'How sweet do you want it – can it be darker?'

JB   'Yes.'

AB   'Yes. We want to see a great variety of productions of *Drama, Baby*. You could write down the title of the play on the wall, then ask yourself: "Why am I doing this? Why am I teaching drama and directing a play with teenagers?" To do this play, there's going to be a bit of you in it, your personality will be in it . . . and somewhere in the answer to those questions will be the words "Drama, baby!"'

AB   'Don't get caught in the trap of trying to present *authentic* teenage characters onstage. These characters are an *imagined* version of teenagers. The characters are in the play, and *the play* is the thing.'

'How to do convincing drunk acting?'

A common observation is that people who are drunk often don't believe they are drunk, and crucially don't try to behave as if they're drunk. Another interesting observation to consider is that there is a big difference between young people being drunk and adults being drunk. Some young people like to act drunk even when they're not! But being cool is still very important and there might be a battle between indulging in that drunken feeling and resisting an increasing lack of self-control.

One effective exercise that can lead to good 'drunken' movement is to imagine a ball spinning around your body and being aware of it, while trying to continue your usual course of movement.

Suggested references

Companies may find it useful to research other stories that are set 'backstage', such as: *Noises Off, 42nd Street, Kiss Me Kate, A Chorus Line, A Chorus of Disapproval, The Habit of Art, The Phantom of the Opera, Shakespeare in Love.*

Hood

By Katherine Chandler

Hood's mam has run off with a bacon-licking vegetarian, while her dad spends his days and nights lost in a chair, feeding his addiction to The Waterboys.

There's no money left, there's five struggling kids to feed, and interfering Father Tuck just won't let them be.

But our modern-day hero Robyn Hood is determined to keep her family together, whatever it takes . . .

A modern-day tale about family and food.

Age suitability: 13+

Cast size:
8 main characters,
plus ensemble and physical performers

Katherine Chandler is a Welsh playwright who has had plays produced by National Theatre Wales, Bristol Old Vic, Sherman Cymru, Theatr Nan'Og, Spectacle Theatre and Dirty Protest. Her play *Before it Rains* won the Writers' Guild Playwright Award at the Theatre Critics of Wales Awards and was shortlisted for the prestigious Susan Smith Blackburn Prize 2012.

Katherine was the inaugural winner of the Wales Drama Award of the BBC and National Theatre Wales, and received a Creative Wales Award from Arts Council Wales. Her adaptation of Terry Jones's fairy tales *The Silly Kings* won critical acclaim and was produced and performed by National Theatre Wales in Europe's largest Spiegeltent, in the grounds of Cardiff Castle.

While on attachment at the National Theatre Studio, Katherine wrote her new play *Bird* which won the 2013 Bruntwood Judges Prize, and is now in development with Manchester Royal Exchange Theatre. Her first film *Tag* was released on BBC iPlayer as part of the BBC3/BBC iPlayer drama launch in 2014. Currently she is working on commissions for the National Theatre Wales, Sherman Cymru and BBC Drama.

Author's notes

All adult characters (excluding Tuck) should be played by representations/puppets/caricatures or in absurd costumes. Run free with your creative expression!

For example: Dad could be a beret on a broom handle (remembering the importance of his beret) or a mop with a pair of boots and a beret . . . Mam could be a wig on a cushion with a Che Guevara T-shirt (remembering the importance of the T-shirt) or a sock puppet with lipstick.

The characters have lines that are to be played directly to the audience and also lines that are dialogue with other characters. It should be clear where the audience is to be directly addressed but, again, play with it and see what feels appropriate.

There are lines at the beginning and end of the play that are assigned to 'Estate Kids'. A separate chorus or the main cast could be used for this. Please split the lines or not accordingly, and again have fun with them. The audience is to be played with and teased and directly addressed throughout the play, when appropriate. Keep them on their toes.

Silent Muz doesn't speak, but when his name appears it generally suggests a moment of focus for the characeter.

The two songs are hugely important for the feel of the piece.

The energy and bounce of the performance is really important. This family is generally not gloomy and morose. They are matter of fact and hopeful, salt-of-the-earth characters on the whole. Their general positive energy will make the stillness and inner thoughts of the more serious monologues more poignant.

Characters
in order of appearance

Estate Kids
Hood
Dad
Mam
Al
Will
Silent Muz
Tuck
John
Nas
Security Guards

Estate Kids *split the following lines, addressing the audience directly, playing with the audience. They could be placed among the audience.*

Estate Kids   We want to talk to you.

To share with you.

We want to tell you a story.

We'll try not to make it too long.

Cos him, over there with the jacket.

Him?

That's the one.

He wants to get back to the telly.

It's raining for God's sake . . .

. . . and he's sat here when he could be sat on his sofa in the comfort of his own home.

We'll try not to make it too dull.

Not too boring.

Cos her.

This one?

She wants it to be funny.

For heaven's sake, at the very least let it be funny.

She got things to do.

Washing.

Cleaning.

Sterilising.

Cleaning the clean.

He's thinking about the time he used to be able to do whatever he wanted to do on a Saturday night.

No one to answer to.

No responsibilities.

And now look at him.

What happened?

Where did it all go wrong?

Kids.

Mortgages.

That's what happened.

Life.

This one's hoping for some songs.

To make it go quicker.

So she don't have to think.

About lost dreams.

They are wondering how long it's gonna take.

Who's looking at their watch.

Yawning. (*Exaggerated yawn.*) Argh.

We don't blame you.

I'm only here cos I lack confidence.

Someone told his mam it's good for confidence.

It's not.

I'm here to meet girls.

Statistically speaking the odds are in his favour.

Eight girls to every one boy.

Still haven't found no one.

We want to tell you a story.

A story that's happening now.

Round our way.

About an ordinary family.

The birds are singing.

Of our time.

And your time.

Round our way.

It's alright.

It's all wrong.

A piece of our world.

A world of our peace.

The world we live in with you.

The world where you was us and we'll be you, still.

Spotlight on a plastic supermarket skip.
A person stands, back to us, in the skip.
Dressed in a green hoody.

All   This is Hood.

Hood *throws a holdall out of the skip.*
A siren sounds.
The holdall falls to the floor, spilling its contents.
Torch light flashes around the stage, flashing glimpses of **Hood***.*
Eventually resting on **Hood***.*
She turns around.
Startled.
Looks to run.
There's no way out.
To run is futile.
Holds up her hands in surrender.

Hood   I was born on June 14th.

She jumps out of the skip and stands centre stage.
Our focus is on her as the skip is removed.
Dad *is wearing a Che Guevara beret.*

Dad   My girl, born on the same day as Che Guevera.
It's a sign.

Hood   That's what my dad thought.

Dad   You'll be a man of the people.

Hood   I'm a girl.

Dad   A man of the people. A family man. Because it's all
that matters when it comes down to it. Humankind and
human contact.
Love.
Love is all you need.

Hood   I'm a girl!

Dad   A selfless giver.

Hood   My dad wants this more than anything.
On account of him being in the Socialist Workers Party.

Mam   You'll be famous.

Hood   My mam wants this.
More than anything.

Mam   Good famous. Famous for being good.

Hood   On account of her addiction to all things celebrity.

Mam   It's fate and it happens, when society is struggling
and humanity is lost.
Someone comes.

Hood   Someone came, didn't they, Mam? (*To audience.*)
Rayo Miller.

Mam *takes off the Che Guevara T-shirt and throws it at* **Dad**.
Dad *sinks into his chair with his back to us.*

Hood   My mam went to live with him nine weeks ago.
Which is typical of her.
He's a vegetarian.
Which is hypocritical.
Considering my mam's obsession with protein.

She pulls her hood up.

All   This is Hood.

Hood   An ordinary girl.
Who lives in a house.
On a crappy council estate.
With my dad . . .

The back of a chair and a beret.

And my brother John.
And Silent Muz. Who doesn't speak.
And the twins. Al and Will.
Our dad has his problems.
He is a man with alternative thought processes and
addictions. Having battled long and hard with alcohol he
transfered his obsessive needs to fighting the injustices of life.

Dad   From my chair. I love my chair. A man needs a chair.

All   Family.

Dad   And The Waterboys. There's not much that needs to
be said in life that's not said by them.

All   Family.

Hood   It's all we've got. That's what they said. That's what
they told us.
All you need is love.
Her and him. Him and her.
My dad sits in his beloved chair playing 'The Whole of the
Moon' by The Waterboys.
Over and over and over.
Some might think it's not much of a life.

Because we have nothing.
This is how I start the day, every day like this:

Loud noise of alarm.

Hood   Hrmmph.
Argh.
No.
Dear God.

Shuts off the alarm.

In my head, I think these thoughts:
Sleep. Sleep. Sleep.
But then I remember this:
If I don't get up then no one will. And they'll be late for
school and maybe won't even make it to school. And there'll
be questions, like 'How are you?' and 'How are things at
home?' and 'We thought we might send someone to see your
dad, just to see how he's getting on', 'How's he coping?'
because he doesn't always cope. Me dad. He's not been
historically known for coping and he can be quite
exhibitionist in his not coping.

Al   He is an addictive personality and he turns to things.

Will   He's a drunk and he turns to booze.

Hood   So I get up.
Today this happened.
Will! John! Al! Muz!

*One by one they slowly come to her, sleepily putting on school uniform as
they walk (except for **John**, who takes his and goes back to sleep). As
they pass **Hood** she hands them a slice of toast off a plate. There is one
piece of toast left on the plate.*

Hood   Only one.
Put it back.
No jam.
Peanut butter? Who d'you think we are!

Al   Is there no milk?

Will   There's no milk.

Al   I want a drink.

Hood   There's a tap full of water.

Al *and* **Will**   Water?

Hood   It's good for you. I'll get milk. I'll get some later.

Al *and* **Will**   There's no crisps.

Hood   There was crisps there.

Al *and* **Will**   There's none. There's nothing. There's nothing here. We'll starve. That's the thing. That'll be next. It happens. It's happening to us. We're gonna starve.

Hood   You're going to be late.

She looks around for money. In her pockets, under things.
Al *and* **Will** *give up.*

Will   I'm wasting away.

They leave.
Silent Muz *watches. Holds his rucksack.*
The first beats of 'The Whole of the Moon' start.
Hood *finds a note.*
Has it in her hand.
John *is out of sight in the house.*
Hood *takes a second.*
Looks at the money that's left in her hand.
She turns to the chair.
She walks to the chair.
Looks at the money in her hand.
Song stops abruptly.

Hood   Since my mam went that is how our mornings go. Doorbell goes.

Hood   Apart from that.

Doorbell goes again.

Hood   That doesn't happen.

Doorbell goes again.

*It is **Tuck**, community vicar with sandals, with a collection box.*
*He is part of the pastoral care team at **Hood**'s school and is known to*
the family.

Tuck   Room for a little one?
It's only me.

He rattles the box.
*Looks at the money in **Hood**'s hand.*

Hood (*to audience*)   Tuck. The vicar. The vicar Tuck.
Also pastoral care at my school.
Which is weird because he should be there – not here. So
why is he here?

Tuck   For the needy.

Hood   Oh.

Tuck   Are you not in school?

Hood   Yes. I mean no. Why are you here? I am in school
but not now.
So yes but no.

Tuck   Not in school. Again.

Hood   I'm stood here. Talking to you.

Tuck   Is your mam in?

Hood   No. She . . .
She's off shagging a vegetarian with highlights.
He's forty-six, which makes it all the more disgusting.

Tuck   Your dad?

Hood   He's sick.

Tuck   As in cool?

Hood   As in not well.
That's why I'm . . .
I'm looking after him. Not always. Just. He's not feeling well.
Normally he's fine.
Today he's not.
He's not feeling too good.

Dad *speaks to audience, not heard by* **Tuck**. *His words could be projected or maybe another theatrical means of seeing his thoughts could be found.*

Dad   I'm feeling bad. Worse than bad. My head is heavy and my heart is broken and my mind has thoughts that are dark and dangerous and I am filled with total and utter despair.

Silent Muz

Hood   Okay there, Muz?

Silent Muz *says nothing.*

Hood   Good then. Off to school. Like you do every day. All normal. Everything's normal.
Holding his rucksack.

Silent Muz *leaves.*

Hood   He doesn't speak. But you know that.
He's great, though. But you know that too. He's young. Just fourteen. He's going through a phase.
We're okay though.
We're fine.
I'm just here because it was better, we thought, if I stayed off.
Just for a bit. Because I'm seventeen, aren't I? So I thought it should be me.

Tuck   What about your courses? Your A-levels? You're doing well by all accounts. Really well. you'll throw it all away.

John *walks past her and takes the last piece of toast off the plate.*

Hood   We're fine.

Smiles at **Tuck***. Wants him to leave.*

John   I'm going back to bed.

Hood   You should go to school.

John   No.

He walks off.

Hood   Look, do you want something?

Tuck   Your form tutor thought that you might be in need of some pastoral care.

Hood   Mr Prosser – the Tosser.

Tuck   It's just. There has been some concern expressed about your welfare. As to whether you're um coping with the . . . um . . . loss.

Hood   She's not dead.

Tuck   No. Of course. It's just. There's help, you know . . . if you're not . . .

Hood   Not?

Tuck   Coping?

Hood   Coping.
We are fine.
We are more fine than you could even begin to imagine fine to be. We have it good. So good. I mean only this morning we were laughing, all of us together, over a full cooked breakfast, sausage, bacon, even hash browns. The works. We were all laughing about how lucky we were.
Not just the food. Things. Just things because they're so great.

John   I'm going out.

He takes the money that **Hood** *has in her hand.*

John   I'll get the milk.

Hood *is left looking at her empty hand.*
Beats of 'The Whole of the Moon'.

Hood   Having each other, you see.

Tuck   There are people that can help you.

Hood   We don't need your help.
With us being so great and everything.

Tuck   There's a meeting. Tomorrow. We have them. Once a month. To discuss. I wonder if there's more we could be doing for you.

Hood   A meeting?

Tuck   I might just mention . . .

Hood   That everything is good. Mention that.

Tuck   Is your father not working, Hood? I thought he was working?

Hood   He was. He was working. But he felt a bit off-colour for a while there. Since. And then.
Yes, he's working.

Tuck   He's not working.

Hood   No.

Tuck   Is he drunk?

Hood   No.

Tuck   They want to talk about you. This . . . erm . . . situation. I think I should tell them. About your dad and your mam.

Hood   This is working out better for us though, having him home. To look after things.

Tuck   It's just a meeting. Just a chat.
I think I have to. I think we need to talk about about this.
I'll come and see you.
Tomorrow.

After school.
Keep you in the loop.

Tuck *takes a second.*
Puts the box down.
Hood *looks at the box.*
Tuck *leaves.*
Hood *takes a moment.*
Turns to the chair.
Walks to the chair.

Hood   You have to get out of the chair, Dad.

Music stops.
Blackout.

Spot on **Will**.

Will (*to audience*)   I'm getting out of this as soon as I'm sixteen. On our sixteenth birthday that's it, I'm done. I'm out of here straight after breakfast. I won't look back. I'm getting a job and a flat. I'll do anything. I'm not staying here, not for nothing. People say – all the time – oh it must be lovely to have a big family – you're so lucky. It's not. It's shit.
I spend all day with clenched teeth. On Sundays my cheeks ache from it. Last week I clenched my teeth for so long my left cheek went into spasm and I thought I'd had a stroke.
I thought to myself, is it not bad enough that you are poor? Motherless? With a father who has an addiction to The Waterboys? As if that's not bad enough you are now having a stroke at fifteen.

(*To* **Al**.) There was this girl on the news yesterday. She'd gone to school with the wrong shoes. They couldn't afford new shoes and they punished her. Put her in the store cupboard for wearing the wrong shoes. That'll be us soon. You know that, don't you?

Al   We'll be fine.

Will   Shut your stupid mouth.

Al (*to audience*)   Welcome to the house of fun.

Will   Keep it shut.

Al   Daaadd!

Will   Daadd!

Al   He has anger issues due to the sense of abandonment caused by our mother leaving us for the vegetarian.
DAAAAD!

Will   He won't do nothing. He never does nothing. Sits. In there. In his chair.
Did you see the telly's gone?

Al   You is kind, you is smart, you is important.

Will   What the?

Al   You is kind, you is smart, you is important . . . (*Repeats continuously.*)

Will   Is that from that film? Is it?

Al   . . . You is kind, you is smart, you is important . . .

Will   What are you doing?
Shut up.

Al   . . . You is kind, you is smart, you is important . . .

Silent Muz *walks through with his rucksack.*

Will   He sold it. The telly. Dad sold our telly.
At first, I thought he was just being his normal shitty self, getting rid of the telly, thought it was another one of his protests or something and then for a minute, for a frozen moment in time, I thought he was doing it for us. For us, cos we needed him.

Al   You is kind . . .

Will   Then he drunk it. The money.

Al   You is smart . . .

Will   I'm not calling him Dad.

Al   You is important.

Will   Not until he starts behaving like he is.

Al   He didn't leave us.

Will   You don't know nothing. You don't know nothing about anything.

Al   You is kind. You is smart. And you is important.

Will   Shut up.
Shut up!
SHUT UP! . . .

Will *continues with his 'SHUT UP!' and* **Al** *continues her repetition until they are screaming at each other.*
Will *pushes* **Al**, *who falls back.*

Will   You got her mouth and you got her eyes. And when I look at you, I see her. And then yesterday we was sat at the table, remember? and I realised that you'd pulled your leg under you and you was sat on the side of the chair like you was riding it side-saddle or something. And it was her again. In you. Sat in the same way.
At the table.

As he talks **Silent Muz**, *who is on his own, opens his rucksack and pours the contents unseen into a bin bag.*

Hood   We had a visitor.

Al   Oh.

Hood   Tuck.

Will   That's it then.

Al   It? What's it?

Will   We're finished.

Al   Finished?

Will   It's the process. You know what this means.

Al   No?

Will   We'll be in a system. He'll put us in a system. He's going to put us in care.

Al   Care!

Will   That's what this is. It's the start of it. He's young isn't he? New to the job. He wants to make his mark. It's how it starts. A visit. He'll be coming back. Is he coming back?

Hood   Yes, he said he's coming back tomorrow.

Will   Told you. He's coming back tomorrow. We'll be referred.

Al   Referred?

Will   That's what they do. They refer.

Al   We'll be referred.

Will   They'll split us up.

Hood   They won't.

Will   There's too many of us. Look at us.

(*At* **Dad**.) Two kids you should have had, maybe three. Not five! Who has five?! They'll split us up.

Hood   The state of this place.

Al   The state of us.

Will   We're a sitting target. He'll be filling in his forms tonight. Making a start.

Hood   No.
He won't. I won't let him.
We're doing okay.

Will   We're not doing okay.

Hood   We'll show him.

Al   We'll clean it up.

Hood   We'll clean us up.

Al   We'll be grand.

Hood   When he comes. This place will shine like a pin.
Satellites will be dazzled by the gazing reflection of this house.
Pilots will be blinded.
We'll get Dad out of the chair.

Al   We'll show him.

Hood   When he comes tomorrow. We'll offer him tea and
cakes.

Al *and* **Hood**   A feast!

Hood   We'll show him.

Silent Muz *leaves with his rucksack.*

Hood   We're just fine.

Will   Where's John with the milk?

Blackout.

Lights on **John** *with his friend* **Nas**.

John   Being poor is the same as being rich except that it's
completely different.

Nas *drags on a rolly and exhales heavily.*

Nas   That makes no sense.

John   But it does though.

Nas   Oh yeah!

John   Yeah!

Nas   No.

John   It's like being small is the same as being big. Although
the thing is, it's different.

Nas *offers the spliff to* **John**.

John   What d'you reckon you'll be doing in ten years?

Nas   Don't know.

John   Not a clue?

Nas   Nope.

John   Will you be a doctor, you?

Nas   No.

John   A dentist?

Nas   Just because my parents . . .

John   Good money.

Nas   Got the highest suicide rate of all the professions.

John   Doctor?

Nas   Dentist. Doctors in the top five.

John   Shit.

Nas   True that.

John   But you'll go and study? They'll want you to study.

Nas   Yes.

John   What?

Nas   Maybe I'll be a vet.

John   Or a teacher. Would you be a teacher, Nas? Teaching all the little shits like us?

Nas   No.

John   Like me. I'm the little shit in this scenario. Teaching me, Nas?

Nas   No.

John   Making my life better. Enriching my life with your knowledge. How 'bout that?

Nas   I want to be a painter.

John   There's a fair wedge to be made in that game, Nas. My dad's mate Tony, he's a painter. Driving a top-of-the-range Beemer. Five hundred pounds a day, just to slap paint on some old lady's walls. And with you being a girl an' all. You could charge more than that I reckon.

Nas   Not a painter. An artist. I want to be an artist.

John   That's gonna blow their minds, that is, Nas.

Nas   Yes.

John   Rebel you are.
I'd like to be a rebel. But with my lot.
You know with my lot, I got nothing to rebel against.

Nas   You should study. Get a good job.

John   That'd show 'em. Raging against the machine with my A grades.

Nas   One day we'll be forty.

John   Shit.

Nas   One day.

John   Forty.

Nas   One day I'll be sat behind a big desk in a big office – I'm seeing dark brown wood, is that oak or some shit – it doesn't matter, because one day I'll be sat behind my big brown desk and a shaft of sunlight will shine in through my window and hit the bit of my desk that I've been staring at blankly for the last fifteen minutes but I won't even have realised that's what I've been doing until this sunlight comes and hits me and that sunlight reminds me of the time when I wanted to be an artist.
And I follow the gaze of the light.

And I follow it through the window and I look out of the
window, for the first time, not for the actual first time but for
the first time properly, and I see the trees that are outside my
window and I notice how the sun hits the leaves and the light
dances off them. And I see sky and it's endless, the peace and
space of the sky, its depth and its colours all of them hypnotic
and vivid, and the sun seems – what is it – and the sky it
seems – it seems eternal – and alive – and I am mesmerised.
And I am an artist – and I pick up a pencil and I have a
notebook on my desk and I start, I put the pencil on the
paper and I look at it, the blank page and the nib of the
pencil breaks, I put the pencil down just at the moment that
the sun disappears behind a cloud.
I go to my window but the sun has gone and the tree doesn't
look the same.

John *takes a slow, theatrical drag of the rolly and breathes deep. Holds
in the smoke. Holds. Holds.*

Nas *is in her own world.*

John *exhales the smoke.*

John   You wants to be an artist.

Nas   But I'll be a doctor.

John *starts to leave.*

John   I'll see you.

Nas   Where are you going?

John *pulls the tenner out of his pocket.*

John   I want to buy you something.

Blackout.

John *and* **Hood**.

Hood   You lost it?

John   I had it and then I put it in my pocket and then when I went to the shop it had gone.

Hood   Tuck is coming tomorrow. Officially. He is coming as an official person to 'see' us and we can't even offer him a cup of tea . . .

Al   Or a biscuit.

Or cake.

Hood   There is no milk.

Al   Or biscuits.
Or cake.

Hood   Because you 'lost' the money.

Will   I'm gonna kill him!

They hold **Will** *back.*

Hood   For God's sake, Will!

(*To audience.*) He's lying. I know he's lying. He's knows he's lying.
Before she left my mam told me three things.
1. All men are liars.
2. Even the one man she thought was not a liar (the vegetarian) turned out to be a liar (she caught him licking bacon in the kitchen).
3. John's a liar.

John   I'm not.

Hood   The cupboards! Look in the cupboards! Get everything out. We're looking for cleaning things. And anything we can eat. Let's see where we are on this.

John   We have sheets.

Hood   Sheets?

John   We can use them for clean rags.

Hood   Good, John. Good.

John   We have soap. We can put the soap in a bowl with hot water. That'll clean stuff.

Al   I found a tin of fruit salad.
Fruit in juice. Food and drink.

Will   What's this?

He holds up **Tuck**'s *collection box.*

Hood   No. That's not for us.

Will   It's money. There's money in there.

Hood   It's not ours. It's for the needy.

Will   Take a look at us.

Hood   He didn't pick it up.

Will   He left it for us and you won't use it. For what? Pride? Look at us! We have no pride.

Hood   Flour. There's flour. We can do a lot with flour. Pancakes.

John   Corned beef. Is that dried milk? I've never seen that. Milk that is powder.

Al   There's sugar. I think this is sugar? I think it's from when Mam tried to make that Christmas cake a few years back. It's got damp so it's got all stuck together but I'm sure it's sugar so that's good, isn't it? We can do stuff with flour and sugar. What is that?

John   I think it's a banana?

Al   It's black.

Will   I have never seen a banana that's black.

Al   A banana cake. We'll make a banana cake. It'll be fine when it's cooked. It won't be black.

She carries on searching. The rest of the family are gathered round the items. **Al** *searches under the cushions of* **Dad***'s chair and under the chair. She finds various low denomination coins.*

Al   Fifty . . . oh . . . one . . . 51p!

She puts the coins with the pile.

Al   Okay, that's it.
That's everything.

They look at the pile of things silently for a while.
Silent Muz *walks off.*
Slow realisation that it's not looking good.

Will   Is this it?
This is all we have.
I'm gonna kill him!

Again goes for **John** *and is restrained.*
They look at the items.

Hood   It appears we have a situation.
We are having a visit from Tuck tomorrow. Who claims to be offering help. However, we believe this to be a lie as we are aware that men are liars (*Looks at* **John**.) and even though he is a man of the cloth, Tuck is no exception.
It is our belief that the true purpose of his visit will be having a good look round and assessing how well we are coping with our current domestic situation of having a mother who has run off with a bacon-licking vegetarian and a recovering alcoholic of a father who sits in a chair listening to The Waterboys.
We cannot even offer the assessing holy father a cup of tea due to our last pennies being 'lost'.

Again looks at **John**. **Will** *shuffles.*

Hood   So we have to rack our brains.
We have to come up with our Plan B. Because Plan A is failing and it's not looking good.

Silent Muz *returns and empties out a black bag of random things on the floor in front of them.*

Hood   Things are definitely not looking good here, guys.

Trainers, shirts, jumpers with labels and stickers left on.
Books, magazines, DVDs, CDs, all unused with stickers on.
Cleaning products.
Food items. Mostly tins but among the tins are ten packets of brownie
mixture, powdered milk and teabags.
Everyone stares at the pile of things in silence.
Silence as they all look at each other.
The beats of 'The Whole of the Moon' start.

Hood *looks at* **Silent Muz**.

Silent Muz *breaks into an uncomfortable smile.*

They all look at each other, look at the stuff. Start to giggle. Get excited.
Hood *looks silently, sternly at the stuff.*

Hood   You have to take this back.

Will, Al *and* **John**   What!

Hood   It's stealing.

Will, Al *and* **John**   What!

John *looks through the stuff.*

Hood   We don't steal. That is not who we are.

Will   He can't take them back, he'll get arrested.

Hood   They have to go back. You can't just go around
stealing things.

John   It's from Tesco's. All of it.

Hood   What?

John   He's stole it from Tesco's. It's Tesco's!

Hood   It doesn't matter.

Will   It matters.

Hood   No.

John   I'm proud of him. Making a stand against the evil capitalist corporation.

Will   Robbing the rich.

Al   I don't want Muz to get into trouble.

Hood   It goes back.

John   But they are a huge monopoly with loads of money. More money than we can ever even imagine. Millions, billions, trillions of money.

Will   We have nothing.
We. Have. Nothing.
We have less than nothing.
It's not fair. It's not right.
They won't miss it, they don't even know!

Hood   We don't steal.

Will   I want to keep it.

John   I really like the trainers.

Will   I want to eat the noodles.

John   The chocolate.

Al   Books. Books are good.

Will   And pens.

Al   Can we keep the books?

John   I mostly want the food.

Will   I only want the food.

Hood   Why did you steal this?

John   Didn't know you had it in you there, mate.

Hood   What if you'd been caught?

Al   Were you trying to help?

Hood   What would we do?

Will   I want a phone. Next time . . .

Hood   Why did you steal?

Silent Muz   . . .

Will   This is stupid. He won't say nothing. Hasn't said
nothing since she went so just . . . SHUT UP because it's all
stupid and it's all wrong and it's all lies.
He doesn't speak because words are lies. This is real. He's
feeding us. Not just talking about it. Talking about socialism
and injustice and Che bloody Guevara.

Beats of 'The Whole of the Moon' start.
Will *looks to the chair.*

Will   Did you know Che Guevara shot a child for stealing?
Shot him. Did you know that when you was busy putting him
up there on a pedestal?
Did you know that, Dad?

Nothing.

Hood   I'll take it back.

John   Please don't take it back.

Al   Just keep the food?

Hood   I'm sorry but we can't.
I'll take it back tonight.

John   We have to eat.

Will   We need food.

He picks up a scrumpled receipt from the floor.

Al   We need each other.

Opens it, confused.

Will   A sketch pad and paints?

John   We need dreams.

Lights on **John** *and* **Nas**.

John   Going away is the same as being here but it's almost entirely different.

Nas   Right.

John   Because what you'll find is. It's all the same.

Nas   Except it's not.

John   I've never been abroad, me.

Nas   I know.

John   I've never said that.

Nas   I just know.

John   What is it, hot is it?

Nas   Sometimes.

John   Have you been to South America?

Nas   I have.

John   My dad always talks about South America.

Nas   Did he go?

John   No.

Nas   You should go.

John   I'll not go.

Nas   You'd like it.

John   I like it here.

Nas   They speak Spanish.

John   Do they? Spanish?

Nas   And Portuguese. And English.

John   Like here?

Nas   Yes.

John   And so that's disappointing. Which is why I won't go.

Nas   Because they speak English?

John   Because a little bit of me just died when you said that, right there, Nas.
A little bit of hope. Because I dreamed of this place.
It's right here – (*Head.*)
I dreamed it all. So I don't need to go there. And I never will because if I go there then that, what you said about 'English', that will happen. That's disappointing, that is.
English?

Nas   Mostly Portuguese.

John   Or Spanish?

Nas   Yes.

John   I'm going to think of that. I prefer that they speak Spanish.

Nas   Have you been?

John   I'm almost certain I've never been out of the country. I've been to Anglesey. We borrowed my Uncle Tony's old Cortina once and our mam drove us all there.

Nas   Did you like it?

John   I did.

Nas   Would you go back?

John   No.

Nas   Is there nowhere you want to go?
Jesus, John.
Have you any dreams?
Is this all you want?
In ten years will you be here? Still here?

Pause.

John   I got dreams. But I think you and me both know that there ain't much point in me having dreams, Nas. I didn't have the start you got, so it ain't looking too good for me, I reckon.

Pause.

I'd like to be in politics, Nas. Cos I reckon I'm good with people and what I've got is a good heart.
I give a shit. So maybe that don't make me cut out for politics as it is now but what I also got on account of my dad is a revolutionary way of thinking, so maybe succeeding as a politician who gives a shit would be my personal revolution. I'd like to be a politician who makes people change the way they thinks about themselves and the world.
There's a line in a song my dad used to play before. The line says 'Kindness knows no shame' and I reckons that if that was a mantra for people, I reckon that would change a lot of things.
It's underrated is kindness. That's what I'd like to – I dunno . . .

Pause.

In ten years I'll be in some mental ward in some hospital. That's if we still got hospitals, Nas. I'll be there on account of my habitual use of marijuana. I'll have developed some borderline psychotic state of craziness. I'll be wrapping myself in silver foil and avoiding people with hats. And the thing is, I'm not dreading it. There's a part of me that is looking forward to the complete and utter state of not having a rational or sane thought again. Because even though I'll be worrying about hats and silver foil I won't have to think any more about the real stuff.

Pause.

The voices'll piss me off though, with me being a fan of peace.

Pause.

We haven't got any money.
Hood is worried they are going to take us away.

Split us up.
Starting to look bad.
Starting to look really bad.

Pause.

Nas Shit.

They look at each other for a while.

John I got something for you.

John *gives her a sketch pad and paints.*

Blackout.

Light on **Hood.**

Hood (*to audience*)   The plan for operation 'Return of the Stolen Goods' is as follows:
1. Dress in black – check.
2. Collect all stolen items from Muz and put in holdall – check.
3. Wait for dark – check.
4. Go to back of Tesco's and put holdall by staff entrance next to skips. Not too close to skips as don't want holdall mistaken for rubbish making return of stolen goods exercise completely pointless.
5. Run home.
And then Tuck . . .

Blackout.

Will (*to audience*)   I have days where I feel like I'm falling. Not tripping-and-grazing-my-knee type of falling but proper black-hole-nothing-to-grip-on-to type of falling. Down and down. No bottom. No end. Just falling. And I'm fifteen so I know that I have the world.
The whole world in my hand.

All that life ahead of me. But when I look back it looks better than looking forward.

Al *is tidying. Cleaning. Fussing.*

Al   I love you, Will.

Will   I know.

Al   Focus on the things you love. The good things.
Happiness. I love happiness.
Are you okay?

Will   What? Me? Yes. I'm fine. What d'you mean?

Al   Not angry?

Will   No. Not. I will be. I will be if you talk.

Al   You're clenching.

Will   Shut up.

Al   I want to talk about her.

Will   She left. She left us. She thought knobbing the vegetarian was a better option than us.
What is there to talk about?

Al   I think she had enough.
I think she would have taken you with her if she could.
Because she loved you, Will. Adored you. You have her eyes. Her mouth. You even sit like her. I see it. She saw it. I think she might have taken you but she couldn't because then she would have had to take me – you can't separate twins, see, that's not right, and then she couldn't just up and leave Muz because he's the baby and if she took three then how could she leave John. And Hood.
I think she needed to not be around this any more.
Around this chaos.
I don't think she could cope.
I think she woke up one day and she left and I don't think it's anyone's fault.
I think it is what it is.

Will   Somebody stopped me.

Al   What?

Will   On the way home from school.

Al   What d'you mean?

Will   They said Dad owed them money. Told me to tell him. Said he owed them fifty quid. And if they don't get it by next week then it will double.

Al   Fifty quid.

Will   And next week it will be double.

Al   What will we do?

Will   I think we should take the money from the box.

Al   It's not our money.

Will   Pay off the man.

Al   There won't be enough.

Will   It's there and we should take it.

Al   How much?

Will   £62.53.
We could blame John. Everyone will think it was him anyway.

Al   We can't blame John.

Will   I'll blame him. I'll say I saw him with money, which is true because I did.

Al   And we'll use the money to pay back the man?

Will   Yes.

Al   I'll take the blame.
We won't blame John.

Will *stops in his tracks*

Will   It's gone!

They look at each other. Look to where the box was. Look at each other again.

Al *and* **Will**   JOHN!

Hood   So to recap. Tuck is to have how many cups of tea, Al?

Al   He's to have only one cup of tea.

John   Therefore eliminating the need for urination.

Al   And stalling exposure to the bathroom –

Will   – and the filthy mess within.

John   And the chance glimpse into any of the upstairs rooms.

Will   Which are also in need of a good clean.

Hood   Good, good.
And if he asks?

Al   Silent Muz shall be in desperate need of a poo.

John   And will go to the aforementioned bathroom –

Will   – and lock the door for the entire duration of the visit.

Hood   There shall be a plate of biscuits.

Will   Custard creams.

John   Which I shall purchase from Spar –

Al   – with the grand total of 51p.

Hood   He shall ring the bell and he shall say –

All   'Room for a little one? It's only me?'

Hood   And we shall say –

All   'Of course, Father, do come in. How lovely to see you.'

Hood   And you, Will, shall take his jacket.

Will   Should I bow?

Hood   And you, Al, shall offer him a cup of tea.

Al   'Cup of tea, Father?'

Hood   And you, John, shall offer him a biscuit which shall be presented on a plate.

John   Just the one.

Hood   Put them all on the plate, John. Arrange them. Let the plate look as if we have biscuits to burn.

Silent Muz   . . .

Hood   And Silent Muz shall be sat in position by the door, ready to act in case of the words, 'Would you mind if I popped to the loo?'
How are you feeling, John?

John   Fine, thank you, Father.

Hood   How have these last few months been for you, Al?

Al   Never better, thank you for asking.

Hood   And Will. You're quiet, Will, it's been tough for you, I can see.

Will   I'm having a blast, Father, a right blast.

Hood   And your father here. How is he doing?

John   Wonderful. If you like 'The Whole of the Moon', Father, he's your man.

Hood   Good. So we're all sorted. We're all ready. We know what we have to do.
Everything's in place.

All   Yes.

Will   Apart from

The back of the chair.

John   Apart from –

The back of the chair.

Al   Apart from –

The back of the chair.

Beats of 'The Whole of the Moon' start.
Will *kicks the air and leaves, frustrated.* **Al** *goes after him.*
Disappointed, **John** *leaves.*
Spotlight on back of the chair.
Beats of 'The Whole of the Moon' get louder.
The back of the chair.

Pause.

Hood   Che Guevera wasn't born on June 14th, Dad, He
was born on May 14th.
Did you know that?
No?
Mam didn't either.
But I did.
But I didn't tell you and I didn't tell her.
Because.
Everything was disappointing. That's what I think.
Everything was disappointing for her.
So I didn't tell her.
But then I did. Because I saw her with him. The vegetarian.
So I told her.
I told her on that morning.
She said that she had fallen in love with him. The vegetarian.
She said that she couldn't help it.
That she had to be truthful and that she didn't want to live
a lie.
So I told her then.
I said 'Che was born on May 14th. His mother had lied,' I
said, 'because she wasn't married when she got pregnant. She
couldn't face the scandal and that's the truth.'
And,' I said, 'and his name wasn't even Che.

It was Ernest. Ernest Lynch. So,' I said, 'I'd been living a lie
my whole life.'
I said, 'You wanna know who was born on June 14th?
Donald Trump that's who. One of the world's most
wealthiest men. Top hundred on the world's wealthiest rich
lists.
And,' I said, 'I didn't know how I was gonna live with that.
So,' I said, 'I'm not going to be a revolutionary after all,
Mam. Not going to be a man of the people.
I'm going to be a capitalist with a comb-over.
So tell that to your vegetarian. Put that in his monthly meat-
free newsletter.'
I think that's why she left, Dad.
Secrets and lies.

She picks up the holdall.

Will you get out of the chair, Dad? Please.

The back of the chair.
Nothing.
She leaves.

The back of the chair

Silent Muz *goes to the CD player, takes out the disc and jumps up*
and down on it shouting and screaming. Destroys the disc.
The back of the chair.

Silent Muz   Get out of the chair, Dad.

Dad *pulls off his Che Guevara beret.*

Blackout.

Spotlight on a plastic supermarket skip.
Hood *throws a holdall out of the skip.*
A siren sounds.
The holdall falls to the floor, spilling its contents.
Torchlight flashes.
Hood *turns around.*
Startled.

Looks to run.
There's no way out.
To run is futile.
Holds up her hands in surrender.

Hood (*to the* **Security Guard**, *but also directly to audience members*)   Sorry. Please. Please. It's not what you think. I was returning this stuff I . . . er . . . found and then I saw these people and they were in here and they were getting food. And it was in here. Food. Proper food. In the bin. There were custard creams and I thought I'll just take the custard creams because we have the visit tomorrow and it's not stealing, I thought, because they thrown it away, it's more wrong, I thought, just to leave it there. And then when I looked. There's a cauliflower. And cheese. It's out of date but then that's what cheese is, isn't it! And I thought I could make it, you know? Cauliflower cheese. Then I saw the Christmas puddings, there's seventeen of them. And they can't ever go out of date can they? Not Christmas puddings. And there's some tins, they're a bit battered but they'll be fine. And then I saw the crisps and peanut butter and I thought . . . I thought it was funny because earlier the twins they'd been asking, you see, about peanut butter and crisps . . .
I just thought . . .
You see it, don't you, on the news, the people who lose it all, on documentaries an' that and you thinks it couldn't happen to us, not us.
But then a little bit of bad luck turns into a shitload of the stuff, like snow.
And before you know it you're stood in a bin in the middle of the night cos you don't know what else to do.
Please.
Don't do anything.
Don't call the police or anything.
I'll put it back.

Hood *empties her holdall of the rest of its food.*

Tuck   Is there a problem here?

Security Guard 1   Is she with you?

Tuck *and* **Hood** *look at each other.*

Hood *expects* **Tuck** *to hand her over.*

Tuck   What is it she's done?

Security Guard 2   She's stealing food.

Tuck   I see.

Resigned to the trouble she's about to be in, **Hood** *is utterly deflated.*

Tuck   She's with me.

Security Guards 1 *and* **2**   You what?!

Hood   You what?

Tuck   I run a food bank, you see.

Hood   A food bank?

Tuck   It's small but we struggle a bit and um, I saw this thing, this article, there was an article on the news about this sort of thing. Wastage. Food wastage. And I thought it doesn't seem right, does it? All this food going to waste when there are people who are trying really hard to . . .
I mean it's food, we should all be able to eat, shouldn't we? So. Normally a few of us come, adults you know, but tonight . . .
She's a good kid. She's kind and thoughtful. She looks out for people. Is there anything more to ask of a human being than that?
Will you be calling the police?

Security Guards *exchange glances.*

Security Guard 1   No.

Hood   No?

Security Guard 2   No.

Hood   I can go?

Security Guards 1 *and* **2**   No.

Hood   No?

Security Guard 2 *fills* **Hood***'s holdall with food and gives her the bag.*

Security Guards 1 *and* **2**   Take it.

Hood   But . . .

Security Guard 1   Go home.

Security Guard 2   Eat Christmas pudding.

Security Guard 1   And peanut butter.

Hood*'s family home.*

John, **Al**, **Will** *and* **Silent Muz** *are cleaning in a choreographed routine to the Electric Light Orchestra's 'Mr Blue Sky'.*

John *exits.*

Hood   Life, I'm told, is a box of chocolates.
Full of surprises.
Or perhaps more relevant to this story, life is a skip of unlabelled tins.

Tuck   Room for a little one? It's only me!

All (*mixed up*)   Of course, do come in, how lovely to see you.
Lovely come in.
Of course, how to see you.
Do come in lovely.

Hood   Please do sit down.

Will   But first I should take your jacket.

Tuck   I don't have one.

Will   Oh.

Al   Cup of tea?

Tuck   White, no sugar, thank you.

Al   Lovely. Isn't everything lovely?

A loud crash and a smash from offstage.

John   Shit!

Al   I'll get you that tea.

John *enters with two plates.*

John   Custard creams.

Nas   Cauliflower cheese.

Tuck   Thank you.

He takes a biscuit.

John   There was Christmas pudding but it's on the floor.

Tuck   Is your dad around at all?
Hood?
Hood?

Hood   Normally I would say –
He's sick.

Tuck   As in cool?

Hood   As in not well. Which is sort of true but –
But today I say.
My dad.
My dad is there. Sat in his chair.
That's just who he is.
But Tuck doesn't mind.
He sits with him.
And they sit and they talk and there are forms and leaflets.
And help.
There is help. And he – my dad – he is talking and he's
crying a bit but mostly he's talking and he is getting us help.
He's our dad. And he stayed.
And that's who he is.

All   Family.

'Mr Blue Sky' plays.

Hood   I am Hood.
An ordinary girl.
Who lives in an extraordinary house.
On a crappy council estate.
With my brother . . .

John   John.

Hood   And Silent Muz.

Silent Muz   Who doesn't speak.

Hood   And the twins.

Will   Al –

Al   – and Will.

All   My band of brothers.

Hood   My merry men.
And our dad . . .
Some might think its not much of a life.

John   Because we have nothing.

Will   But we are fine.

Al   Having each other, you see.

Hood   It's all that matters when you come to think of it.

'Mr Blue Sky' plays and everyone dances.

Hood *dances along with her family.*

Estate Kids *split the following lines, again addressing the audience directly:*

Estate Kids   So there we go.

All done.

Wasn't too long?

You liked the songs?

There were some laughs.

But best of all it was short.

They kept it short.

Thank the Lord, they kept it short.

You need the loo.

Bars still open.

Catch the end of that film.

They won't be long.

Just getting changed.

Get a takeaway on the way home.

They've had fun.

Your duties done.

Till the next one . . .

Blackout.

The end.

Hood

BY KATHERINE CHANDLER

*Notes on rehearsal and staging drawn from a workshop
with the writer held at the National Theatre, October 2014.
Workshop led by Melly Still, with notes by David Ralfe.*

How Katherine came to write the play

Class was an important starting point for Katherine. The way
in which the characters speak to each other – blunt and
straight to the point – is familiar to Katherine from her own
working-class upbringing. She sees this as a kind of honesty
and frankness.

Katherine also wanted to write something for a younger age
group which was political, without the political element being
too laboured. She noted that working-class culture had
changed since she was a teenager. The working-class socialism
she grew up with, which we see in Dad, now seems old-
fashioned; but as teenagers, Katherine and her peers were
interested in revolutionary politics and brought up with a
strong allegiance to the Labour Party.

Themes

At the workshop, a brief discussion of the themes of the play
produced the following ideas:

- Class
- Family
- Survival
- Reality versus dreams
- Poverty
- Inequality
- Big corporations
- Waste.

Style and genre

Katherine said that she had set out to write something less
bleak than much of her other work. She describes the style as

'comedic', but the characters' pain is real and not to be laughed at, so she does not think of the play as simply 'a comedy'.

Some of the situations the characters find themselves in are so extreme they might become funny, and this humour is reflected in the rhythm of the writing and punctuation. But it is not necessary to 'play for laughs'. The comedy will be created by playing the situation truthfully.

The play has a happy ending, which certainly puts it closer to comedy than tragedy. Melly also noted that, etymologically, the word 'comedy' comes from the same place as the word 'common', because Greek and Roman comedies dealt with normal people, from the same time and place as the audience, much like *Hood*.

Staging

The play is set in a number of different locations. The stage could be divided into sections, with each section representing a different location. But perhaps a more interesting way to stage it is with a playing space that can be transformed from one location to the next.

Katherine would prefer that specific choices of songs named in the script are respected, but said that all other incidental music in the play could be freely chosen by directors.

Casting

Katherine advised that, where necessary, genders of characters can be changed (with the exception of Mam and Dad), or actors can play against their gender.

When casting puppeteers, it is worth choosing people with physical and mental stamina as it's a tricky, technical process requiring concentration and physical strength. Cast people who will be willing to practise and practise until they can do it brilliantly.

Also look for people who can do puppetry without pulling focus from the puppet. There are certain actors (sometimes the ones with big egos) who are not very good at making themselves invisible!

Language and characterisation

Throughout the workshop, Melly stressed that characterisation should not come from 'characteristics' that are decided in advance and then imposed on the text. Characterisation in this play should come from the wants and intentions of the characters that are found in the text and felt by the characters in every moment.

What a character wants and what they intend to do to other characters by saying or doing something *is* characterisation. We might also call this 'subtext', and this is where the real drama is found. In this way, language and characterisation should be seen as interdependent, and Melly showed us several exercises for exploring both.

WALKING ON PUNCTUATION EXERCISE

This is an exercise for exploring trains of thought and the rhythm of a text. It can be done by actors, directors or teachers.

- Take a section of the play and start reading out loud whilst walking. Read all the parts and the stage directions. Every time you reach some punctuation, change direction. You should read with the meaning of the text but try not to think about 'acting'.

- Develop the exercise further by giving each piece of punctuation its own action: pause for a comma, change direction for a full stop, jump once on the spot for a question mark, throw your hand in the air for an exclamation mark, take three tiny steps for an ellipsis and take a side-step for a dash.

- Do this with some of the fast-paced dialogue and then compare it to Nas's monologue (p. 82–3).

In the workshop, this exercise made the group think about the meaning of the text, avoiding the problem of actors saying text without really knowing what it means. People quickly got out of breath, because the dialogue is so fast. Heart rates were raised and the group were in a higher state of tension, which suggests something about the characters' almost constant state of anxiety. The exercise reveals how rapidly the characters move from thought to thought. There are lots of exclamation marks, with the characters using lots of imperatives, as they fight for attention.

John and Nas's sentences are much longer, perhaps because they're more relaxed, or because they're stoned or because they are away from the hectic home space. This place, where they smoke weed and chat together, is John's safe space, away from the home. It was noticed that Nas's dreams come out in a big rush of long sentences, before she reverts to shorter sentences when she is brought back to reality.

This exercise also unlocks the rhythmic, almost musical quality of language in the play. This was the first thing Melly noticed when she read the play and she compares it to a symphonic poem.

GRAB THE BATON EXERCISE

This exercise forces actors into active listening and reveals the intentions behind the text.

- Take a passage of group dialogue from the play, assign parts to actors (including characters who are onstage but have no lines) and then ask those actors to stand in a circle. Place an actor playing Dad in a chair outside the circle.

- Find an everyday object to use as a baton. Ask your actors to read the text, taking the baton every time they speak. (Silent Muz can also take the baton, when people are waiting for him to speak but he is refusing.) Where a character is referred to by another character, everyone taps the character being talked about on the shoulder. Characters also read any stage directions that refer to themselves. Your actors should read for meaning but not be self-consciously 'acting'.

This is an active listening exercise, which will force your actors to listen for their cue to take the baton. It's like a read-through but it forces everyone to concentrate all the time. It also makes actors much more aware of when they are not speaking and they'll start to question whether that's because they don't want to speak (and why) or if they are not being allowed to speak. To explore this, the exercise can be developed, so that every time an actor feels that their character wants to speak, they try to take the baton. The script will dictate who wins the baton and is allowed to speak, but it will mean that each character has to fight to be able to speak, making the exercise even more active and bringing out even more clearly the breakneck pace and verve of the writing.

The actor playing Dad should discuss their experience of being separate and unable to get involved. In the workshop, actors playing Dad said they found it quite unsettling and even upsetting being isolated in this way. It also makes Dad's not speaking more of an active choice.

When characters refer to objects or possessions, the baton effectively becomes whatever object is being talked about (for example, the food that the children find in the cupboards or Tuck's money box). The exercise becomes a way of exploring how the characters fight over these objects.

Melly uses this exercise with every play she directs and she gets actors to do it every day. It forces actors to concentrate and to be in the present. It's also a good warm-up to do just before a performance. It is a way of exploring the wants and intentions behind a text, without getting into the overly cerebral, psychological dissections of character which often take place round a table. Without consciously 'acting', the readings had a real truth and energy to them. What the characters want is made very clear by this exercise.

Once again, Melly emphasised that characterisation in this play does not come from 'characteristics' that are decided and then imposed on the text, but from wants and actions that exist and are felt in the moment.

VERB/INTENTION CARDS EXERCISE

This is a useful exercise for actors who want to explore the intentions behind their lines or who are having difficulty with one particular line. It will encourage actors to think about characters in terms of verbs not adjectives, in other words actions not feelings. (NB: the word 'act' comes from 'action'!)

- Your actors can work in pairs or one pair can do the exercise, with everyone else watching and contributing to the discussion about which intentions work best for which lines.

- Everyone in the group picks a verb and writes it on a card (e.g. to accuse, to deny, to attack, to defend). The verb will become the intention behind a piece of text; in other words, what a character wants to do to the other characters by saying these lines. One person chooses a verb-card at random and holds it up and an actor takes a line and says it with the verb/intention written on the card. Then they can try the same line with a different verb/intention. By exploring different options, instinctively you will see which makes sense.

For example, what is the intention behind Al's lines 'You is kind, you is smart, you is important'?* It could be to infuriate, to reassure or to hurt. Try each of them and if it's still not clear which feels right, ask yourself which is most likely, given what we know of Al?

Keep in mind that a character wouldn't say something if they didn't want it to have an effect on another character. What

---

* These lines are a quote from the feature film *The Help*, in which a black nanny, living in the Deep South of America in the 1960s, tells the white child she looks after 'You is kind, you is smart, you is important' every day because the child receives no affection from her parents. Al may or may not imitate the woman's Deep South accent!

do they want *to do* to the other characters? Keep them doing by giving your actors active verbs not adjectives or feelings.

WHAT DOES EACH CHARACTER WANT?

It's useful to discuss with your actors what they think each character wants. Every character will have specific wants at specific moments in the play but do they have something they want throughout the play? (This is sometimes called a 'super objective'.) Identifying what characters *want* will give your actors more to *do* than if you just discuss how they feel. In the workshop, our brief discussion gave a few suggestions:

HOOD: to be better than her parents, to be the parent figure, to make her family normal, to protect her siblings.

MUZ: to be seen, to be heard, to be invisible, to help.

JOHN: to be with Nas.

WILL: to leave, to be independent, to have his own space.

AL: to look after Will.

Katherine noted that, while the children don't know if Tuck has their best interests at heart, for her his intentions are noble and he leaves the money deliberately. He wants to help the family.

Puppetry

SQUATS: A WARM-UP AND STRENGTH EXERCISE

Puppetry is a physical skill and puppeteers will benefit from a good physical warm-up, with plenty of stretching. Moving around the stage with a puppet puts extra strain on the legs and knees, so squats are a good way to build strength throughout rehearsals and to warm up before a show.

• With feet slightly wider than shoulder-width apart, keep the back straight with bum tucked in and your arms held out loosely in front of you, whilst you bend the knees and go just a bit lower than you would if sitting in a chair; then straighten the legs to stand up again. Start by doing five to

ten squats at a time – they're tiring! Ask your puppeteers to
do more and more each rehearsal.

'Squats' also develop the crucial puppetry skill of lowering
your centre of gravity while retaining complete balance and
control. Wherever possible, a puppeteer's head should be
lower than the puppet's to encourage us to look at the puppet
not the puppeteer. Professional puppeteers can often stay low
by walking on their feet with their knees completely bent, in a
full squat position. But if your puppeteers find this hard and
have to walk on their knees, make sure they wear knee pads
under their costumes.

Basic puppetry exercises, for early exploration

1 ANIMATE YOUR HAND
- Sit with the palm of your hand on the floor. Look at your
  hand and notice details that you've never seen before.
  Make small movements with your hand and observe very
  closely. (This creates a strange distancing effect.) Then
  imagine your hand has a life of its own and starts to move
  around. It can explore, discover, react or meet other
  hands. How do its movements change depending on its
  mood? How do you physicalise its intentions, reactions and
  emotions? Apply what you learn to the next two exercises.

2 FLYING A PAPER BIRD
- Fold a piece of A4 paper in half so the two shortest sides
  meet. Hold the middle of the fold between thumb and
  forefinger and allow the two halves of the paper to fall
  open, so they become the wings of a bird. Use it as a
  puppet and fly it around the room. Search for the
  connection between your breath and the bird's flight.

3 ANIMATING AN EVERYDAY OBJECT
- Take an everyday object and try to bring it to life. How
  does it move around? It can explore, discover, react or
  meet other objects. How do its movements change
  according to its mood? Experiment with a voice for the
  object (just making sounds, not saying words). How do

sound and movement go together? How does the puppeteer's breath relate to the puppet's movement?

- Do this with several different objects and see how different objects suggest different ways of moving and different voices giving different 'personalities'. Encourage your actors to be playful and imaginative but not silly. They should be searching for the best, most sensitive and most expressive quality of movement.

What should you make your puppet out of?

The puppets for this play will be created using objects. At the workshop, Melly shared a useful exercise for exploring how the Mam and Dad characters inform the design of the puppet.

Brainstorm words or phrases we associate with each character. For Dad, we came up with: drunk, heartbroken, a shadow of himself, unkempt, impotent, inert, unwashed, not in the present, broken, heavy, carrying the weight of the world. Already some of these words, like 'broken' or 'heavy', are easy to visualise or physicalise. Perhaps Dad is made of broken or heavy objects. Phrases with a more poetic feel, like 'a shadow of himself', could also inform the design. How would you create a shadow of Dad from the objects at your disposal?

There might be a link between the design for Dad's puppet and Mam's. For instance, they are both made of broken objects. Or perhaps Dad is made of soft things, while Mam is hard and brittle.

The objects you use could have particular significance or relate to the characters. Mam could be made of things from the house. Perhaps Dad has a transparent bin bag full of beer cans for a belly. In the workshop, one group created a Mam made of a suitcase, referring to her leaving the family home.

Think carefully about what materials you use to make your puppet. Consider how different materials absorb or reflect light, what they are like to handle, whether they are malleable or rigid, whether they make a noise. Consider how they will need to be handled and how easy they are to manipulate.

Working with and building your puppet

When designing puppets, less is often more. Leaving more to
the audience's imagination can mean they feel a greater
connection to the puppet, because they're doing some of the
work to bring it to life. Avoid giving your puppet a clearly
drawn face. It reduces the puppet's potential for expression
because the face is fixed.

Think about who operates the puppet. Are the puppeteers the
same every time? Do they control the same parts of the puppet
every time? Perhaps the Estate Kids also do the puppetry.
Do the puppeteers divide Mam and Dad's lines between them
or say them together, as a chorus?

If you want to develop the puppetry further, it's possible that
Mam or Dad could pop up as part of a memory, thought or
fantasy at any point in the play where you feel it's right.
Perhaps the memory of Mam haunts the house throughout
the play.

Operating your puppet

Start by exploring how your puppet breathes. Your puppeteers
should themselves be breathing in unison and giving that
breath to the puppet, looking for the small movements to
show a chest expanding and contracting, shoulders rising and
falling, to bring their puppet to life. As ever, the puppeteers
should be looking directly at the puppet and keeping their
eyes still; it will be very distracting if their eyes flicker around.
The puppeteers should feel what the puppet feels, but they
should put that emotion into the puppet, not express it
themselves. Their movements should always be as economic
as possible, otherwise we'll be looking at the puppeteers not
the puppet. Puppetry is largely about making yourself invisible.

Encourage your puppeteers to study human movement,
including how people walk, stand up or sit down. They may
like to video themselves moving and then watch themselves in
slow motion. Asking the puppeteers to move in slow motion
will force them to analyse and break down movement. They

should feed all of this knowledge into the way they animate the puppet.

Don't forget, the different parts of your puppet must move in relation to each other, like different parts of the same machine. But if a puppet is walking, one part might go up as another goes down. As a puppet sits down, the hand might remain a fixed point while the legs bend, with the hands following as the body leans back into the chair. How a puppet stands, sits and walks are starting points for early investigation and good daily warm-ups.

Don't feel every part of the puppet needs to be moving all the time. If only one part is moving, it can give greater focus and force to that movement; for example, the movements of a head as the puppet looks around or a hand as someone waves goodbye. But do think about how all parts of the puppet can contribute to other actions. For example, ask your puppeteers to investigate how the puppet can cross its legs. Perhaps they'll need to watch each other sitting in a chair and crossing their legs before they see clearly that we move many more parts of the body than just one leg!

If your puppet is made of several objects, those parts don't need to be stuck to each other. In fact, the space between them plays as much of a part as the objects themselves. Make sure all parts of the puppet are animated, otherwise that part will become simply decorative, not alive. Stay in control of all parts of the puppet at all times.

Experiment with the scale and proportions of how your puppet fits together. If your puppet has a human-sized head, an upper body made of a normal-sized coat and shoes for feet, for consistency it might be best to to stick to real human proportions when you place them in relation to each other. In other words, it wouldn't look right to have the coat three inches above the shoes because real legs are much longer than that.

But once you've tried real human proportions, you might find that breaking the rules produces interesting and uncanny effects. What if the head floats much higher than the body? Can a long or extendable neck suggest a sad character, searching or yearning for something? An unusual body shape might end up being much more exciting, but if you're giving the puppet a strange body shape, be aware of that, understand why you've made that choice and be in control of it.

Exploring the Estate Kids

SNAPSHOT EXERCISE

This exercise gives a structure to exploratory improvisation, which can be used to explore 'back story'. This sort of work will give depth to the Estate Kids by exploring who they are and what life on the estate is like.

- Ask your actors to sit on chairs in a big circle. In the middle of the circle, create a still image, a snapshot of the moment when Mam leaves, including members of the family and a group of Estate Kids watching. Build up the image slowly by having one actor at a time stand up and enter the image. If you are entering the image you should do so confidently. There is no need to explain who you are playing.

- Once the image is complete, ask the actors in the image to think as clearly as they can about time of day, weather and who they are. Then the director brings the image to life for ten seconds with every actor working to keep the scene alive. It should be as realistic as possible: this is not about making something for an audience to watch. Then freeze and see what picture we are left with.

This exercise gives a structure to improvisations that can be used to build the back story for characters and to discover what life on the estate is like. You can invent images that are nothing to do with the story but that allow us to imagine life on the estate (e.g. the Estate Kids out drinking, a snowball fight). You can explore moments such as Mam leaving, which we know have taken place but which do not appear in the play.

- Ask your actors to improvise for longer and longer and insist that they don't pause or stop acting in the middle of an improvisation.

- To use this exercise in relation to the Estate Kids' text, assign lines to half the people in the circle and ask the other half to build up an image of life on the estate. Bring the image to life for ten seconds, then freeze it. Then the people outside the image can deliver the text and feel as though their performance is situated within some concrete understanding of where they are and what this estate is like.

- You can keep exploring the text in this way, sitting in a circle, without an image in the middle but making sure actors are really engaged and not slumped in their chairs. Ask your actors to try out intentions – to tease, to surprise, to challenge, to invite, to engage the audience – and discuss which worked best. (You will discover different intentions for different lines.) Keep coming back to those active verbs. What do the Estate Kids want to *do* to the audience, what do they *want* to get from them?

You should avoid caricaturing the Estate Kids. Make sure each of them has a name, an age and a sense of their home life. It should not be a chorus of stereotypes.

The Boy
Preference

By Elinor Cook

In an affluent suburb in the near future, the birth of a boy is welcomed with shouts of joy and firecrackers, but when a girl is born the neighbours say nothing. One night, Joey looks out of his bedroom window and sees many young women with a strange glow around them – are they the 'missing women'? Why have they come back?

Age suitability: 13+

Cast size:
12 or 18
(depending on whether doubling or not)

Elinor Cook was the winner of the George Devine Award 2013 for Most Promising Playwright. She was part of the Royal Court Writing Super Group in 2012, during which she wrote *The Girl's Guide to Saving the World*, which was produced by HighTide in April as part of their 2014 festival, directed by Amelia Sears. Elinor has recently finished writing an episode of *The Secret*, a new series project with Working Title Television which is now filming, directed by Dominic Savage for BBC1.

Her play *Pilgrims* received a rehearsed reading at Soho Theatre in 2012, and another of her plays, *Pastoral*, was a commission from the Bush Theatre under Josie Rourke.

Elinor's short play *The Circle Game* was winner of the Old Vic New Voices Time Warner Ignite 3 competition and was also performed at the Latitude Festival. Her play *Head Music* toured recently with Box of Tricks' Head/ Heart project, while *Microwave* was shortlisted for the Old Vic/Theatre 503 Award for new writing and received a rehearsed reading at Theatre 503 as part of their Foundations Programme and more recently a week's workshop and reading at the National Theatre Studio.

A distinct bias of 'boy preference' can be found in countries extending from North Africa and West Asia to South Asia, including India, and East Asia, including China. That such discrimination has a place in a large part of the modern world is distressing: the number of 'missing women' can be quite large.

Amartya Sen

The birth of a boy is welcomed with shouts of joy and firecrackers, but when a girl is born, the neighbours say nothing.

Anonymous

Characters

GIRLS
Lila
Verity
June

BOYS
Joey
Otto
Beetle
Riley
Mo

THE NEW GIRLS
Adelaide
Alice
Abbie
Anna

FOR DOUBLING
Can either be roles in themselves or doubled with existing characters
Husband
Wife
Young Man
Journalist
Farmer
Psychologist

The play is set at some point in the near future, in an affluent suburb of a developing country.

The world's temperature has risen by a couple of degrees.
It is high summer, and very hot.

Scene One

Late at night.

Joey, *alone, in his bedroom.*

He is looking out of his window.

He sees something.

He peers harder.

He jumps and turns away.

He takes his telephone and dials.

Joey   Hello?
I'm not sure if you're the people to call but –
There's a weird –
Girl?
In my front garden.
She's just –
Standing there.
Staring at me.
OK.
Right.
Yes, I'm closing the curtains.
I've turned the light off, yes.
So, now what?
OK.
I'll try that.
I'll try and pretend she just isn't there.
Thank you.
Thank you, yes.

He sits

He closes his eyes.

He takes a deep breath.

He opens his eyes.

He can't stop himself from peering out again.

He jerks away hastily and breathes deeply.

He dials the number again.

Joey   Hello?
Yes, it's me again.
I'm sorry to bother you so soon but.
The thing is –
She's not alone.
The girl.
There are –

He swallows.

Hundreds of them.
Just –
Standing there.
Looking at me.

Scene Two

The lights come up on **Alice**, **Anna**, **Abbie** *and* **Adelaide**.

They glow, brightly.

The light fades.

Nothing.

Scene Three

The next day.

Lila's *house.*

Lila *is sitting at the kitchen table, writing in her exercise book.*

She speaks the words out to the audience as she reads back over what she has just written.

Lila   I always wanted a sister.
But I got a brother instead.
Then I got another one.
For their birthdays they get Playstations and gilt-edged

encyclopaedias.
Their food is sprinkled with supplements.
Plumped up with vitamins –

Otto (*offstage*)   Lila?

Beetle (*offstage*)   Sis?

Lila   They exercise three hours a day.
They sleep ten hours a night.
On weekends they have massages whilst eating chocolate-
covered almonds.
The Emperor and The Prince.

Otto *and* **Beetle** *enter, wearing tennis whites.*

They fling their rackets and rucksacks onto the ground.

Otto *puts the radio on loudly.*

Lila *puts her hands over her ears.*

Beetle *rushes over to his sister and cuddles her, knocking her things off the table.*

Lila   Beetle – !

Beetle   You're the *best* sister in the whole wide world.

She picks her fallen items up from the floor.

Beetle *doesn't help.*

Beetle   You're so pretty.
And kind.
And *lovely*.

Otto   Did you mend my swimming trunks?

Lila   On the chair.

Otto   Oh.
Bit wonky but.
Cheers.

Beetle   I *love* my sister!

Lila   Get off –

Beetle   Can't I have a cuddle?

Lila   Not right now.

Otto   Have you heard?

Lila   Heard what?

Otto   Dad says they're closing your school.

Beat.

Lila   Yeah OK.
Hilarious.

Beetle   Do you fancy stretching your legs?
Getting some fresh air?
Sis?

Otto   They're turning it into a sports centre for us, Dad
says.

Beetle   Maybe strolling over the road, popping into the
shop, and buying me a choc-ice?
Maybe?

Lila   What do you mean, 'Dad says'?

Otto   Uh –
I mean 'Dad says'.

Lila   Of course they aren't.
They can't be.

Beetle   And a can of fizzy something.

Otto   They've contracted the bulldozers.

Lila   But –

Beetle   Cos the thing is I'm *boiling*.

Otto   That's how Dad knows about it.

Lila   They can't do that.
They can't just do that.

Otto   Yes they can.
It makes sense.

Lila   Not to me it doesn't.

Otto   You've got to look at it pragmatically, right?
Ultimately it's an economic decision.

Lila   Do you even know what you're talking about?

Otto   If there aren't enough girls to fill the seats then what
are they meant to do?

Lila   Well –
Not give up on us, for one thing.

Otto   The Girl Deficit is having serious financial
consequences.
Dad says.

Lila   Please don't say that phrase.
I hate it.

Otto   What?

Lila   It's propaganda.

Otto   It's the truth.

Beetle   Lemon and lime flavour.
No, Cherry Coke!

Otto   Anyway.
There's going to be an Olympic swimming pool.
Bosh!

Beetle   Please-oh-please.

Beetle   And a dry ski-slope.
A boxing ring.

Lila   But –
Jesus.
I've got exams!

Beetle   Um, hello?
Lila?

Otto   God, calm down.

Lila   Calm *down*?

Otto   They're going to try and squeeze you in at the school
over the river.
So that's alright.

Lila   But that's –
No.
That's forty minutes away.

Otto   Forty-five.

Lila   How will I get there?

Otto   I could drive you.
If you ask me very, very nicely.

Lila   I'll drive myself, dip-shit.

Otto   Whoah.
No you won't.

Lila   I can and I will.

Otto   I swear if you even –
If you even *look* at my car –

Beetle   Sis?

Lila   I drive your car all the time.
So what?

Otto   You better be joking.
My God, you had seriously better be joking.

Beetle   Sissy!

Lila *What?*

Beetle Alright!
Don't snap at me!

Lila What do you want, Beetle?

Beetle Only a choc-ice . . . ?

Lila No.
No way.

Beetle What?!

Otto Cos seriously, Lila.
If that's true, I honestly don't even know how to process that information.

Lila You're on a diet.

Beetle No I'm not!

Lila You should be.

Beetle Otto?!

Lila Haven't they found a bride for you yet?
Oh yeah, I forgot.
No one will have you.

Beetle *grabs her exercise book and rips it.*

Lila What do you think you're doing?!

Beetle Guess you don't need to do your homework if you don't even have a school.

He rips more pages.

Lila Oh my God, you did not just do that.

Beetle You basically don't exist.

Lila I'll kill you.

Beetle You're basically a dodo –

Lila I will actually kill you.

Beetle   And dodos don't need to do anything except sit behind glass in museums and be stared at by bored school-children eating sweets.

Lila   Well, at least I won't be sent away.

Otto   Lila –

Lila   We all know what happens to the left-over boys.

Beetle   I won't get sent away!
Otto!
Tell her!

Lila   They make them disappear.

Otto   Lila, I'm warning you –

Lila   Before they contaminate the world with the stink of their loneliness.

Beetle   You're such a *bitch*.

Lila   Before they get their sticky hands on black-market machine guns.
Start slaughtering innocent civilians on their way to the supermarket.
Because they're just so *lonely* –

Otto *manhandles* **Lila** *to the floor.*

He holds her there.

She can't move.

Otto   Will you respect your brothers?

Lila   Get OFF.

Otto   Will you.
Respect.
Your brothers?

Lila   As *if*.

Otto   Would you like to spend the night in the garage?
With the spiders and the rats and the giant moths?

Lila   You're hurting me.

Otto   Cos that can be arranged.

Lila   Ow.
My hair.

Otto   Beetle, get the door.

Lila   No.
Wait.

Otto   No?
Does that mean you're going to apologise to him?

Lila   No . . .

Otto   OK.
Now grab her legs –
That's it –

He has her arms, **Beetle** *has her legs.*

Otto   And it's down to the basement we go –

Lila   I'll bite you –

Otto   I thought you would have learned from last time.
But maybe you like the dankness, the darkness, the locusts
scuttling over your toes –

Lila   OK, OK, OK I'm SORRY.

Otto   You're sorry?

Lila   Yes.

Otto   Because you said unspeakable things?

Lila   Yes.

Otto   Because Beetle is going to be a Great Man.

Lila   Yes.

Otto   He's going to be a rich, successful entrepreneur with a gold watch and a beautiful wife and three strong sons who'll win all the prizes and trophies and tournaments?

Lila   Yes . . .

Otto   OK.
Good.

He puts her down.

We love you, sis.
We just need you to understand and accept certain facts.

Lila   OK.

Otto   Love you.
OK?

Lila   Yes.

Otto   Say it.

Beat.

Lila   Love you too.

Scene Four

The **Husband**, *the* **Wife**.

The **Husband** *has his arm around his wife's shoulders.*

She is holding a baby who is wrapped in blue blankets.

Husband   The doctor pointed at the screen and he said –
You see that here?
That means it's a girl.
You're going to have a little girl.
My heart!
It leapt.

I looked down at my wife and she –
It took me aback because –
Because she was frowning.
She looked at the doctor and her lips were set and the doctor nodded.
He said 'Can you come in next Wednesday?' and she said –
'Yes.'

Wife   This is Luke.
Our son.
He's going to be very tall and successful and clever.
I can tell.

She displays the baby proudly.

Adelaide *walks past.*

The **Husband** *looks at her.*

Husband   From time to time, I wonder about who she would have been.
My wife says –

Wife   You're being sentimental.

Husband   And I suppose I am.
But yes.
I do wonder.
Sometimes.

Scene Five

Later that day.

The park.

Joey *is lying down, listening to music with his eyes closed.*

Adelaide *is standing over him, watching him.*

She is wearing a sun hat.

Joey *becomes aware of her.*

He opens his eyes.

He starts.

Adelaide   Do you realise you're bright red?

Joey   Um.

Adelaide   I'm protecting you from the sun.
See?

She stretches her arms out so he's in shadow.

Joey   That's OK, I uh –
I was just leaving.

He starts to gather his things.

He tries not to look at **Adelaide**.

Adelaide   No you weren't.

Joey   I was, I –

Adelaide   Don't you remember me?

Beat.

Last night.
I saw you at the window.
You saw me.

Joey   Look, whatever it is you want I don't think I'm the –

Adelaide   I don't want anything.
Honest!
I just saw you were getting sunburned and so I –
Anyway.
Do you want my hat?

Beat.

He inspects the hat.

Joey   This is a girl's hat.

Adelaide   It's unisex.

Joey   You reckon?

She touches his head.

Joey   What are you – ?

Adelaide   Your head is broiled.

Joey   Yeah, well.
I like it broiled.

Adelaide   Don't you know anything about UV rays?

Joey   God, you sound like my mum.

Adelaide   Put it on.

Joey *sighs.*

He puts it on – his head is really hot after all.

Adelaide *tries not to smile.*

Joey   What were you doing in my garden anyway?
You and the other –
Girls.

Adelaide   Ha!
We ate your carrots.

Joey   I saw.

Adelaide   And your radishes.
What are you listening to?

Joey   Uh –
Just –

He offers her a headphone.

Adelaide   I like it.

Joey   Yeah?

Adelaide   Very loud.

Joey   Yeah I know but −

Adelaide   Can't be good for you.

Joey   Where did you all come from?

Adelaide   Just think of what's happening to your eardrums!

Joey   Are you from across the border?

Adelaide *turns the music up really loud.*

Joey   Hey.

Adelaide   Doesn't it go any louder?

Joey   Hey don't, you'll break it −

They tussle over his phone.

Verity *and* **June** *appear and sit on a bench slightly apart from* **Joey**.

Joey *is immediately alert − he lets* **Adelaide** *take his phone.*

He sits up straighter.

Verity *and* **June** *do not appear to be aware of him.*

Adelaide *observes the situation.*

Adelaide   Which one you got the hots for then?

Joey   Can you not?!

Adelaide   Go on!
I won't tell.

Verity *and* **June** *shake their hair out of their ponytails.*

They run their fingers through their hair.

They tie their hair up again.

Joey   To be honest −
I'd go for either.

Adelaide   Pah.
That's not very discriminating.

Joey   You can't afford to be picky.
There isn't the time.
Or the resources.

Adelaide   Why's that?

Joey   Because of the Girl Deficit.
Obviously!

Beat.

Adelaide   Go and talk to them then.
Sounds like you haven't got a moment to lose.

Joey   Don't feel like it.

Adelaide   Aww go on!

Joey   I can't just –
Go up to them and start –
Babbling!

Adelaide   Yeah you can.

Joey   Do you not know anything?
There are systems.
Hierarchies.

Adelaide   So?

Joey   So they're way, way, way at the top.
And I'm *way* down at the bottom because, *durr*.
Weird taste in music according to *everyone*.
And my inhaler.

Adelaide   Oh, stop feeling so sorry for yourself.

Joey   What?

Adelaide   Go and tell the small one she's the most
ravishing creature you've ever seen.

Joey   God!
Do you not know – ?!
That is *so* not how it works.

Adelaide   How does it work then?

Joey   You wait.
For them to pick you.
Based on your attributes and skills.

Adelaide   What are your attributes and skills?

Joey   Well –

Adelaide   Exactly.

She picks up a pebble and chucks it at **Verity** *and* **June**.

They look up.

Verity   Yes?

Joey *looks at* **Adelaide** *in panic.*

She nods at him encouragingly.

Joey   Uh.
I was just thinking that it's uh –
Lovely day!

Verity   Is it?

Joey   Well . . .

June   It's about a million degrees.
As usual.

Verity   It stinks.

June   As usual.

Beat.

He turns to **Adelaide**.

Joey (*hissed*)   What did you do that for?

Adelaide   Well, what kind of piss-poor effort was that?!

Joey (*hissed*)   You panicked me!

June (*to* **Joey**)   Don't you live on my road?

Joey, *amazed, swings back round to face her.*

Joey   Do I?

June   Yeah.
I hear your music through the walls sometimes.

Joey   Oh.
Sorry.

June   No, I like it.

Joey   Really?!

Verity *nudges* **June**.

Otto, **Beetle** *and* **Riley** *approach.*

June *adopts a bored face.*

June   Whatever.
It's OK.

Verity (*under her breath*)   Why is he wearing a girl's hat?

Joey   Cos I'll make you a tape, if you like?

Verity   Shouldn't you be watching *Star Trek* or something?

Joey   I –
I hate *Star Trek*.

Otto *and* **Beetle** *cluster possessively around the girls.*

Riley *towers over* **Joey**.

Riley   Is the nerd pestering you?

June   Aw leave him alone.
He's alright.

Verity   He keeps going on and on about *Star Trek*.

Riley   Yeah?

Joey (*under his breath*)   I hate *Star Trek*.

Riley   Pardon?

Pause.

Joey   I was just explaining that I don't even watch, let alone *enjoy* –

Riley   Why are you wearing a girl's hat?

Joey   It's –
It's unisex . . .

He looks expectantly to **Adelaide** *for confirmation.*

She shrugs.

Riley   Look at the state of you, Joey.
Aren't you ashamed?
Aren't you ashamed to let these beautiful, graceful women see you in this state?
Where's your pride, man?
Where's your dignity?

Joey   It's –
I was just thinking about the UV rays . . .

Riley *goes right up to* **Joey**.

He holds him by his collar and pulls him really close.

Joey *holds his breath and squeezes his eyes tightly shut.*

Riley *seems to think about it then gradually lets him go.*

Riley   Listen, Joey.
It's the weekend.
We just want to relax in the park and feel good about ourselves, yeah?

Joey   Yes.

Riley   And it would probably make everyone feel better if you just took yourself off.
Maybe to a darkened room somewhere.

That smells of dirty socks and empty yoghurt cartons.
Communing with your Dungeons and Dragons or whatever.
Yeah?

Joey OK.

Riley Cos this is a space for –
Well –
Real Men.

Pause.

Joey OK, I'm going.

Riley Have a good one, Joey!
Hey –
We're mates, right?

Joey Yeah.

Riley Course we are!

Verity *and* **June** *laugh as* **Joey** *slinks away.*

Joey (*to* **Adelaide**)   See.
Told you.

Adelaide They'll get their come-uppance in the end.

Joey I bet they won't.

Adelaide Bet you they will.

Joey What do you know about it?

Adelaide Never you mind.
Bye.

Scene Six

Psychologist *and* **Mo**.

Psychologist Now I'm just going to ask you a series of
very simple questions which I'd like you to answer as

honestly as you can.
OK?

Mo   Um, OK.

Psychologist   Don't look so terrified!
It's easy as pie, I promise.

Mo   Right.

*The **Psychologist** flicks a switch on a recording device.*

He clears his throat.

Psychologist   Now.
Do you ever feel unhappy?

Mo   Uh.
Not particularly?

Psychologist   Stressed?
Strung out?

Mo   Well.
Exams are coming up so –

Psychologist   Does the extreme competitiveness of the
male environment unsettle you?

Mo   I don't think so . . . ?

Psychologist   Do you feel you have attributes and skills
that lend you a competitive edge?

Mo   Well.
I do alright.
In school, and stuff.

Psychologist   Any sisters?

Mo   No.

Psychologist   Girlfriend?

Beat.

Mo   Not at the moment.

The **Psychologist** *makes a note.*

Psychologist   What about urges?

Mo   Urges?

Psychologist   Strong urges.

Mo   Uh . . .

Psychologist   Do you feel that you suffer from excessive
uh –
Energies?

Mo   I play a lot of sport?

Psychologist   Ah?

Mo   I'm in the tennis firsts.
And the football team.
Second division.

Psychologist   Which position?

Mo   Right midfield.

Psychologist   Ah ha.

Mo   Cross-country.
Fencing.
Indoor rock-climbing.

Psychologist   I'm a rugby man myself!

Mo   Oh?

Psychologist   Do you play?

Mo   No.

Psychologist   Not to worry.
Excellent.
Sporty.
We like that!
A fine way to manage the masculine propensity for violence,

wouldn't you say?
Do you shoot?

Mo   No.

Psychologist   Shame but.
Probably for the best.
Ha!

Mo   Mm.

Psychologist   Very well!
Thank you very much indeed for answering my questions.
Fascinating!
Now if you wouldn't mind sending in the next –

Mo   Sorry but –
Why does everyone always say that?

Psychologist   Hm?

Mo   The 'masculine propensity for violence'.

Psychologist   Well now . . .

Mo   As if we're all just –
I don't know –
Lunks.

Psychologist   Dear oh dear, don't take it personally!
We're merely taking precautions.

Mo   You can't just –
Write us off like that.
As if we're just this unwieldy mass of, I don't know –
Toxic testosterone.

Psychologist   Listen.
You're nervous.
Worried.
It's understandable.

Mo   I'm not nervous –

Psychologist You're concerned you might not get picked and have to be sent away.
Of course you are!
But between you and me, you're a very attractive candidate.

Mo That's not what I was –

Psychologist Strong!
Tall!
Reassuring!
It's what every girl wants!
Just be patient.

Mo You're not listening to me.
That's not my concern.
That is not my concern at all.

Psychologist That will be all, uh, Mo.

Mo That's it?

Psychologist NEXT!

Scene Seven

Outside the girls' school.

The next day.

Alice, **Abbie** and **Anna** *are sitting in a circle on the ground, playing a clapping game.*

Lila *watches them, puzzled.*

Pause.

Lila Excuse me, um.
Excuse me?

They ignore her.

I've actually been told to –
Well.
Ask you to leave.

Pause.

Lila   I'm a monitor.
I'm Head Monitor.
Which I'm not proud of or anything, I'm not being a dick,
but it gives me this tiny piece of authority that I get to wield
every now and again and –
Well.

Pause.

Lila   Look.
The thing is you're on school property.
So . . .
Can you –
Go?

The girls smile to each other and continue.

Lila   Hello?
Um.
Hi?

A **Young Man** *appears in a hard hat, wearing a badge, carrying a clipboard and a tape-measure.*

He starts measuring things importantly.

Lila *stares at him.*

Lila *(to the girls)*   Okay.
I'll come back to you in a –
Because I really can't let you stay here but –
But just wait for one minute, okay?

She steels herself and then marches up to the **Young Man**.

Lila   Um, excuse me.
Excuse me?

Young Man   What?

Lila   What exactly are you doing?

Young Man   Uh, measuring.

Lila   I can see that.
Why?

Young Man   What's it to you?

Lila (*pointing to his badge*)   You work for my dad's company.

Young Man   Then you'll know what we're doing, won't you?

Lila   Yes.
But I want to hear you say it out loud.

Young Man   Tsk.
We're preparing for the imminent demolition.
Out of the way, please.

Lila   Do you realise just what it is you're demolishing?

Young Man   I don't have time for this.

Lila   You're demolishing people's future.
You're demolishing people's *dreams*.

Young Man   Oh no!
Not people's dreams!
Boo-hoo!

Alice *jumps up, sneaks up behind him, and grabs the* **Young Man***'s tape-measure.*

Young Man   Oi!

He lunges for it.

Alice *throws it to* **Abbie**.

Abbie *throws it to* **Anna**.

Young Man   I really don't have time for stupid girls' games
–

Anna *throws it to* **Lila** *who holds it high above her head.*

Young Man   What the hell do you think you're doing?

Lila   What do you think *you're* doing?
Mindlessly obeying orders without a thought for the consequences.

Young Man   I'm telling your dad –

Lila   People like you are dangerous.
Your ignorance should come with a, a toxic warning!

He lunges yet again for the tape-measure.

Anna *grabs the hard hat off his head and frisbees it offstage.*

He stares after it, appalled.

He looks to **Lila**, *then in the direction of his hat.*

He chooses the hat and begins to run offstage.

Young Man   This isn't over!

Lila   Nope!
Next time I'll castrate you with that tape-measure!

He exits.

Lila *clears her throat and looks sheepishly at the other girls.*

They smile at each other – a moment of intimacy between them.

Lila   Well, uh.
Small victories.
Um.
Thanks.

Pause.

Do I know you?

Alice   Just how imminent is this imminent demolition?

Lila   I'm not sure.
Dad won't tell me.

Abbie   Can you find out?

Lila   Believe me, I'm trying.

Anna   Hack into his computer.

Lila   I've tried.

Alice   What you need is a riot.

Lila   Exactly.

Alice   Loudspeakers.

Lila   Yes!

Abbie   Placards and slogans.

Lila   Perfect!

Anna   You could chain yourself to the bulldozers.

Abbie   Create a human shield.

Lila   There's just one small problem.

Abbie   Which is?

Lila   Crowds.
That's one thing we don't have.
And it's the one thing a riot definitely needs.

Pause.

Abbie   We're a crowd.

Lila   Not really.

Abbie   There's more of us.

Beat.

Lila   Is there?

Abbie   Uh-huh.

Lila   Enough for a riot?

Anna   Enough for several.

Lila   Wow.
OK.

Anna   Think about it.

Lila   I will.
Thanks.

Beat.

Alice   We've got company.

Lila   What?

Alice   Look.

Riley, **Mo**, **Otto** *and* **Beetle** *are trying to peer into a window of the school.*

Beetle *stands on* **Otto**'s *shoulders.*

Lila   Oh God.

Anna   Who are they?

Lila   They're from the boys' school next door.
Two of them unfortunately happen to be related to me.

Abbie   What are they doing?

Lila   They're trying to see into the changing room.

Anna   Why?

Lila   Verity and June just finished ballet class.

Beat.

Alice *whistles.*

The boys turn.

They see the girls.

They amble over.

The boys stare at the girls.

Riley *steps forward.*

Riley Hi.

Alice Hello.

Anna Hello.

Abbie Hello.

Pause.

Riley Have we met?

Lila You're not supposed to be here –

Otto Shut up, Lila.

Riley I don't believe I've had the pleasure.

Beetle (*to* **Lila**) He wasn't talking to you.

Riley I was talking to –

Alice Alice.

Riley Alice.
And . . . ?

Abbie I'm Abbie.

Anna Anna.

Riley Hi.

He smiles.

Pause.

Riley Whereabouts you from?

Abbie We're from around.

Riley Round where?

Anna The other side.

Riley Of?

Beat.

Abbie The town.

Riley   I see.

Beetle (*to* **Anna**)   Are you wearing perfume?

Anna   No. It's just my natural smell.

Beetle   Wow.

Otto   Can I carry your bag for you?

Abbie   I don't have a bag.

Otto   Can I carry –
You?

Abbie   Alright.

He lifts her up.

Lila   What the hell are you doing?

Mo   Hey, Lila.

Lila   Oh.
Hi.

Mo   I like your –
Hair today.

Beetle *guffaws.*

Lila   Um.
Thanks.

Pause.

Alice   So.
What is there to do around here then?

Riley   Everything.

Alice   I don't believe you.

Riley   I can show you.

Alice   Is that your motorbike?

Riley   Yeah.

Alice   How fast does it go?

Riley   As fast as you want.

Alice   Okay.
We'll see about that.

Beetle (*to* **Anna**)   Do you want a piggyback too?

Anna   Sure.

She climbs on to **Beetle***'s back.*

They exit, apart from **Lila** *and* **Mo***.*

Lila   Why do you hang out with them?

Mo   You know.
Something to do.

Beat.

Mo   I'd rather hang out with –
You though.
But you know that.

Beat.

Lila   Mo, I –

Mo   I know.

Lila   I can't –
I don't want to just be someone's saviour.

Mo   I know.
I get it.

Pause.

Lila   You should go with them.

Mo   Lila –

Lila   I'm sorry.

Mo *hesitates.*

Then he runs to catch up with the others.

Scene Eight

Verity *and* **June** *in the changing room – the one the boys were just peering into.*

A few minutes earlier.

Verity   Are they there?

June   Yes.

Verity   You sure?

June   I can see the tip of Otto's nose.
Oh, and Beetle's on his shoulders.

Verity   Is Riley there?

June   Yes.

Verity   Is he looking at me.

June   He's trying to.

Verity *preens for a second.*

Then she shifts.

For God's sake.
What do they think we are?

June   Yeah.
Performing monkeys?

Verity   They think we exist just for them?
Their delectation?

June   What are we?
Pieces of art hanging in a big white gallery?

Verity   We should charge them.

June   We *should* charge them.

Verity *takes her top off so she is just standing in her bra.*

Verity   What do they expect me to do?
Strip naked and do a little dance?

June   Basically they do expect that.

Verity   You know what I'd like?

June   What?

Verity   I'd like to be able to sit on a bench.
By myself.
With a massive plate of chocolate cake.
No one loitering behind the trees.
No panting boy asking if he can touch my hair.
No pretend-men flexing their pretend-muscles.
Just me.
On my own.
Eating an entire chocolate cake in the sunshine.
And then burping.

June   Sounds amazing.

Pause.

Verity   But the depressing thing is –
I'd probably miss it.

June   Yeah.

Verity   I like them looking at me.
Waiting for me.
Tucking little love letters in my blazer pocket.

June   I know.

Verity   Makes me feel kind of special.
Powerful.

June   Yes.

Verity   How messed up is that?

June   It makes sense.

Verity   Does he even like me?
I mean *like* me.
Like *me*.

June   Riley?
Course he does.

Verity   I dunno.

June   He *totally* does!

Verity   Sometimes I think he doesn't even see me.
He just sees –
Something girl-shaped.

June   Go on then.
Show him your girl shape.

Verity   No, dickhead!

June   Go on –
Or flash him!

Verity   Nooooo!

June *tries to push* **Verity** *up against the window.*

They struggle, laughing.

Up close to the window, **June** *notices something.*

June   Shit.
They've gone.

Verity   What?!

She rubs the window and peers out.

They stare.

Who –
Who are all those girls?

June   Dunno . . .

They look.

June   Maybe they're visiting . . .

Verity   From where?

June   Dunno.

They look.

Verity   What's Riley doing?

June   He's helping her on to the back of his motorbike –

Verity   I can *see* that –

June   You asked.

Verity   Who is she?

June   Never seen her before in my life.

Verity   What the hell does she think she's playing at?

June   God.
Look at them.

They look.

They're a bit beautiful.
Aren't they?

Verity   Don't *say* that.

June   They're sort of –
Glowing.

Pause.

She's got her arms around his waist –

Verity   I can't watch.

June   She's laying her head on his back.
Ugh, vomit.

Verity   No.

June   She's holding on really tight –

Verity   Shut *up*.

June   She's laughing.
They're all really, really laughing.
God's sake, nothing's *that* funny.

Verity *starts angrily putting her top back on.*

Verity   This isn't how it goes.
This is our territory.
They can't just march in and, and trample on our territory!

June   Yeah.
Bitches.

Verity   We need to –
Mark it somehow.

June   Pee on it?

Verity   Don't be *stupid*.

June   I'm sorry.

Verity   Well.
If they want a war.
They can have one.

Scene Nine

Journalist *and* **Farmer**.

The **Journalist** *has a microphone.*

He/she thrusts it in the **Farmer**'s *face.*

Journalist   Can you tell us a little bit about what you saw?

Farmer   Oh it was very strange!

Journalist   Could you elaborate?

Farmer   Now I was getting the cows into the barn for the night, with the help of Pam (she's my dog and very dutiful she is too).

Journalist   Uh-huh.
And – ?

Farmer   And the cows –
They seemed very agitated.
Which is rather unusual as they're generally very placid creatures.
As you'll know.

Journalist   Uh-huh.
If you could stick to the . . . ?

Farmer   So I swung my torch around, bit curious I was, and, lo and behold, the absolute last thing I expected to see I can tell you!

Journalist   And what was that?

Farmer   Why, it was crowded with young women!
Hundreds of them there were!
All bunched up on bales of hay and washing themselves in the water troughs!

Journalist   Without any clothes on?

Farmer   I –
Shouldn't like to say.

Journalist   Extraordinary.

Farmer   That is absolutely the word for it!

Journalist   And what do you make of the theory that these are girls who have been trafficked against their will from across the border, in order to rectify the Girl Deficit?

Farmer   Oh no!
Nothing like that.
They were happy as anything they were.
Laughing.

Journalist   And where are they now?

Farmer   Oh, they're still there.
We've grown quite fond of them as it happens.
Although the cows aren't so sure!
What with dropping dead with the ague every few minutes!

Journalist   So you're saying the girls have infected your cows with some kind of deadly disease?

Farmer   Ah well.
Easy come, easy go.

Journalist   You're saying the girls are actually damaging your livelihood, in a manner of speaking?

Farmer   Way I see it –
It's nice to have them around, that's the honest truth of it.
It's nice to have them around.

Beat.

Journalist   Thank you very much for speaking with me.

Scene Ten

Lila *walks by with a placard saying* SAVE OUR SCHOOL.

She waves it encouragingly.

Lila   Save our SCHOOL!
Down with the sports centre!
Save the GIRLS' SCHOOL!

Scene Eleven

The local swimming pool.

There is a very tall diving board.

Joey *is alone, wearing a hoodie and reading a book, headphones in.*

Riley, **Mo** *and* **Beetle** *sit with* **Alice**, **Abbie** *and* **Anna**.

They rub sun-cream on their backs.

Alice   You missed a spot.

Riley *obediently rubs in more cream.*

Adelaide *appears and sits down beside* **Joey**.

Adelaide   Aren't you boiling?

Joey   No.
A bit.

Adelaide   Take it off then.

Joey   I dunno.
It smells nice.

Adelaide   It smells of whatever you ate for dinner last night.

She sniffs.

Spam?

Joey *tuts and flings his hoodie off.*

Pause.

Adelaide   What's up?

Joey   Nothing.

Adelaide   Come on.
You can tell me.

Joey   It's just –
Well, look!

Adelaide *looks.*

Joey   I don't get it.
There's girls everywhere all of a sudden!
You can't move for girls!

All smiling and sun-kissed and smelling of sun-cream.
And *still* none of them want to talk to me.

Adelaide   *I'm* talking to you.

Joey   Yeah but.
You don't count.

Adelaide   Why don't I count?

Joey   Well.
You're like me.

Adelaide   What?

Joey   Invisible.

Pause.

Alice   So what now?

Riley   What do you mean – now?
We're relaxing in the sun.
It's beautiful!

Alice   We're bored of that.
Now we want to do something else.

Abbie   Something interesting.

Anna   Something different.

Beat.

Riley   Different, eh?
How about something truly amazing?

Anna   I'm intrigued.

Riley   Wanna see me dive?

Alice   Are you any good?

Riley   I'm the best.

Otto *laughs to himself.*

Riley   How about a competition?
Me and Mo.

Beetle   Why Mo?

Mo   Yeah.
Why me?

Riley   Ooh.
Are you scared?

Mo   No.

Riley   Scared of falling flat on your belly?
KER-PLASH!

Mo   What?

Riley   Embarrassing!

Abbie   Are you scared, Mo?

Mo   Course I'm not.

Anna   It's really high.

Mo   I'm not scared.
I just –
Don't fancy it.

Riley   Chicken!

Beetle   Why not my brother?
He's better than Riley.

Anna   Is he?

Beetle   You should see back home!
Trophies and medals and framed certificates!
Literally everywhere!

Otto   That is true.

Riley   Bullshit.

Beetle   When he dives he doesn't even break the surface of
the water.

Otto   I don't.

Alice   Now that I'd like to see.

Abbie   A contest!

Anna   We can mark you both out of ten.

Abbie   But be warned – we're a very tough crowd.

Anna   Very exacting standards.

Riley   I'd expect nothing less.

Alice   So is it on?

Riley   Course it's on!
That's right, isn't it, Otto?

Pause.

Otto   Fine.
It's on.

Otto and **Riley** *stand up and face each other.*

Adelaide (*to* **Joey**)   It's starting.

Joey   What is?

Adelaide   You'll see.

Otto and **Riley** *shake hands.*

Alice   We want a perfect swallow's dive to start.

Anna   Not a ripple on the water.

Alice   Strong, straight arms.
Legs taut.
Chin tucked in.

Riley   Not a problem.

Otto   May the best man win.

They look at each other.

Alice   The highest board, of course.

Riley Obviously.

Otto Naturally.

Mo But –
It's rotten.

Beetle What?

Mo They've got a bit of tape across it.
Look.

They look.

Alice He's right.

Anna That just makes it extra exciting.

Abbie Extra dramatic.

Riley Yeah!
You reckon that's gonna stop me?

Mo It might give you pause for thought . . .

Riley Am I a man or am I a mouse?

Otto I don't care about a bit of tape.

Beetle He doesn't care!

Alice So who's going first?

Beat.

Riley I will.

He begins to climb the steps of the diving board, slowly.

He is more nervous than he is letting on.

He reaches the top.

Mo Careful, Riley.

Riley Shut up.
Don't need to be careful.

Mo It looks a bit –

Riley   Shut *up*.

He walks to the very end of the diving board.

He looks down.

He swallows.

He raises his arms above his head.

He prepares to jump –

Scene Twelve

The next day.

The park.

Otto, **Beetle** *and* **Mo**.

Mo   Are we gonna talk about it or or what?

Pause.

Mo   Are we gonna talk about Riley?

Pause.

Guys?
Don't you think we should at least –

Beetle   They're just –
Beautiful.
Aren't they?
The girls.

Otto   Yes.

Pause.

Beetle   It gives me a pain.
Here.

Otto   Yeah.

Beetle   A good pain.
A sort of –
Pure pain.

Otto   That's exactly it.

Beetle   I just want to look at her all the time.

Otto   Yes.

Beetle   I want to –
Hold her earlobes.

Otto   Yeah.

Beetle   Squeeze them.
Really gently.

Otto   I'd like to do that.

Beetle   I miss her.

Otto   I know.
It's agony.

Beetle   You feel it too?

Otto   Yes.

Beetle   They wouldn't leave us.
Would they?

Otto   Course not.

Mo   Guys?
Seriously.
Why aren't we talking about what happened yesterday?

Pause.

You don't think it's strange?

Otto   Think what's strange?

Mo   The way they've just –
Appeared.
Out of thin air.

Beetle   No.

Mo   And then Riley goes and –
You know?

Otto   You question things too much.

Mo   But –

Otto   The point is they're here.
And we have to do whatever it takes to make sure they stay.
Right?

Beetle   Right.

Otto   Because they're basically our salvation.

Pause.

Mo   You ever heard of the Furies?

Otto   What?

Mo   Infernal goddesses with snakes in their hair.
Wreaking divine vengeance.
Justice.

Beetle   What's justice got to do with anything?

Mo   Just cos we can't see those snakes.
Doesn't mean they're not there.

Beetle (*pointing*)   They're here!

Alice, **Abbie** and **Anna** *enter carrying beach towels, hats, sunglasses, etc.*

Alice   Is the car ready?

Beetle   You came!
We were getting worried.

Abbie   You got air-conditioning?

Otto   Only the best for you.

Anna   Shotgun!

Beetle   Don't you want to sit next to me?

Anna   I will on the way back.

Beetle   You promise?

Mo *edges away.*

Abbie   Where you going, Mo?

Pause.

Mo   I'm not gonna come.

Otto   What?!

Mo   Don't fancy it.

Abbie   Oh.
That's a shame.

Beetle   Why don't you want to come to the beach?
It'll be brilliant!

Mo   I just –
Maybe I got too much sun yesterday.

Beetle   Ah, don't be boring!

Mo   Bit of sunstroke.

Pause.

Alice   Oh well.
We'll see you later though.

Pause.

We'll come and find you.
Alright, Mo?

Pause.

Mo   Don't drive too fast.
The cliff road's a bit hairy.

Otto   I know what I'm doing.

Mo   Yeah.
I hope you do.

Scene Thirteen

The girls' school playground.

Verity *is weeping dramatically.*

June *strokes her hair.*

Lila *enters brandishing her placard saying* SAVE OUR SCHOOL.

Lila   Save our SCHOOL!
Education for ALL!
NO discrimin-ATION!

Verity *weeps.*

Lila   What's the matter with her?

June   What do you think?
She's *devastated*.

Lila   Why?

June   Didn't you hear?
About Riley?

Lila   Hear what?

June   God, Lila.
Do you live on the moon or something?

Lila   I've been campaigning –

June   First he dumps her for that stupid new girl.
Then he goes and drowns.
In the *swimming* pool.
Such an *idiot*.

Lila   He –
What?

June   He dived all wrong and smashed his head open.
And broke his neck apparently.

Lila   My –
God.

June   He was with *them*.

Lila   Them?

June   You know.
The *new* girls.

Lila   I –
I can't believe it.

Verity   Fucking *bastard*.

June   She's completely *mad* with *grief*.

Verity   How dare he?
How *dare* he?
How dare he go and *die*?

Lila   I don't think he did it on purpose –

Verity   It's them.
Them.
Ever since they came to this town they've snaked their way
into the heart of everything.
And made it *rot*.

Lila   But.
It was an accident.
Just an accident.

Verity   Ugh, they give me the *creeps*!

Lila   I –
I don't know what you mean.

Verity   They want us to suffer even though we haven't *done*
anything.

Lila   But –
What about the school?
They're going to help us save the school.

June   How can you be thinking about *school* at a time like this?

Lila   Because it's important.

June   Not as important as Riley's head exploding like a *pumpkin*.

Lila   Well no, but.
That's awful of course but.
I don't think you can really blame them for an *accident* –

Verity   You're kidding yourself, Lila.
They're trying to mess us up.
Rip us apart.
And it's working.

Lila   What are you talking about?!
Rip us apart!
That's ridiculous!

Beetle   LILA!

He runs onstage and straight into **Lila***'s arms.*

He is soaking wet.

Lila   What?
What's the matter?

Beetle *moans.*

Lila   Beetle?
Why are you soaking wet?

Beetle   They –
The car, it –
I don't know how it happened, it –

Lila   What are you talking about?
What car?

Beetle   Otto was driving.
I was in the back with, with the . . .
We were singing and we had the windows down and it was
all great –

Lila   Who was singing?

Beetle   And then something ran out –
It looked like a girl but I couldn't –
I didn't –

Lila   Slow down.

Beetle   Otto swerved to avoid her and we –
He pranged into the barrier.
But the barrier just –
It just crumbled away.

Lila   What?

Beetle   And we just –
Into the water.
I got the door open somehow but Otto –

Lila   Otto –
What?

Beetle   I can't find him.
I can't find him.

June   Oh my God?!

Lila   What do you mean, you can't find him?

Beetle   And the girls they just –
They were just sitting on the shore.
Watching me.
They were completely dry.

Lila   Beetle you're not making any sense.

Adelaide *enters.*

Beetle   It was *her*.
She's the one who walked out into the road.
She did it!

Adelaide *sees* **Beetle**.

She grins, waves, then runs.

Beetle *chases after her.*

Beetle   Hey!
You!
Come back here!
You killed my brother!

He exits.

Lila *sinks to her knees.*

Verity   Now do you believe me?

Lila   He can't be dead.
He can't be.
It must be a mistake.

Verity   I personally am not standing for any more of this
nonsense.

June   Bloody hell.
Bloody *hell*.

Verity   Maybe they're like zombies.

June   What do you mean?

Verity   Blunt instruments to the head.

June   We don't have any blunt instruments.

Verity *spots* **Lila***'s sign.*

Verity   Yes we do.

She picks up the sign.

She and **June** *look at each other.*

Verity   Come on.

She and **June** *exit carrying* **Lila***'s sign.*

Lila *is alone.*

Mo *enters.*

They look at each other.

Lila   Did –
Were you there?

Mo   No.
I'm really sorry, Lila –

Lila   Did I get it all wrong?
Did I?

Mo   You weren't to know.

Lila   I didn't question it.
I just got so caught up in what I wanted that I didn't notice –

Mo   It's not your fault.

Lila   Well.
Maybe there's still time.

Mo   For what?

Lila   To fix it.

Pause.

Lila   Will you help me?

Mo   Course I will.

Lila   OK.
We're going to have to break into my dad's warehouse.
And steal some heavy-duty machinery.

Mo   Uh . . .
Right . . .

Lila   Right?

He nods.

Mo   Right.

Scene Fourteen

Joey *is pacing, agitated.*

Adelaide *enters.*

Joey   Where have you been?

Adelaide   Just around.

Joey   What have you been doing?

Adelaide   Nothing much –

Joey   What are you doing to them?

Adelaide   Enjoying the sunshine.

Joey   What.
Are you doing to them?

Adelaide   To who?

Joey   You know who!
The boys.

Adelaide   Oh.
Them.

Beat.

Joey   Well?!

Adelaide   What do you care?
They're not your friends.

Joey   That's not the point!

Adelaide   You wanted my help.

Joey   What?
I never said –

Adelaide 'Oh poor me, the game's so hard, I can't win the race, it's just *too* competitive!'

Joey I never said it like that –

Adelaide So I'm just evening it out a little bit.
Redressing the balance.

Joey But –

Adelaide I just want to look out for you.

Joey Why?

Adelaide No one else really does, do they?
You just don't really have anyone, Joey.
Except me.

Pause.

What happened to your sister anyway?

Pause.

Joey How do you know about my sister?

Pause.

She died.
Not that it's any of your business.

Adelaide How did she die?

Joey I don't know.
She was a baby.
Sometimes babies die.

Adelaide Was she covered in spots?

Joey I don't know.
Maybe?

Adelaide How come she got sick and you didn't?

Joey I don't know, do I?!

Adelaide Didn't you share the same room?

Joey   Yes.
So?
Maybe I'm stronger.

Adelaide   You wheeze even when you're sitting still.

Joey   I do not.

Adelaide   You sound like a little drowning turtle most of the time.

Joey   Shut up!

Adelaide   I bet your mum was sad when she died.

Joey   Can you stop going on about it?

Adelaide   Did she cry loads?

Joey   I was a baby, wasn't I?
How should I know?

Adelaide   Or was it your mum all along?

Joey   What?

Adelaide   Did she take a hammer and crack her tiny skull like an egg?

Joey   Okay, now you're being crazy.

Adelaide   Or put her hands around her neck and twist?

Joey   Stop saying this stuff.

Adelaide   Did she creep out into the garden and bury her behind a rosemary bush?

Joey   What?
No.

Anna, **Alice** and **Abbie** *enter*.

They watch.

Adelaide   Funny, isn't it?
When you were born there was a huge feast.

People gorged on teeny-tiny canapés and went blind they drank so much champagne.

Joey   Whatever.
Go away.

Adelaide   The fireworks were so spectacular that a television crew came to film it all.
They were in the *news*!

Joey   Yeah.
So?

Adelaide   But when I was born
Mum and Dad just pursed their lips and frowned and made a tacit agreement.

Joey   I genuinely do not know what you're talking about.

Adelaide   That's because you're not listening –

Joey   Why should I listen to you?!
Since you came along it's just been –
Messy.
Confusing.
Scary.

Adelaide   We just want to make you hear us.
We want to make everyone hear us.

Joey   Hear what?
WHAT?

Alice *steps forward.*

Alice   Is this yours?

She holds out an inhaler.

Joey   No.
I've got mine right –

He pats his pocket.

He pats his other pocket.

Panic.

He starts to wheeze, ever so slightly.

Joey   Okay.
Give it back.

Alice   What'll you give me for it?

Joey   I –
I'm not going to give you anything.
You're just going to –
Give it back.

Alice   That's just typical isn't it?
Such a sense of entitlement.

Abbie *and* **Anna** *nod.*

Joey   You –
Stole it from my –
Pocket.
Why should I –
Beg for it?

Anna   Just another pampered little prince!

Abbie   An exulted little sultan!

Joey   That's not –
Fair.

Alice   It's just take, take, take with you lot.
Isn't it?

Adelaide   Okay.
I think he gets the point.
Maybe you should give it back now –

Abbie   'Oh Mummy, can I have a car?'

Anna   'An iPad in every colour of the rainbow?'

Abbie   'A jacuzzi in my bedroom?'

Joey   What do you –
Want?

Alice   We want you to love us.
Respect us.
Value us.

Abbie   Will you?

Anna   Will you?

Joey   I'm not the one you should be –
I never did –
Anything –

His wheezing gets worse.

Adelaide   Maybe we should . . . ?

June *and* **Verity** *enter, followed by* **Mo** *and* **Beetle**.

June *and* **Verity** *hold up the placard threateningly.*

June   Leave him alone!

Alice   Oh.
How sweet.
The cavalry.

June   He can't breathe, you stupid witch!

Beetle   He never did anything to you.

Alice (*to* **Beetle**)   You had a lucky escape, didn't you?

Beetle   I'm a good swimmer.

Alice   We'll see.

Joey *gasps, barely able to breathe.*

Adelaide *starts to look increasingly worried.*

June *lunges for* **Alice**.

June   Give it *back* or I'll cause you some serious damage!

She wrestles with **Alice**, *attempting to snatch the inhaler.*

Alice *is too strong for her.*

After a moment, **Adelaide** *helps pin* **Alice***'s hands behind her back so that she drops the inhaler.*

June *snatches it quickly and hands it to* **Joey***.*

He breathes into it thankfully.

Verity   Now bugger off!
Or I'll smash your head to a pulp.

Alice   You should be thanking us.
We're doing it for you.

Verity   Yeah well.
What if we don't need your help?

Alice   The bulldozers are coming tomorrow.

Anna   The girls' school will be rubble by the afternoon.

Abbie   Your textbooks and pencil cases and protractors all ground into the dirt.

Alice   How are you going to stop it without us?

Verity   You'd be surprised how loud we can shout.

June (*to* **Joey**)   Are you okay?

Joey   Thanks.
That was amazingly cool.

Verity   Mo?
Are they coming?

Mo   They should be.

Verity   Where are they then?

Beetle   Wait!
I can hear them.

Alice   What are you talking about?

A low rumble.

It gets louder.

The bulldozers.

Adelaide, **Alice**, **Abbie** *and* **Anna** *look at each other.*

Verity, **June**, **Mo** *and* **Beetle** *prepare to run.*

June (*to* **Joey**)   Come on.

Joey   What's happening?

June   It's Lila!

Lila *appears on top of a bulldozer.*

Lila   Woo-hoooo!
Take THAT!

The sound of bulldozers fills the stage.

Scene Fifteen

A few months later.

The park.

Lila *and* **Mo**.

Lila *is writing in her exercise book.*

Mo *sits a little apart from her, reading.*

Every now and again he glances up at her, and smiles to himself.

Lila *looks at him.*

Lila   What?!

Mo   Nothing.

Pause.

I'm glad you don't have to go to the school across the river.

Lila   Me too.
Bloody pain in the arse . . .

Pause.

Mo   Do you think your dad will ever forgive you?

Lila   For hijacking his bulldozers?

Mo   Among other things . . .

Lila   I actually think he's starting to understand.
Slowly.

Pause.

Oh, by the way . . .

She holds out a small photograph.

Mo *takes it.*

He looks at it, then turns it upside down.

Um . . .
What is this?

Lila   A picture of my mum's uterus.

Mo   Uh . . . ?
Okay.

Lila   She's pregnant.

Mo   Seriously?!

Lila   Well, you know . . .
After Otto . . .
Well.

Mo   Yeah.
Yeah.

Pause.

So.
Do you know what it is, yet?

Lila   Yep.

Pause.

It's a girl.

The sound of fireworks.

They look up.

Verity, **June**, **Joey** and **Beetle** *come onstage and watch them too.*

Alice, **Adelaide**, **Anna** and **Abbie** *appear fleetingly.*

They fade into the background.

The rest of them watch the fireworks.

The Boy Preference

BY ELINOR COOK

*Notes on rehearsal and staging drawn from a workshop
with the writer held at the National Theatre, October 2014.
Workshop led by Maria Aberg, with notes by Laura Keefe.*

How the writer came to write the play

Writer Elinor Cook approaches all her work from a feminist perspective. She was inspired to write *The Boy Preference* by Malala Yousafzai's father, who said: 'In order to change the world you have to educate the boys.' Although she was heavily influenced by the growing gender gap in parts of Asia she believes the same attitude towards women pervades here. She wanted to write something for Connections that was fun and joyful, but also harrowing and disturbing without being preachy. She didn't want anyone to be a villain.

Approaching the play

After reading the play director Maria Aberg asked the group: 'What does it mean? What is the play trying to say?' She explained that in preparation for the workshop she had been reading articles about India and China and questioned what happens when men outnumber women and society fears they will become violent. Maria says the job of director is turning ideas into action, analysing the text and then making it practical. Let your actors solve problems and find solutions for difficulties in the script.

Themes

Maria encouraged directors to have a conversation about the themes within the play with their company. Split the cast into groups to do research into each theme. Which themes within the play apply to our world today?

Elinor spoke about the importance of heat within the play as it raises the stakes, and she asked actors and directors to think about what exposing flesh does to young boys' and girls' hormones? It is a 'coming of age' summer that is set in the future, so the temperature has risen due to global warming. She says it is not set in a specific city or country, but she had imagined a wealthy suburb of Delhi when she was writing it.

The play also explores the theme of gender and the difference between male and female behaviour. Maria encouraged companies to think about how being educated separately affects how sexes interact with each other.

Maria suggested finding the rules of the world of the play. This may be making decisions about the following questions.

- Do boys take tests?
- How corporate is the world?
- Do the girls get a choice of boys?
- What are gated communities?
- Is the other school across the river?
- What are the rules about women driving, in reference to the brother being annoyed at Lila?
- At what age can boys drive?
- Define what beauty is in the play? There are so few girls that girls have a lot of value, but their value is their gender.
- What is attractive about what they wear? Is how they look what we deem attractive here and now, or is there a new standard?

If you don't get matched with a girl you get sent away. Elinor saw the leftover boys being sent away to fight wars. The adult society is worried about all the single young men, so all boys have regular psychology meetings.

When do the boys need to marry? In the world of the play, Elinor suggested probably at quite a young age, so the pressure is on. The girls probably get to choose the boys they marry.

Do the boys need to find a woman before being sent away? Elinor said this is a society that is worried about what has happened (the deficit of girls) and is trying to address the imbalance.

Structure

The event at the end of the play is a catalyst for change which allows Lila's mum, only a few months later, to have a baby girl. Lila's act of taking bulldozers from her father's warehouse shows him her strength and changes his opinion of her, as is made clear in the last scene.

Give each scene a title, so your actors have a starting point when you come to rehearse the scene. Choose a title that includes all the characters, so all actors feel involved. It will get your actors thinking about what the scene is about and helps to develop a shared language for the play.

Then decide what each character wants in the scene. Be specific as to what the character wants in the scene, not the entire play. Another way to look at it is: what would be the ideal outcome of the scene for each character? This should give you the characters' 'wants'. Again it is helpful to find 'wants' that involve all characters within the scene. There are no right or wrong answers. Find 'wants' that are helpful to the actor playing the character in that scene. The 'wants' may change during the course of rehearsals.

Language

Furies in Greek mythology were deities of vengeance. Gods used the Furies to effect change.

Ague is a Shakespearean term for disease.

Elinor said that the play mentions 'borders' to highlight that the characters can't leave the world or regime they live in.

Maria said be careful about making decisions where there aren't any clues in the text. It can be unhelpful creating a reality that doesn't exist in the text. Build up profiles from the information within the play.

Scenes Four and Nine, with the Husband and Wife and the Journalist and Farmer, sit slightly outside the play. Suggestions of how that could be staged are: TV adverts; propaganda; live feed; heightened reality; sung or cabaret style. The scenes give the context of the society and wider world of the play.

If a group feels uncomfortable about the implied abortion in the mother and father scene, Elinor is happy for them to change the language used or cut as needed, although it doesn't explicitly state that she is going to have an abortion.

Characters and characterisation

THE NEW GIRLS

Who are they? Are they girls not yet born, or are they ghosts? It is ambiguous who the girls are. Perhaps they are aborted, abandoned or trafficked girls? The new girls bring the boys and girls together to effect change. It would be good to agree as a group who the girls are, as it is hard to play ambiguity.

What happens to the girls at the end? Again this is ambiguous. Are they mown down? Do they leave because their job is done, bringing men and women together – empowering the girls? Are the girls happy or sad at the end?

The power the new girls have over the boys is a hypnotic, sexual attraction. They are new, exciting and exotic. The farmer is affected by them in the same way the boys are. Why are they killing the cows?

Are the new girls always visible to the audience and/or other characters? Are they always present onstage like a Greek chorus, or in the audience always watching/observing?

The girls' actions need to push Lila into action. She becomes a vehicle for their wants. Their 'want' is to warn rather than eliminate all men!

ADELAIDE   Sister of Joey (she looks out for him). Who is Adelaide visible to in each scene? The first beach scene may be a good place to set this up.

JOEY   Fifteen years old.

VERITY AND JUNE   Mean girls. Conforming to what is expected of them. For Verity the 'want' to be desired is probably greater than actually being with that person.

LILA   Lila's mother is deliberately not mentioned as she doesn't have a voice until the end, when she is pregnant with a girl. Lila's dad runs the construction firm. Lila and Mo have an implied love story.

BEETLE   Overweight.

Hierarchy within the groups

THE BOYS
1 Riley
2 Otto
3 Mo
3 Beetle
5 Joey

THE GIRLS
1 Verity
2 Lila
3 June

THE NEW GIRLS
1 Alice
2 Anna
3 Abbie
4 Adelaide

When choosing character names Elinor did not want to locate them in a country or certain ethnicity.

Casting

Elinor had imagined the characters to be around sixteen to eighteen years old.

Doubling the new girls' characters would give more parts. Like a Greek chorus, each girl role could be split between a number of women.

When casting Verity it isn't about who is most beautiful but who plays the part best.

Think of ways you could include more cast members and involve more performers, such as using them as a choir or to make the sound effects.

Production, staging and design

The world in which the play is set is affluent. Elinor sees the world as sharp, bright and clean. Maria suggested it could be useful to find visual references, such as photos, films, art, music videos, etc. When thinking about designing and staging a show, get the cast involved in the design. Ask them to bring in images.

DESIGN EXERCISE

Come up with a concept for the entire play using only one of the following elements:

Sound and music

Food and drink

Colour

Lighting

Costume

Here are some examples.

Sound and music

Use music to locate the world of the play and also the location of each scene. Perhaps by using electro/Asian-inspired music, or clean-cut pop. It could be very effective to have a sound motif for certain characters or locations. For example, to identify the new girls, a siren could be sounded whenever they appear. Sound could be used to suggest heat, e.g. crickets. Other possible sound effects could be firecrackers or fireworks as mentioned in the text, and summer holiday songs to show the season. Sound could also be used for the bulldozers (you don't need a literal bulldozer). Similarly, for the diving-board scene you could record some sound from your local swimming pool.

Food and drink

Everyone except the other girls eats. To show the heat, characters could always be drinking fluids and eating ice creams and lollipops.

Colour

You could put the new girls all in the same colour. Or use colour to be gender specific. Boys in blue, girls in pink. The strength and shade of the colour could show the hierarchy and social status of characters, for example going from black and white to colour. The presence of the girls could infiltrate colour into the costumes and/or the set. If you choose a colour, think about how it can then be used, not only in costumes but also in props and setting. What colour writing is on the placards, for example?

Lighting

You could use lights to make the girls glow. This could be achieved with torches or with UV light if the girls wear white. To create the heat, warm, bright colours could be used on stage. The diving board could be marked out with lights on the floor and two strong lights could represent the headlights of a bulldozer. You could use an overhead projector to do the diving scene with water. Light could also be used to create shadow when the girls are on stage, to make it feel like there are more of them.

Costume

It may be helpful to find a visual aid to show the characters conforming and to identify the various tribes. Costume could be an easy way to do this. Different groups could be identified by colour or style. How do you identify hierarchy within tribes? How do you get girls to glow? Perhaps by using glow-in-the-dark wristbands or LED lights in costumes. Maybe the audience is given glow sticks so they glow and create the illusion there are more girls. Maybe only female audience members are given glow sticks.

Costumes suggestions for the boys: sporty, Krazy Gang, Edwardian schoolboys, public schoolboys, rugby kit.

The new girls: saris, colourful, feminine, Greek chorus, floaty.

Costume could show heat: board shorts, Hawaian shirts, etc.

You could mix eras of costumes to differentiate between new girls and others, i.e modern costumes for the boys and girls and Greek classical costumes for new girls.

How to costume the new girls probably ties in to who you see them as.

Style and technique

To find or demonstrate the style or atmosphere for the play you are trying to create maybe find other films, plays, etc. as points of reference to share with the company.

The clapping game played by the new girls draws on the witches from *Macbeth* and has a ritualistic feeling, like an incantation. The game is very young and childish – almost at odds with their age. When developing the clapping game with your actors it might be interesting to get them to make up the clap themselves.

Character exercises for use in rehearsals

CHARACTER EXERCISE

- Choose a character. Extract all the facts from the text about the character. Then decide what questions would be helpful to answer about them. What is the super-objective for your character (their overall 'want' in the play)? What is at stake for them if they don't achieve their super-objective?

Be careful with super-objectives. There is a difference between what someone wants to achieve in their lifetime and what they want to achieve in the play.

This exercise points out the complexities and contradictions in the characters and will encourage actors not to resort to stock characters or stereotypes.

STATUS GAMES

• Pick a leader in the group and walk around the space. Everyone tries to emulate the leader. Then create a greeting and use it throughout the group. Walk around greeting each other and see how it filters down the hierarchy of the group. How responsive are the group to the leader and their presence?

Suggested references

Both Maria and Elinor suggested researching the one-child policy in China and other areas. This research may be interesting to do with your group.

The Edelweiss Pirates

Pirates

By Ayub Khan Din

Germany, 1943. The Second World War rages into its fourth year. All internal opposition has been viciously silenced and the population follow blindly behind Adolf Hitler and his policies of total war and domination. Though the majority of young Germans have been brainwashed into Nazi Party policies from an early age, others are becoming disgruntled by the lack of basic freedoms, tired of every aspect of their lives being dictated by the state, from what they are allowed to do in their free time to who is acceptable to the Nazi state to call a friend.

Around Germany, small groups of youths form themselves into societies, some just to listen and dance to banned music and be with like-minded teenagers, others becoming more aware that it is they, the youth of the country, who have to start resisting the Nazis, in whatever ways they can. One such group was the 'Edelweiss Pirates' of Cologne, a group who found the courage to say no, enough is enough: there are still people in Germany with a conscience and moral convictions to stand up to the regime, even though they may have to pay a terrible price for their convictions.

Age suitability: 13+

Cast size:
10 main characters
and large chorus which includes singing.

Contains strong themes throughout.

Ayub Khan Din was born in 1961 and grew up in Salford. After leaving school he worked briefly as a hairdresser before enrolling in drama school, where he wrote his first stage play, *East Is East* (1997), for Tamasha Theatre Company. It was first staged at the Royal Court Theatre in London and has been produced many times since. It was subsequently adapted by Ayub into a highly successful feature film. Both play and film have won numerous awards including Evening Standard Best Film Award, the Writers' Guild Awards for Best New Writer and Best West End Play, and the John Whiting Award for Best Stage Play. *West Is West*, a sequel film, was released in 2010.

Other plays include *All the Way Home*, produced at the Lowry Theatre, Salford, in 2011, and *Rafta Rafta* (2007), an adaptation of Bill Naughton's 1960s play *All in Good Time*, which was first produced at the National Theatre, London, and then by the New Group in New York. *Rafta Rafta* won an Olivier Award for Best New Comedy in 2008. Ayub's screen adaptation of *All in Good Time* was released as a feature film in 2012.

Characters

Juergan Bauer
Klaus Becker
Dieter Ackerman
Petra Gleissner
Benjamin Dressler
Rutger Shriener
Narrator
Chorus
Oberkameradshaftsführer

Scene One

Cologne, Germany, 1943.

Blackout. Slowly a single spotlight comes up on the centre of a swastika banner that hangs over the stage. We hear Adolf Hitler finishing his speech to the Hitler Youth in Nuremberg in 1938, to loud cheers and applause.

The **Narrator** *comes on to the stage. He is dressed in full Hitler Youth leaders' uniform.*

Narrator   1938! Adolf Hitler addresses a rally of 50,000 members of the Hitler Youth in Nuremberg. They are representing the eight million members around the country.

Below the banner is a wall. Standing in front of it are: **Dieter Ackerman**, *seventeen;* **Klaus Becker**, *sixteen; and* **Juergan Bauer**, *seventeem. All three wear Hitler Youth uniforms.* **Juergan** *paints a slogan on the wall, while the other two keep watch at either end. The slogan says 'All Germans must find a way to . . .'*

Juergan   How do you spell sabotage?

Klaus *looks back in disbelief.*

Klaus   You've got to be kidding me!

Dieter   For God's sake, Juergan!

Klaus *rushes over and looks at the wall.*

Klaus   S-A-B-O-T-A-G . . .

Dieter   E!

Klaus   E.

Juergan *starts finishing the slogan.*

Klaus   Can you spell Hitler?

Juergan   Oh, yes.

Klaus   Remember the possessive, for Hitler's war. And don't use quotation marks.

Offstage, we hear the **Chorus** *start to sing the anthem of the Hitler Jugend, 'Vorwärts! Vorwärts!'* **Klaus**, **Dieter** *and* **Juergan** *run off behind the wall. They join the back of the chorus as the others march on.*

Chorus
> *Vorwärts! Vorwärts!*
> *Schmettern die hellen Fanfaren,*
> *Vorwärts! Vorwärts!*
> *Jugend kennt keine Gefahren.*
> *Deutschland, du wirst leuchtend stehn*
> *Mögen wir auch untergehn.*

They all hold Nazi flags, The boys are wearing brown shirts and Nazi armbands, the girls white shirts and ankle-length dresses. If this costume is not possible, all members of the **Chorus** *should wear black, with Nazi armbands.* **Dieter**, **Klaus** *and* **Juergan** *have now joined the line.*

Chorus
> *Uns're Fahne flattert uns voran.*
> *In die Zukunft ziehen wir Mann für Mann*
> *Wir marschieren für Hitler*
> *Durch Nacht und durch Not*
> *Mit der Fahne der Jugend*
> *Für Freiheit und Brot.*
> *Uns're Fahne flattert uns voran,*
> *Uns're Fahne ist die neue Zeit.*
> *Und die Fahne führt uns in die Ewigkeit!*
> *Ja die Fahne ist mehr als der Tod!*

They stop and come to attention. The sound of trumpets and a roll of drums.

Oberkameradshaftsführer   Following the regulation to protect musical cultural works of 29th March 1939 the Reich Music Examination Office has declared the following musical works as undesired and harmful. Publishing, distributing or performing these works is forbidden in the German Reich.

'The Lambeth Walk'.
'Your Broadway and My Broadway'.
'Swinging High and Swinging Low'.
'Swing for Sale'.
'The Dipsey Doodle'.
'Adolf Hitler's Favourite Flower is the Simple Edelweiss'.
'Pent up in the Penthouse'.
'Swing Low Sweet Chariot'.
'The Flat Foot Floogie'.

And all other works by degenerate Negro and Jewish musicians.

Chorus
Vorwärts! Vorwärts!
Schmettern die hellen Fanfaren,
Vorwärts! Vorwärts!
Jugend kennt keine Gefahren.
Ist das Ziel auch noch so hoch,
Jugend zwingt es doch.

The **Chorus** *march off leaving* **Dieter**, **Juergan**, **Klaus** *and the* **Oberkameradshaftsführer**.

Dieter   Oberkameradshaftsführer, 'Adolf Hitler's Favourite Flower is the Simple Edelweiss' –

Oberkameradshaftsführer   What about it?

Dieter   Is it not his favourite flower, then?

Beat.

Oberkameradshaftsführer   I cannot speak for the Führer on what he considers to be his favourite flower. Though I believe all indigenous flora and fauna of the German Reich are dear to his heart. But there is no official statement on the matter, from the party. Therefore the matter, in this instance, is closed. And the official verdict on the song 'Adolf Hitler's Favourite Flower is the Simple Edelweiss' stands.

Dieter   It is one of my favourite songs. I know all the words by heart. I learnt them especially. My grandma loves me to sing it to her.

He starts to sing a few lines of the song.

> *Adolf Hitlers lieblingsblume*
> *Ist das shlichte Edelweiss!*
> *Adolf Hitlers lieblingsblume*
> *Ist das shlichte Edelweiss!*

Oberkameradshaftsführer   Quiet! I can arrest you for that! Do you want to end up in a concentration camp?! Tell your grandma to find another favourite song for you to sing.

Dieter   Arrested? Will having the words in my head be a crime?

Oberkameradshaftsführer   Yes. Unlearn them. Learn some martial party songs and they will eventually eliminate the words from your head.

Dieter   And my grandmother?

Oberkameradshaftsführer   Must do the same!

He walks around them, looking at them. The boys are sniggering.

Oberkameradshaftsführer   Ackerman, your hair is too long –

Dieter   I thought I could use it as a weapon on the battlefield. To trip our enemies up, Oberkameradshafts-führer!

Oberkameradshaftsführer   You're clever, aren't you, Ackerman?

Dieter   No, Oberkameradshaftsführer! That's not what they say in school. But I'll tell them you think so, Oberkameradshaftsführer!

Klaus *and* **Juergan** *suppress their smiles.*

Oberkameradshaftsführer   You think this is funny, Ackerman? I expect all members of my unit to show proper respect to the standards of National Socialism. If you have no respect for yourselves, you have no respect for the country, the people or the Führer. These transgressions won't just reflect badly on you, but will have to be taken up with your family as well. Penalties will have to be paid.

Dieter   My father fell for the Fatherland at Stalingrad, Oberkameradshaftsführer!

Oberkameradshaftsführer   Then you of all people should follow his example.

Dieter   But the Russians have it back now, Oberkameradshaftsführer!

Oberkameradshaftsführer   What?

Dieter   Stalingrad, Oberkameradshaftsführer!

Oberkameradshaftsführer   What about it?

Dieter   You wish me to follow my father's example and fall for the Fatherland.

Oberkameradshaftsführer   We will retake Stalingrad, have no fear of that. Then our armies will be knocking on the gates of Moscow.

Dieter   Then should I wait till we retake it, or should I wait till we're at the gates of Moscow before I sacrifice myself for Volk, Reich and Führer?

Oberkameradshaftsführer   Do you doubt our ultimate victory, Bauer?

Dieter   No, Oberkameradshaftsführer! I want to die. I'm just not sure when and where.

Oberkameradshaftsführer   Any more insubordination and you might find it occurring sooner rather than later. Heil Hitler! Dismissed.

He gives the Nazi salute. The boys return it. The **Oberkameradshaftsführer** *walks off.*

Klaus   You've gotta watch it, Dieter.

Dieter   What?

Juergan   Don't rub them up the wrong way. Especially him. He's a weasel. He'll rat you up to the Gestapo soon as look at you.

Klaus   He had his own mother arrested and sent to a concentration camp for re-education.

Dieter   I'm not kissing anyone's arse. Especially that little Nazi shit.

Klaus   No one's asking you to. I'm just saying fade into the background a bit.

Dieter   When are we gonna do something about them, eh? I'm fed up of painting slogans on walls and sticking pamphlets through letterboxes.

Klaus   You've got to be patient.

Dieter   That's all I ever hear. Be patient, be patient! Well, I'm fed up of being sodding patient! If we're patient for much longer they'll have won the bloody war!

Juergan   You're not going to be good to anyone stuck in prison.

Dieter   I'm no good sat on my arse doing nothing now! What will it take for you to realise that these bastards only understand force! I want to do something now! I want to start hurting them now!

The others walk off, leaving **Dieter**.

Dieter   I never knew anything different. I was born in
1927. Hitler and the Nazis, they were all I ever knew. Flags
and uniforms . . . It was fun at first, the marching. Going on
camping trips. My parents weren't too happy about it. But
they didn't say anything . . . They couldn't. It wasn't until
1938, Kristallnacht . . . we attacked the Jews, their businesses,
synagogues, anything. We were made to take part, our troop.
Smash windows and that. Everyone was really excited. My
parents didn't want me to go out – I went anyway. I wanted
to be with my friends. But amongst all that shouting and
crashing and the fires . . . all I could think of, as we walked
the streets, was how my parents had always taught me never
to throw stones . . . It was dangerous and I could hurt
someone . . . I could hurt someone . . . All that night, that's
all I could think of . . . and I suddenly knew that this was
wrong. That these leaders, the ones who brought us out,
shouldn't be telling us to do this. They should know better,
they were adults, and they were telling us to do and shout
these terrible things . . . They laughed when we did it. It
wasn't right . . . and I knew it . . . I did throw some stones,
at first . . . But I never thought the same way again. Never
thought the same way they did. In my head, I got away from
them. Turned my back on what they'd taught me. They
never knew . . . but my parents did.

He walks off. The **Narrator** *comes on. He's dictating a letter. A
secretary takes down what he says.*

Narrator   These adolescents aged between twelve and
seventeen hang around late in the evening with musical
instruments and young impressionable females. They like to
indulge in mixed-sex hiking and camping trips and sing songs.
Since this riff raff is in large part outside the Hitler Youth
and adopts a hostile attitude to the organisation, they
represent a danger to young people . . . There is suspicion
that it is these youths who have covered the walls of the
pedestrian subway with slogans. 'Down with Hitler', 'Medals
for Murder', 'Down with Nazi Brutality'. However often

these inscriptions are removed within a few days new ones appear on the walls.

Klaus *comes on.*

Klaus   My parents were political. I grew up with politics. They were Communists. They were always out on the streets demonstrating against the Nazis. All my life, all I ever remember are smoky rooms full of people talking and arguing politics. First, of all, how to bring about revolution, then, how to combat the Nazis . . . And then . . . then it all went quiet, no more open talk of Russia or Comrade Stalin. Suddenly, our world was whispered and shadowed . . . hidden. The worry of my parents every time there was a knock on the door. It's as if we were waiting for them to come. They were always expected, anticipated. Then one day they did come. I was playing with my friend across the hall. The boots came up the stairs, I saw them coming. Climbing up. The black boots. Shiny boots. They stopped outside our apartment and knocked. I knew inside the apartment my parents would have turned to the door instantly, knew they would have turned to each other. Knew my father's look would have told my mother not to worry. His always reassuring look. But not this time . . . I saw the door open . . . heard my mother screaming, my father on the floor, blood pouring from his nose and mouth, as the shiny boots rained down on his face and body. My mother, as she is dragged along the hall by her hair, screaming. My father looked at me as he passed and even through the blood and the pain, the look . . . he gave me the reassuring look . . . the look of my father, the look that said, all would be well . . . I never saw them again. They were both shot in Dachau.

We hear the Willi Berking Orchestra with Rudi Shuricke singing 'Traumorchester'.

Scene Two

A bombed-out apartment, Cologne, 1943.

The music fades. We we can now hear the low humming of aircraft engines and the sound of an air raid in progress. Bomb flashes and the light from the fires light up the room. The apartment is furnished with old bits of mismatched furniture. Across the door a beam has fallen in and fills the area with rubble. The windows are smashed but are covered in old blinds. **Petra Gleissner***, sixteen, leads* **Benjamin Dressler***, seventeen, into the apartment. They squeeze in through the door.* **Benjamin** *stands looking about the apartment.* **Petra** *starts to empty things from her knapsack onto a table. She turns and looks at* **Benjamin***. She rushes over to him and hugs him.*

Petra   I'm glad you came. I don't know what I would have done if you hadn't. I know I'm being selfish.

Benjamin   You? I'm the one that's left everyone behind. Abandoned everyone.

Petra   You didn't. Don't think that way, Benji. It's what your parents wanted.

Beat.

It's what I wanted. They understood.

Benjamin   Did you see them leave?

Petra   Yes . . . I followed them all the way to the station. They have my address. I'm sure they'll write as soon as they get there.

Benjamin   I don't know if I'm strong enough to do this.

Petra   Yes, you can. You can do it for them. For your sisters.

Benjamin   But to just disappear. Go underground. Can you do this?

Petra   Of course.

Benjamin Have you thought about it? I mean, really thought about what it is we're going to do?

Petra I wouldn't have it any other way. I hate the way we're living, the way we treat each other. The suspicion – the fear. I hate what they've done to you.

There is a knock on the door. She puts her finger to her lips. They both stand still. There's a further three knocks. **Petra** *goes over and opens it.* **Dieter** *and* **Klaus** *enter. They are now dressed in the casual clothes worn by Edelweiss Pirates.*

Dieter Well, how do you like your new home?

Benjamin *smiles and he and* **Dieter** *embrace.* **Klaus** *shakes his hand.*

Klaus I'm glad you're safe.

Dieter I'm sorry we couldn't bring your family as well . . . It would have looked too suspicious. We have contacts with the railways, though, so we'll know exactly where they're being resettled.

Benjamin Thanks.

Klaus What have you got planned?

Petra Isn't it a bit early for that, Klaus? Benji's only just got here.

Benjamin *sits down. The others look at him.*

Benjamin It's alright, Petra, he's right. But first of all we need to make sure that we can trust the others. I mean, absolutely sure.

Juergan No one with parents in the party?

Petra I'll go now then, shall I?

Juergan I didn't mean you.

Petra Who did you mean?

Benjamin We can't blame everyone because of what their parents think. Even my father believed Hitler was good for the country. Now, he's on his way to a resettlement camp in the East. We just have to be careful. No one else must know about this apartment or what happened to me. As far as anyone else is concerned, I've been resettled with my family. Dieter, whose is this place?

Dieter   It's my cousin's. He's serving in Russia. He let the *Blockleiter* know that I'd be looking after it while he was away.

Petra   What if he comes back on leave?

Dieter   He's married now. They've got a place in Berlin. Besides, he knows it was bombed. I spoke to the *Blockleiter* and told him I'll be using it for Hitler Youth meetings.

Benjamin   And he believed you?

Klaus   Of course he did. My cousin's a *Hauptsturmführer* in the SS.

Benjamin   Good.

Klaus   The place above is bomb damaged. Unlivable. The flat on this side, too. Which leaves the one below and that's Herr Shultz, and he's deaf. There's a window in the bathroom that opens out into a well area. I've got a rope there for a quick getaway if the need arises. From there a sewer outlet into the street systems.

Benjamin   Excellent.

Klaus   Just stay away from the windows during the day. Keep the noise down to a minimum. Only use the radio when me or the others are around.

Benjamin   What about going outside?

Petra and **Dieter** *look at each other.*

Petra   Maybe, at night. Daytimes are out of the question.

Dieter   You said yourself we have to start being extra careful.

Petra   People say the Gestapo have got Jews hunting Jews on the street.

There's another knock on the door. **Petra** *opens it and* **Juergan** *comes in. He's surprised to see* **Benjamin**.

Juergan   Good. You're here. Now at last we can get on with planning what we're going to do next.

Benjamin *rushes over, throws his arms around him and gives him a hug.*

Juergan   What was that for?

Benjamin   For being you! Straight to business.

He turns to the others.

We have to let these bastards know there's someone else in the ring again.

Dieter   We just have to be careful.

Klaus   Look what happened to the Scholls.

Juergan   That's why we have to hit them hard. No more bloody pamphlets.

Dieter   Letting people know the truth is as important as fighting on the streets.

Juergan   Pamphlets are for kids!

Klaus   We are kids!

Juergan   All over Europe there's armed resistance. We've got to show the Allies that there are people here that can fight back too.

Petra   How are you going to do that?

Juergan *pulls out a gun.*

Juergan   With this.

Dieter   Where the hell did you get that?

Juergan   I took it off a Nazi. Now, I want to use it on one.

Benjamin   You'll get your chance. We all will. Anything we do that shows resistance is important. I just want to be sure you all know what you're getting yourself into. You know what will happen if we're caught? So make sure you're going into this for the right reasons. If anyone wants to walk away now, I'll understand, we all would.

He looks at the others. The lights fade. **Petra** *steps into a spotlight.*

Petra   My father is a Nazi. He always has been. Right from the beginning. I never knew what he was like before Hitler. My grandmother tells me he was a quiet young man. I find that hard to believe . . . She said the Kaiser's war changed him. When he came back, he was always unhappy. Because he'd lost so many comrades, uselessly. They all came back to nothing. To chaos, she said. That's why he took to Hitler and the Nazis. He believed Hitler gave us back our self-esteem. He said we could hold our heads high in the world again. Everybody worked. Nobody went without. He's so proud of his uniform. My mother went away. They argued a lot. She didn't like Hitler. She didn't want my father to be so involved with the party. The party won in the end, and they made me stay with my father. Said she was an unfit mother. I can't forgive my father. Because he knows what he's doing is wrong. He knows that these people are morally corrupt. He's very intelligent. But he believes so much in them that he is willing to sacrifice everything for it. Even his humanity. I think that's his greatest crime . . . That he knows it's wrong, but continues to go along with the lies. I'm not like him . . . A lot of my friends are. I've never been scared by the Nazis. That's what they want, you see. They want you to be frightened. They want you to fear the loss of everything you hold dear. I don't. I'd gladly give it all up to see them finished.

Scene Three

The apartment. Some months later.

The radio plays 'Wann wirst du wieder bei mir sein?' sung by Ilse Werner. **Dieter** *and* **Petra** *dance together.* **Benjamin** *dances alone around the room, smoking a cigarette. He wears a heavy overcoat.*

Klaus *stands, hand-cranking a printer. He holds up one of the printed copies to the light and reads it.*

Klaus 'Hitler has led Germany into a criminal war against its own citizens and the peace-loving nations of the world. It is imperative that all Germans realise that following this lunatic can only bring death and destruction to the country.'

Benjamin You're getting good at this, Klaus.

A bomb drops quite close by, which makes everybody flinch.

You're mad! Go on, get down to the shelter before you're all killed!

Klaus We're not going anywhere you can't go, Benji.

Dieter We'll be together, even unto death!

Benjamin That's a very romantic notion, Dieter. But large bombs make very messy bedfellows.

Petra *dances over to him and takes him in her arms.*

Petra You still owe me a dance.

Benjamin And how's that going to look when they dig you out and find you in the arms of a dead Jew, my Aryan maiden?

Klaus They'll probably send the bomb-aimer the Iron Cross.

They laugh. A bomb drops quite close.

Dieter *picks up the leaflets.*

Dieter Come on, Klaus, we need to get these out while the raid's still on.

Benjamin I'm coming as well.

Klaus You're not. It's one thing us getting caught, but –

Benjamin   How many crimes can they kill me for? Distributing leaflets and being a Jew? They can only chop off my head once.

Petra   Don't say such things.

Benjamin   I'll be fine.

Petra   Dieter, no.

Benjamin   I'm coming, so don't try and stop me. It's the only time I ever get out of this rat-hole.

Dieter   Alright, Klaus, you stay and keep Petra company. Look out for Juergan. He's bringing someone over.

Petra   What?

Benjamin   Here?

Petra   Who? He knows not to bring strangers. What's he thinking of?

Klaus   We said no one else comes here. This is just for Benji.

Petra   We can't have more than two people in the same place. It's too dangerous. Tell him no. It's out of the question!

Dieter   It's just for a couple of days, till we sort something else out.

Petra   It's not fair. It puts Benji at risk.

Klaus   It puts us all at risk.

Petra   This should have gone through the group first.

Dieter   He didn't have time. He got a message to me, it was urgent. I said it was alright.

Petra   Why couldn't anyone else take him?

Dieter   They're hiding or arrested.

Klaus   More reason we should be sticking to the rules. The city's crawling with informers.

Petra   Who is it? Has anyone vouched for him? Found out his background?

Dieter   A soldier. He doesn't want to go back to the front.

Petra   That tells us nothing. There are plenty of Nazis who'll do anything to avoid being sent back to Russia. Klaus is right, he could be Gestapo. No. It's too dangerous.

Dieter   I've already told Juergan to bring him.

Petra   What do you think, Benji?

Benjamin   We can't turn people away. It's not who we are. Let him stay. I don't have a problem sharing for a few days.

There's a loud knock at the door. They all freeze.

There's another three knocks. **Dieter** *goes over to the fallen beam with* **Klaus** *and they pull it aside.* **Juergan** *comes in with a dishevelled looking* **Rutger Shriener***, nineteen. He looks haunted, as he stands there looking about the room. He is extremely nervous. The boys replace the fallen beam across the door.*

Juergan   Thought it'd be safer to come in the raid. This is Rutger Shriener.

Petra   What the bloody hell do you think you're playing at, Juergan, bringing a complete stranger here?

Juergan   What?

Rutger   I'm sorry, I thought –

Juergan   Hang on a minute! Since when have you been giving the orders?

Petra   Since about the same time you took the decision to start bringing in strangers without them being vetted by all of us first!

Juergan   I thought it's what we do. We help people.

Petra   We do. But we do it together. If we're all taking the risk, we make the decisions together.

Juergan   There was no time –

Petra   Then you should have made time. Or said no. It's when we start bending the rules mistakes happen and we can't afford to make mistakes.

Benjamin   Alright, both of you. It dosen't matter now. He's here, and he's very welcome. Juergan, why don't you introduce us to your friend?

Juergan   This is Rutger Shriener.

Petra   We don't need to know surnames.

Rutger   Look, I'm sorry if this is a problem, I can leave –

Petra *turns to* **Rutger**.

Petra   Stay where you are . . . I'm Petra.

Dieter *gives a little wave.*

Dieter   Dieter.

Klaus *nods his head.*

Klaus   Klaus.

Juergan   And this is Benji.

Benjamin *comes over and offers his hand.* **Rutger** *takes it.*

Benjamin   There! I bet that made you fell very welcome! Come in, take a seat. Don't bother yourself with the bombs. We've got a special dispensation from Mr Churchill: he's promised not to bomb this house. Though as you can see, the news hasn't filtered through to his pilots.

Rutger   You're in contact with the Allies?

Benjamin   Of course. Mr Churchill doesn't do anything without consulting us first.

The others look at each other and start laughing.

Juergan   He's joking, Rutger.

Benjamin   Somebody offer our guest a drink. You do drink alcohol? We do. Don't worry, we shan't inform the authorities. They're far too busy these days to bother themselves with under-age drinkers.

Rutger   Thanks.

Benjamin   Juergan, get our guest a drink. Drinks all round, I think.

Scene Four

We hear 'Du gehst durch all meine Träume' by Willi Berking. The **Chorus** *come on, all dancing an emotionless foxtrot. Searchlights follow them about as they dance, as if in a ballroom. The* **Narrator** *smoothly dances amongst them with a 1940s-style microphone.*

Narrator   There are two possibilities: either we are good Germans or we are bad ones. If we are good Germans, all is well. If we are bad Germans *there are two possibilities:*

Chorus Member 1   Either we believe in victory, or we do not believe in victory.

Chorus Member 2   If we believe in victory, all is well. If we do not believe in victory –

Narrator   Then there are two further possibilities:

Chorus Member 3   Either we hang ourselves, or we do not hang ourselves.

Chorus Member 4   If we hang ourselves, all is well. If we do not hang ourselves –

Narrator   Then there are two possibilities:

Chorus Member 5   Either we give up the fight, or we do not give up the fight.

Chorus Member 6   If we do not give up the fight –

Narrator   Then there are again two possibilities:

Chorus Member 7   Either the criminal Red mob following the Anglo-Americans liquidates us immediately, or following Stalin's wish we are deported to work in the icy wastes of Siberia.

Chorus Member 8   If we are liquidated immediately, that is comparatively speaking, good. If they deport us to Siberia or somewhere else –

Scene Five

The apartment.

The air raid has got heavier. All stand tensely as the explosions get louder and closer. **Rutger** *sits down in an armchair. Another large bomb explodes close by. All flinch.* **Rutger** *throws himself down on the ground.* **Benjamin** *stays seated.*

Benjamin   You must have had worse in Russia?

Rutger   What? . . . Yes.

Petra   Where were you?

Rutger   I'm sorry?

Petra   In Russia?

Rutger   Yes – I mean, all over. Didn't stop in one place long enough to get to know the name. We started near Kursk, I know that, ended up in something unpronounceable in Poland.

Benjamin   Are you hungry? We've got some sausage, do you like sausage? Petra, get Rutger some sausage. And some bread. It's a day old, I'm afraid.

Rutger   Thank you. All of you. I don't want to put you in any danger. I appreciate what you're all doing for me.

Klaus   What is it we're doing?

Petra   What has Juergan told you about us?

Rutger   Nothing . . . Putting me up . . . I'm a –

Juergan   Give him a break, Petra. He's just saying thanks.

Dieter *picks up the leaflets.*

Dieter   Come on, who's going to help me with these. Benji, are you still coming?

Benjamin   No, I think I'll stay, now.

Dieter   Suit yourself. Alright, you two, and you, Jurgen, let's get this lot shifted.

The other boys pick up leaflets and head out of the door. **Benjamin** *and* **Petra** *close it behind them and replace the beam.*

Rutger   What are they?

Benjamin *picks up one of the leaflets and hands it to* **Rutger**, *who starts to read.*

Petra   What do you think?

Rutger *shrugs noncommittally.*

Benjamin   You don't like what's written?

Rutger   Nothing wrong with what's written. But . . .

Petra   What?

Rutger   They're just words, aren't they?

Benjamin   Words are one of the few weapons at our disposal.

Rutger   Yeah, but what real harm can leaflets do?

Beat.

Benjamin   They're a reminder that not everyone's willing to follow them blindly.

Rutger   You think that after what they've done, they'll worry about what a few people have to say on a leaflet?

Benjamin *looks at* **Rutger**.

Benjamin   They're scared of words, Rutger. You see, words are one of the few things that make them vulnerable. Words expose the lies. They're powerless against them.

He goes over and pours another drink. He fills **Rutger**'*s glass as well.*

Benjamin   It's why they went to so much trouble to control words in the first place. Then, when they realised they couldn't, they burnt them. Turned them to ash.

Pause. **Rutger** *shrugs again.*

Rutger   I don't know . . . I'm just a soldier. I don't know about words or politics.

Beat.

Benjamin   How can you say you're just a soldier?

Rutger   It's what I am. I just do what I'm told to do. Go where they send me.

Benjamin   You don't though, do you?

Rutger   What?

Benjamin   Go where they send you.

Rutger   Don't know what you mean.

Benjamin   That's why you're here. With us. You've made a political statement by not going back to the front.

Rutger   I didn't.

Benjamin   You did. You just said, you only follow orders.

Rutger   So?

Benjamin   Did you have orders that told you to desert?

Rutger   No.

Benjamin   Then by refusing to return to fight you made a political statement.

Rutger   I didn't want to die in Russia is all I'm saying.

Benjamin   If that's not a political statement in this day and age I don't know what is . . . You're not eating your sausage, don't you like sausage? We might have a bit of cheese. Do we have any cheese, Petra?

Rutger   How old are you lot?

Benjamin   Seventeen.

Petra   I'm sixteen.

Benjamin   Dieter is eighteen. Klaus is seventeen and Juergan . . . How old is Juergan?

Petra   About six in the head.

Pause.

Rutger   Do you do all this yourself, then . . . write these leaflets and that. Or are there grown-ups involved?

Benjamin *and* **Petra** *start to laugh hysterically.*

Rutger   What's so funny?

Benjamin   I'm sorry, Rutger, we're not laughing at you –

Petra   No, that's not true, we are, we are laughing at you.

Benjamin   It's just . . . 'grown-ups'?

Petra   Making sure we wash our hands after printing.

Petra   Wear an apron if you're going to attack the Führer with ink.

Rutger (*irritated*)   I'm glad you find me amusing.

Benjamin   We don't, Rutger, really we don't. I'm sorry – it's just the idea of having adults involved with what we do.

Petra   I'm sure there are some out there . . . who aren't afraid to do something. But not with us, not with our group.

Rutger   Who are you with then? What are you? Communists? Anarchists? Christian Democrats?

Benjamin   God forbid, no. We're Edelweiss Pirates. The Navajos of Cologne. I thought you knew?

Rutger   You're just kids.

Benjamin   That's as maybe. But they're still scared of us.

Petra   Scared enough to hunt us down.

Benjamin   No, there's no adults overseeing us, Rutger.

Petra   We don't trust them.

Benjamin   It was the adults that gave us Hitler.

We hear some of the introduction to 'Bei mir bist dü schön' sung by Zarah Leander.

Scene Six

*The **Chorus** come back, all dancing the emotionless foxtrot. Again the searchlights follow them about as they dance, as if in a ballroom. The **Narrator** smoothly dances among them with a 1940s-style microphone. Zarah Leander begins to sing as the **Narrator** speaks.*

Narrator   There are again two possibilities:

Chorus Member 9   Either one dies during the long march from the stresses and privations, or one does not die immediately.

Chorus Member 10   If one dies quickly, one has deserved it, but is still lucky. If one does not die quickly, that is unfortunate –

Narrator   Once again, there are two possibilities:

Chorus Member 11   Either one slaves away for foreigners until the end of one's life, without ever seeing one's homeland and one's family again –

Chorus Member 12   Or one gets shot in the back of the neck a little earlier.

Narrator   Since both of the last two possibilities end in death, there are no further possibilities. Therefore:

There are not two possibilities!

There is only one!

We must win the war, and we can win it! Each man and each woman, the entire German people, must call forth their utmost in work, courage, and discipline. Then our future and the future of our children will be assured, and the German people will be saved from a descent into Bolshevist chaos!

Scene Seven

The apartment.

Petra *sits at the table writing. The music still plays. We can hear the shower.* **Benjamin** *walks about the room, peeking now and then through the drawn curtains.*

Benjamin   Right, read that back to me.

Petra   'Dear Mrs Dressler, I hope that this finds you and your family well and in good health. Before I say anything else, I must say that your little doggy Benji is very happy and in good spirits. He sends you lots of little doggy kisses. He is always excited when I read him your letters. It's as if the little fellow knows they're from you. He's settled in with us now, and is eating as well as he can, under the present conditions. But I think he still misses you dreadfully.'

She looks over to him.

Petra   Then what?

Benjamin *turns frustratedly back into the room.*

Benjamin (*sarcastically*)   Tell them my coat's got a lovely shine to it and I've stopped trying to mate with people's legs.

Petra   Look, I'm doing the best I can.

Benjamin   I'm fed up pretending to be a dog!

Petra   You can hardly be the son they left behind in hiding, now, can you? I know it's hard, Benji. But do try . . . I'm sure they really appreciate it.

Benjamin (*starting to dictate again*)   'The bombing continues here and very little is left of the old neighbourhood. You wouldn't recognise the place. Benji has no playmates any more, because they've all been killed. There's not even a cat to chase!'

Petra   They call that sabotaging the morale of our fighting men.

Benjamin   What?

Petra   It's true. My mother's friend was arrested and sent to prison.

Benjamin (*frustrated*)   Fine! 'The bombing continues here, but I am sure the Führer will lead us all into a final victory . . . ' Oh, what's the bloody point?! It's all lies! I'm lying to them. They're probably lying to me . . . Hitler's lying to everyone!

Beat.

Petra   You're their son, Benji. They'll always recognise your voice.

Benjamin *slumps in a chair. He sits forwards and holds his head in his hands.*

Benjamin   I wonder.

Petra   What do you mean?

Benjamin   I'm not the person they left behind any more. Would they really know me again? What would we have to

226 Ayub Khan Din

say to each other . . . after all that's happened? How could we begin to understand what we're all going through . . .

Petra   Because you'd tell them . . . and they'd listen, because they love you and that's what parents do.

Pause. He looks up.

Benjamin   'I had a letter from my son Friedrich, he's serving in Russia, now. You remember Friedrich, my eldest boy? He's a year older than your son, Benjamin.'

He goes over to the window and peeks out.

'It's terrible, isn't it, Mrs Dressler, that it takes this horrible war to make us realise the love we feel for each other . . . for our children, our loved ones, who can't be with us.'

Petra *looks up at him a moment, before continuing to write.*

Benjamin   'How we took each other for granted . . . our world, thinking it would always remain unchanged. That we would walk through the door and all would be as it has always been . . . My boy tells me things in his letters that, he says, he could never say to me at home . . . I would like to share with you, dear Mrs Dressler, a few words my son wrote recently. I think it's something all mothers should hear from their sons.'

Pause.

'Dear Mother, he wrote, though it feels like a vast emptiness that separates us, I've never felt as close to you as I do now, in these dark times. Nor has the love I feel for you, Papa and the girls ever been stronger. I don't want to add to your sadness, but it hurts in every part of my body to think of you and what you may all be going through. I only wish I could be with you, so that I might share some of the burden. I love you, Mother, with every sinew of my body, with every breath I take, and I thank you for making me the person I am. I only have the strength to do what I do, because of you and your love for me. My only wish is that we will all be together again soon and that this time will all seem a horrible nightmare. That I may look again into your beautiful face and see you smile at me and know that all will be well and we are all safe again. Take care of yourself, my dearest Mother. I kiss your face and pray that God takes care of you all. Your loving son . . . '

Petra *looks up at him from writing.*

Benjamin   ' . . . Friedrich.'

Scene Eight

We hear 'Ja, das ist meine Melodie' sung by Ilse Werner. The **Narrator** *starts to mime to the whistling. We should hear part of the whistling and the lyrics of the song as the* **Chorus Members** *speak.*

Chorus Member 2   January 20th 1942. Berlin. Wannsee conference to co-ordinate the 'Final Solution' was convened by Reinhart Heydrich. There was little doubt what the Final Solution was. Heydrich made it clear that it meant the total annihilation of the Jews by a combination of forced labour and mass murder.

Chorus Member 5   June 2nd 1942. SS and police authorities deport approximately 58,087 Jews from the Greater German Reich to Theresienstadt.

Chorus Member 6   41,783 from Germany.

Chorus Member 7   15,266 from Austria.

Chorus Member 8   611 from Sudetenland.

Chorus Member 9   310 from Luxembourg.

Chorus Member 10   117 from Danzig.

Chorus Member 2   Between October 26th 1942 and October 28th 1944 German and SS police deport approximately 46,750 Jews from Theresienstadt to

Auschwitz-Birkenau, in twenty-seven transports. Fewer than three thousand survive.

Chorus Member 2   Extermination begins in Belzec. By the end of 1942, 600,000 Jewish men, women and children have been murdered.

Narrator   It is actually true that the Jews have, so to speak, disappeared from Europe and that the Jewish 'Reservoir of the East' from which the Jewish pestilence has for centuries beset the peoples of Europe has ceased to exist. But the Führer of the German people at the beginning of the war prophesied what has now come to pass.

Scene Nine

The radio continues to play the Ilse Werner song. **Benjamin** *stands carefully peeking out of the window.* **Rutger** *walks in from the bathroom. He has his shirt off and is drying his hair with a towel.*

Rutger   Someone will see you.

Benjamin   I only ever get to see the world in the blackout.

Rutger   What's to look at? It's all ruins, now.

Benjamin   People. I like watching people. I always have done.

Rutger   What's the point of that?

Benjamin   When your life consists of the four walls of this apartment you fantasise about other people's lives. Who they're going home to. Wives, kids, parents . . . What it would be like to just go strolling along the street with them again in broad daylight. Go to the cinema, sit on a park bench. Go to classes at university . . . learn, read the books . . .

Rutger (*surprised*)   You're a Jew? You are, aren't you? Imagine that – a Jew. I'm living with a Jew. You don't look like a Jew.

Benjamin   I shaved off my horns and my tail's strapped between my legs. Otherwise I'd have been a dead giveaway.

Rutger   I didn't know there were any left in Germany. They said we were cleaned up. Jew-free.

Rutger   Pardon me for saying so, Rutger, but you seem somewhat disappointed.

Rutger   Me . . . No. No, not me. Doesn't bother me either way. Never crossed my path, the Jews. So never had anything to do with them.

Benjamin   Well, how would you have known one?

Rutger   The yellow stars.

Benjamin   It's only lately we had to wear a star. You didn't know I was a Jew.

Rutger   You can pass. You must have some German stock in you. Aryan blood. They taught us that at school. How the Aryan race interbred with the minor Germanic tribes. To create the German race. It's scientific. I don't understand it all. But them others . . . The other types of Jews . . .

Benjamin   Yes?

Rutger   Well, they've got other distinctive features.

Benjamin   Like what?

Rutger   More . . . more, pointy.

Benjamin   'Pointy'? You mean to tell me we've been persecuted all these years because we were too pointy?

Rutger   Like I said, it don't bother me.

Benjamin   It should do. It should bother you that a section of your fellow citizens have been robbed of their right to vote, to work, to own businesses, to educate their children. Not allowed to sit on a park bench or swim in a lake or practise their religion. And if that wasn't enough, to be robbed by the state, forcibly removed from their homes and placed in confinement, in a foreign country? None of that bothers you in the slightest?

Rutger   I'm not saying I agree with it. But let's face it, you don't see anyone on the streets demonstrating, do you?

Benjamin   They're scared. I would be too.

Rutger   But before all this . . . the war and that. They all knew what was happening to you lot. Adolf made no bones about it, did he? Wrote about it in his book. And all them new laws and that. Against you lot. Nobody said anything then.

Benjamin   Your point is?

Rutger   Not just me, is it?

Benjamin   No, not just you.

Rutger   And don't forget, a lot of you people . . . well, did alright for yourselves, didn't you? Back in the thirties and that, when we was all on the breadline. You lot didn't suffer much.

Benjamin   Says who?

Rutger   Says everyone. Everyone knows you lot always do alright.

Benjamin   You really are quite an oaf, aren't you?

Rutger   No need for that . . . I don't care, is all I'm saying. Just surprised to find you still here. Thought you'd all been shipped off east.

Benjamin   Resettled . . . Yes, my parents and sisters have.

Rutger   How come you're still here?

Benjamin   Same reason you're not a frozen lump of torn flesh fertilising Mother Russia.

Rutger   Where were they sent, your family?

Benjamin   Theresienstadt.

Rutger They still there?

Benjamin I've got no reason to believe they're not.

Rutger I can see it now.

Benjamin What?

Rutger You a Jew. You've got the talk.

Benjamin Have I?

Rutger Yeah. Clever with it and all. With this lot. You're the organiser, aren't you? They listen to you. You've influenced their thinking. I can see that. Clever. That's what your people were good at. Organising the rest of us.

Benjamin I'm the most disorganised person I know. If it hadn't been for Petra and Klaus, I'd be in Theresienstadt with my family, sitting bored.

Rutger Well, count your lucky stars you're not there.

Benjamin If only racial stereotyping were true, I'd be much more competent and could look forward to a wealthy Jewish future.

Beat.

Why should I count myself lucky?

Rutger What?

Benjamin You just said I should consider myself lucky that I'm not in Theresienstadt.

Rutger I mean . . . Well, you're here, in Cologne . . . You didn't have to leave.

Benjamin But you said 'not there' like you knew what 'there' was like?

Rutger It's just . . . a word isn't it?

Benjamin What's so terrible about 'there'? Do you know Theresienstadt? Have you been?

Rutger   What's with all these questions? Who are you to interrogate me? You're trying to be clever with your words?

Benjamin   You haven't answered my question?

Rutger *(hesitantly)*   I . . . don't have to.

Benjamin   You just have.

Rutger   What? What are you trying to do? You're putting words in my mouth. I never said anything. What are you up to?

Benjamin   I'm being Jewishly clever.

Pause.

Well?

Rutger   Well – nothing! I'm not answering any more of your questions.

Benjamin   You haven't.

Rutger   Haven't what?

Benjamin   Answered any of my questions. You made a statement about my lucky escape from Theresienstadt.

Rutger   What do you want?

Benjamin   Whatever it is you know about Theresienstadt.

Rutger   You're off your rocker, you are. Been in this place too long.

Benjamin   That doesn't tell me anything. What are you hiding?

Rutger   Nothing – everyone's heard the stories. I'm no different.

Benjamin   What stories would they be?

Rutger   Well, not stories, more rumours, they're just rumours. About what was happening with your lot, Jews and that.

Benjamin   What's that got to do with Theresienstadt?

Rutger   Well . . . nothing . . . They're there, aren't they?

Benjamin   Are they? What do you know about it?

Rutger   Nothing . . .

Benjamin (*shouting*)   I said what do you know?!

Rutger   It's all a fake! Alright? Just pretend. So that people'll think we treat Jews well.

Benjamin   What do you mean?

Rutger   They're being shipped east all the time. Thousands of them. It's a transit camp. Most people aren't there long. Not if you're a nobody. Just the important Jews get to stay, artists, politicians and that. Some war veterans. It's all just for show.

Benjamin   You're lying!

Rutger   I'm not.

Benjamin   How do you know all this?

Rutger   I told you. You hear things.

Benjamin *grabs hold of him.*

Rutger   What're you doing!

Benjamin   Not good enough! Answer my question.

Rutger   I don't have to say anything to you!

Benjamin   Answer me!

Rutger   I'll tell the others what you're doing!

Benjamin   Want to find yourself out on the street? Tied up with a notice saying you're a deserter?

Rutger   You can't do that!

Benjamin   Answer me!

Rutger Alright! . . . I was there! I was there! Happy now? I know it's true, 'cause I was there.

The door opens and **Petra**, **Dieter** *and* **Juergan** *come in.*

Dieter What's going on?

Petra Benji, what are you doing?

Benjamin *rips off* **Rutger**'s *shirt and forces up his arm, revealing a small tattoo.*

Benjamin Blood-type tattoo! He's in the SS.

Juergan *suddenly pulls out a gun. He points it at* **Rutger**, *who scrambles over to* **Juergan** *and grabs at his legs.*

Rutger Wait! No! I was, but I'm not any more! I ran away!

Juergan Liar!

Benjamin Dirty lying bastard!

Benjamin *suddenly pushes him to the floor and starts to kick him.*

Petra Benji, no!

She tries to pull him back as **Rutger** *tries to protect himself from the tirade of blows and kicks.*

Benjamin Tell me what you know! Tell me or I'll blow your brains out myself!

Dieter *steps in and manages to pull* **Benjamin** *away.* **Juergan** *cocks the gun and looks as though he is about to shoot* **Rutger**.

Dieter Put that thing away!

Juergan He's SS!

Dieter I don't care! I said put it away! Now! If that goes off, it'll bring more than the neighbours banging on the bloody door!

Juergan *reluctantly lowers the gun.* **Dieter** *looks down at the whimpering* **Rutger**.

Dieter   Get up off the floor. Sit in that chair.

Slowly **Rutger** *raises himself off the ground and slumps into an armchair.*

Dieter   Now, you'd better tell us who you really are.

Rutger   We were sent 'cause we were available – we were on our way east, anyway . . . we didn't know . . .

We hear the 'Trio for Strings 1' by Gideon Klein while members of the **Chorus** *come on as a crowd. They now wear overcoats and carry suitcases and bundles. The* **Narrator** *stands to one side. They come forward individually.*

Chorus Member 2   We walked through the streets. Streets we'd walked down for years. Familiar streets. And all was normal. Everything was how it should have been. Except for us. And they watched us pass by. Never said a word, just watched in silence as we passed.

He sets his bag down and goes and stands in front of the **Narrator**. *Now others slowly start to come forward and place their bags amongst the growing pile. The* **Narrator**, *starts to indicate to people, to go left or right.* **Chorus Member 10** *comes forward.*

Chorus Member 10   We were at the Deutz-Tief train station. We waited. My brother played. He was excited. We only ever came here before when we went on holiday. That's what my parents told him. We were going on holiday. My father cried when he told him.

Chorus Member 1   It was loud! And cold, it was so cold and there were dogs barking. Bright lights. Soldiers shouting. Screaming. The children cried. They forced us down off the train. Hit us, men women and children. We had no time to think. They took away my wife. And my daughters. I never had time to say goodbye. I don't know where they took them. I just wanted to hold them.

He sets his bag down and stands to one side as **Chorus Member 3** *comes forward.*

Chorus Member 3   They sent me and my wife to the left. But they grabbed the baby from my wife's arms and gave it to my mother, who went to the right. My wife started to scream! She wanted the baby. How dare you take my baby away, she said! You have no right to do this! It's inhuman! Give me back my baby!

She ran to the other line . . . and grabbed the child. But they wouldn't let her rejoin me. I have her things . . . and the baby's clothes. Winter things. They'll need them.

He sets his bag down and stands to one side as **Chorus Member 4** *comes forward. The music fades. We hear 'Trio for Strings 2' by Gideon Klein as* **Rutger** *is spotlit.*

Rutger   We were sent to Theresienstadt to pick up a transport for the east. You know, guard it. I knew it was a resettlement camp. They were all German. Some were Czechs, but they were mainly German. Some from here, Cologne. I recognised the accent.

Petra *looks at* **Benjamin**.

Rutger   Funny, I didn't expect them to speak German, made them more . . . They were waiting. It was chaotic. Shouting fathers trying to keep families together. Kids crying, others laughing, playing games. They all had bags and suitcases, bundles. So much stuff. Every one had something. All the time the dogs were barking. We were told to get everyone aboard, into the cattle cars. Slam the doors shut. Then suddenly silence . . . Then this sound started, quietly, a low murmuring, coming from the cars. Even above the locomotive, you could hear it, a mumble or hum . . . it didn't sound like humans . . . Whispers . . . I don't know if it was whispers. I couldn't make out words . . . but there was an urgency in it. A fear, a wonder. Some time later, we arrived in a place called Auschwitz. We got them all off the train. They separated the men from the women and children. Then they were all marched off into the camp. Within two hours they'd gassed all two thousand of them.

Lights up.

Benjamin   You're lying!

Rutger   I'm not. It's not just that place, there are others as well. Where they kill them.

Dieter   They couldn't . . . It's not possible . . . Two thousand people . . . It's just not possible.

Rutger   That's why it is possible. Because no one'll believe it.

Benjamin   You're lying!

Rutger   I saw it. Saw what they did to them.

Juergan   I believe it. I know what they're capable of.

Benjamin   When did these trains start from Theresienstadt?

Rutger   A couple of months ago.

Beat. **Juergan** *turns to* **Benjamin**.

Juergan   When was the last time you had a letter from your parents?

Benjamin *looks up at him but says nothing. We hear 'Das wird ein Frühling ohne Ende' sung by Ilse Werner.*

Chorus Member 2   I was bombed out of my house. It was terrible, I lost everything. Didn't have a thing left to wear, only the clothes I stood up in. Nothing for the kids either . . . One day we were called together. People in our area, who'd been bombed out and lost everything. We were taken to a warehouse. They had lots of clothes on rails, clothes for every occasion . . . all weathers. Shoes of every description. I got a lovely new coat. The kids got fitted out with everything as well. Nice quality and all . . . not rubbish. They were happy running about and showing them off. Then I noticed . . . I noticed that all the children's new clothes had a Jew star sewn on them . . . My coat too . . . It wasn't there, mind, but you

238 Ayub Khan Din

could see where one had been . . . I looked about the room.
I could see other women had noticed too. We looked at each
other . . . we was all thinking the same thing. I mean . . . what
are you expected to do? We had nothing. Lost everything in
the bombing and that and . . . No one said anything . . . we
just started ripping off the stars . . . As we left . . . I looked
back . . . the floor was covered in them . . . Carpeted it was,
yellow Jew stars . . . hundreds of them . . . There were, oh,
dear God, there were hundreds . . .

Scene Ten

Benjamin *stands in front of a wall painting a slogan. He has already written 'Where are the Jews?'* **Petra** *rushes up to him. We hear the sound of police sirens in the distance.*

Petra   For God's sake, Benji. Come on! Leave it now.

Benjamin   No!

Klaus *and* **Dieter** *come running on.*

Klaus   Benji! Enough, they're behind us! Run!

Dieter   Come on, we've got to go, now!

We hear shots being fired and shouting.

Benjamin   No!

The boys try to pull him away but he pushes them off.

Get away from me!

Petra   Please! Benji! Just leave it, please! Do something, Dieter!

Benjamin   Go! I'm going to finish it!

Dieter   This isn't the way, Benji!

Rutger *comes on, dragging* **Juergan**, *along with him.*

Klaus   Oh God, Juergan . . .

Juergan *falls to the ground in pain.*

Rutger   What the hell are you still doing here? Go!

Juergan   For God's sake, leave the lot of you.

He pulls out a gun.

(*In pain.*) Benji, if you don't go now, I'll shoot you myself.

Rutger   Give that to me!

Benjamin   Don't touch me!

Rutger   I'll stay and finish it, alright? Just go . . .

He snatches the brush off **Benji** *and pushes him to the others.* **Benji** *looks as though he is about to fight* **Rutger**.

Rutger   You have to go. Now! Go, all of you!

Klaus *and* **Dieter** *rush to take* **Juergan**, *but he pushes them away.*

Juergan   No . . . Get away . . . Please!

He doubles up in pain. They both hesitantly run off.

Juergan (*shouting*)   Over here, you bastards!

Petra *rushes over and quickly kisses* **Juergan**. *She grabs* **Benji**'s *hand and drags him.* **Benji** *looks at* **Rutger**.

Rutger   It's alright. You can leave the words with me now . . .

Beat.

Petra *and* **Benji** *run off.* **Juergan** *lets out a loud groan.* **Rutger** *starts to write: 'Murdered in your name. Germany awake and revenge them! Revenge them! Revenge' . . . A volley of shots rings out.*

Blackout.

A single spot lights the stage. The **Narrator** *walks into the light.*

Narrator   On 10th November 1944, in Cologne,
Ehrenfeld, thirteen members of the so-called Ehrenfeld
Group were publicly hanged without trial in front of
hundreds of curious onlookers.

We see projected across the stage real pictures of the Ehrenfeld Group on the scaffold. Both before and after the hanging.

Amongst them were six teenage members of the Edelweiss
Pirates: Gustav Bermel, seventeen; Franz Rheinberger,
seventeen; Adolf Shutz, eighteen; Gunther Schwarz, sixteen;
Bethel Shink, sixteen; Johann Miller, sixteen.

We hear Rudi Schuricke singing 'Heimat, deine Sterne'.

Slow fade to black.

The end.

The Edelweiss Pirates

BY AYUB KHAN DIN

*Notes on rehearsal and staging drawn from a workshop
with the writer held at the National Theatre, October 2014.
Workshop led by Bijan Sheibani, with notes by Phil Sheppard.*

Some background to the play's creation

During the 2014 European Parliament elections Ayub Khan
Din was concerned to see a considerable swing to the political
right and young people's progressive disengagement from
politics. He had known about the Edelweiss Pirates for some
time and felt that this was an opportune time to try and
document their story. These young people found a collective
strength to challenge what they saw was wrong in their society
and built a determination to fight for what they believed was
right. Even amidst the extremities of a world war they
struggled to make their voice heard.

Ayub didn't want to write a 'documentary' but an absorbing
drama, so although the play is inspired by real historical
people and events, the play's main characters are fictional.

Determining and investigating the facts

EXERCISE I

At the start of the rehearsal process directors are encouraged
to work through each scene and list the facts provided by the
script. This is a time-consuming exercise but will hopefully
surprise directors with the amount of useful, exploitable and
expandable detail that is in the text that may not be evident
immediately in a conventional read-through.

During the workshop the participants made a list of all
indisputable facts, however seemingly mundane or
inconsequential. For example, at the beginning of Scene
Two:

A bombed-out apartment. Cologne, 1943.

The music fades. We can now hear the low humming of aircraft engines.

Bijan Sheibani suggested using the phrase 'There is/are . . . ' as a prefix to each fact when compiling your lists:

- There are bombs
- There are apartments
- There are bombed-out apartments
- There is Cologne
- There is 1943
- There is music
- There is fading
- There is music that fades
- There is a low humming we couldn't hear before
- There are aircraft engines, etc.

Listing and examining the elements and constituent parts might help to lead to more questions that need to be discussed and investigated in rehearsal. If there are apartments, what kind of apartments are they? Where are the bombs coming from? What does a bombed-out apartment look like? Where is Cologne? What is Cologne like? If it's 1943, what happened in that year? If there is music, how are we hearing it? If it fades, then what causes it to fade out? If we can *now* hear the low humming why couldn't we hear it before, did it exist? If so, where was the humming previously: somewhere in the distance getting nearer or already there but only *theatrically* pertinent now?

Ideally this process should be followed throughout the whole script and might be particularly helpful for illuminating detail in the stage directions.

Time and place

EXERCISE 2

Directors are encouraged to draw up A TIMELINE OF EVENTS IN THE PLAY, to determine what happens and in what order. What is the progression of events within the play? The events within the script are not in chronological order as many characters speak of the past so you will need to start your timeline of facts before the beginning of the play in Cologne, 1943.

As well as a time map, you could also draw macro and micro MAPS OF PLACES in the play. Perhaps start with a map of Europe to determine where Germany and Cologne are: is Cologne on the coast, near a border, at threat of invasion, in the mountains, in the countryside, is it a small agricultural town or a busy city? Then create maps that are more tightly focused: draw a map of Cologne and mark where the different events may be taking place, then focus further by drawing a map of the bombed-out apartment discussing with the cast what is in that room? Discuss how much *stuff* such as furniture and possessions you actually *need* to have in the apartment and what the essentials are that the script prescribes. As rehearsals continue you will be able to finalise your map of the room. This could also be done to scale, using masking or electrical tape on the floor to show the dimensions of the room and possible positions of doors and windows. (Using tape means you can easily pull it up and make alterations as you go.)

Characters

EXERCISE 3

Along with mapping the play's timeline and geography you should also plot TIMELINES FOR ALL THE CHARACTERS in the play, charting what happens to them, what they do and in what order. Within the dialogue there are a number of stories and flashbacks: where do these fall in the progression of the characters' lives? For some of the characters you may have to go back a long way into their personal histories to include all the play's facts. If there is enough time, it was suggested that going back as far as the characters' births, essentially creating a biography, would be a useful research and imagination exercise for your company.

Compile a list of all the information given in the script about the characters. This should not contain conjecture but only facts. For example:

Dieter Ackerman

- He is seventeen
- He spends time with Klaus Becker and Juergan Bauer
- He wears a Hitler Youth uniform
- He can spell 'sabotage'
- He can run
- He can march, etc.

The company should aim to be thorough and meticulous with this exercise. Stay clear of assumptions and association and stick only to facts.

Getting actors involved in the issues of the play

EXERCISE 4

Can your company see any similarities between the events and issues in the play and things happening now? Can they find any contemporary equivalents? The participants at the workshop suggested conflict in the Middle East, the London riots, religious extremism and recent events in Syria could all possibly be helpful analogies. Addressing issues that young people may have personally experienced, such as peer pressure and bullying, could be helpful when analysing some of the arguments and domestic conflict in the play. These thematic investigations could evolve into improvisations so that actors can get used to dramatising the issues, finding solutions through doing rather than just discussing.

Understanding exactly what you're saying

EXERCISE 5

There is a lot of debate in the play and it is vital that the actors know precisely what it is they are arguing about and why.

During the workshop the participants took two of the Ober-kameradshaftführer's speeches in the first scene beginning 'I cannot speak for the Führer' and 'You think this is funny, Bauer?' They were then asked to *draw the image* of each word (this is a bit like charades) and to try and find a clear physical representation for everything that's said. This will hopefully help your actors to avoid generalising and to be more specific with their characters' intentions as they are trying to distinguish specific words in a hope of making their thoughts vibrant and unambiguous.

How can an actor physically differentiate between *want, wish, require* and *deserve?* Between *hate, despise, dislike* and *threaten?* Or between *transgression, crime, sin* and *evil?* You should try this exercise in pairs or small groups and be honest with one another: if it's not clear then keep experimenting until it is. When you feel the *drawing* is clear then return to speaking only the scripted lines and see if you sense any more definition: are the arguments and intentions clearer?

You could then try the speeches with different intentions, different objectives: how does the Oberkameradshaftführer want to affect his listeners: educate them, scare them, intimidate them, win them over? What's the goal, what's the desired outcome for these speeches?

The participants then looked at the dialogue between Dieter and Juergan, starting with 'You've gotta watch it, Dieter' (page 206). with the intention of again finding the argument's 'essence': what is each character's stance, what are the most important words and phrases within the debate? Discuss the effects of using words like 'weasel', 'rat' and the use of repetition in this section. Make sure the actors have a clear objective: what do they want to achieve? This should be thought of in terms of how each character wants to affect the other: what do they want them to do, what do they want from them, what do they want them to understand?

Telling a story from memory

EXERCISE 6

In many ways this is one of the most important exercises for this play, since so much of the play comprises the telling of memories. Being really clear about how your actors tell a story from their own experience, and how one's body and imagination engage in this act is important to work on. This is best achieved by getting your actors to tell their own stories from memory and getting the rest of the company to observe how such personal stories are relayed.

In the workshop weekend this exercise was used for possible approaches to Dieter's monologue 'I never knew anything different' (p. 207); however it can be used throughout the play.

In small groups each describe your journey to rehearsal that day, using as much detail as you can recall. The listeners should, as well as listening intently, observe the way the story is told. How does each fact spring out? How, if the teller goes through a process of visualisation before explaining, do they in some way relive it and then give you the facts as they are moving through the facts of their story? How do they use their hands, their eyes; are they checking in with you to make sure you're keeping up with them; how do they go into detail about specific images or sounds? During their description does the teller find an unexpected emotion: are they amused, saddened or angry about something they experienced, and how does this manifest itself?

Then try telling the story again as if for the first time, as if the listeners haven't heard it before: don't presume they know what you're talking about. Are there any differences between the first and second telling? What are they? Do they still want you to follow and understand, or is it just repetition? Perhaps urge the teller to give more detail if facts become a little hazy.

Try the storytelling exercise again but this time telling a story of something that happened to you five, seven or ten years ago. Do you notice any differences? How is the teller using their hands and eyes? How are they visualising as they go along? Are they plotting a geography for you to follow? Do fun things sound like fun? Do sad things sound sad or has their emotional impact been diluted over time? How does the teller use verbs and adjectives to colour their story? What about sound, taste, smell and touch as well as visual recollection?

When Dieter says 'Flags and uniform . . . It was fun at first, the marching. Going on camping trips,' discuss how this could be played. The text informs us that he is going to move on to 'terrible things', but does he need to play that right now while he's talking about *fun*? Play the speeches moment to moment; don't predict or indicate how the stories, or the play, are going to progress and unfold.

Bringing a monologue to life

EXERCISE 7

In small groups the participants divided Klaus's speech 'My parents were political' (p. 208) into *units*. Units are the building blocks of the action; some directors call them *episodes*. The end of one unit and the beginning of another is where the action or focus of scene or speech palpably changes. The aim of this process is to help to focus actors in rehearsal by offering them bite-sized chunks rather than trying to get their heads around an entire speech or scene. When choosing the beginning of new units it might be helpful to imagine you are directing a film: where would you make the cuts, the close-ups, the flashbacks, the longer takes? You might want to take this one step further and draw a storyboard for each *take*, each change of unit.

When moving forward with these exercises, continue to keep in mind where Klaus is, where is he seeing or hearing all this from?

Once the units have been discussed and established, go through the speech and mark each unit with a tableau (frozen image) or sequence of tableaux that represent the action described in the speech. Then develop these tableaux into a sequence of mini-scenes, effectively filling in the gaps between the frozen images, adding dialogue and movement. Consider what each character is thinking in each mini scene by using thought tracking, call '*Freeze*' at any given point and ask the actors what this person is thinking now in this situation.

Consider a soundscape for each image. If this were a radio play with no dialogue, what noises or music would you choose to tell this story if you were in charge of the sound effects? Think about the arguing, the boots, the knocking, the whispers, the pain and the shots – how might the sounds of these influence the telling of the story; how could they contribute to the tone, tempo and pace of the monologue?

Now try returning to the script and see if these investigations have made the speech sharper, given it more variety and greater clarity.

Many of these exercises were selected to find the reality and humanity of the characters; don't be tempted to exaggerate and create types and caricatures.

Remember that the characters don't know the full horrific extent of what's really going on outside their window and beyond; try and avoid presenting the tragic shadow of the Holocaust, of which the Edelweiss Pirates are relatively unaware until the end of the play. They don't know the war is far from over, that the Allied forces will enter Germany or that by the end of the war almost all of Cologne's Jewish population of 11,000 will either have been deported or killed. Any production should aim to show the Pirates' story moment to moment and not try to predict or telegraph their future. With this in mind, Ayub encourages directors not to restrict their company's research solely to the violence of the war, but to look at day-to-day, 'ordinary' lives in Germany at the time: education, housing, cuisine, fashions, music and cinema.

Design

The results of the determining and investigating facts exercise will be essential when considering the design of your production. There are many resources available for conjuring a Second World War Germany – what Ayub described as 'visual shorthand': an abundance of resonant imagery and sound archives that could help your production.

Bijan suggested that when considering design it is important to take into account the various theatrical *modes* within the play – it's not all naturalistic.There are moments of documentary realism (Hitler's Nuremberg speech), but while the naturalistic dialogue in the apartment suggests a *fourth-wall* convention, the Narrator directly addresses the audience. Then there are the choral moments of the Hitler Youth, the more surreal elements of the Chorus, and the music and dance sequences. What kind of design could handle all these elements, all these different modes?

Ayub said that fluidity should be a primary objective for any design and a minimal approach could be very successful: e.g. a few bricks and damaged and upturned furniture could suggest the bombed-out apartment. If you want to be more elaborate with the set perhaps consider having the Chorus as onstage stage management, swiftly creating and dismantling locations. At all costs Ayub wanted directors to avoid 'patchy' productions clunking between the different modes, but rather to investigate a design that would give coherence and fluidity. He suggested that the wall, both as an inner and an outer wall, could provide some possible solutions.

Ayub encouraged directors to consider the use of film and projection to help with the creation of place; the use of sound could also provide effective and economical solutions for quick transitions of location, and create a sense of the larger offstage world.

Casting

The Chorus could be any size – it could be just one actor. The lines for the Chorus could be divided among the actors to suit your cast size, but they shouldn't be cut, rearranged or paraphrased.

Similarly, the role of the Narrator could be played by more than one actor, but Ayub asked that there be a uniformity of presentation, an individuality about the role. The Narrator needs to have authority, an otherness, an ominousness; the role is open for experimentation but needs consistency as the Narrator is a guide, a Virgil, through the play and the role needs to be clear. The Narrator could be played as a girl but other roles, though they could be played by actors of either sex, should be kept to the gender indicated in the text (e.g. Klaus could be played by a girl but the character needs to remain male – don't make Klaus into Claudia).

The writer encouraged directors to keep the actors playing the named characters separate from the Chorus as this may prove confusing for an audience, and suggested the character roles don't suddenly start speaking choral lines.

Ways to approach the music
from a workshop led by Tom Brady

During the workshop with Ayub it was made clear that the music choices in the script should not be changed. How each production uses the music is open to interpretation, but it was carefully selected while the play was being written and shouldn't be substituted.

Music director Tom Brady encouraged the directors to do as much research as possible when investigating the music. Look at when each piece of music was written, see it in context and consider its social and political stance and its 'intention' – why might it have been written? It is important to translate the lyrics and discuss why the writer might have chosen each piece. Though most of the audience may not understand what's being sung, it is important that the company does. Research each individual artist; some of the singers were also actresses and would have been well known. Life stories such as that of the featured composer Gideon Klein are readily available.

Most of the music in the play is jazz with some atonal music, the majority of which was anathema to the Nazi regime as it embraced freedom of thought, love and sex, and was seen as the spawn of 'degenerate Negro and the Jewish musicians'. The growth of audiences for radio was making this music more widely accessible, and as the regime took action to suppress its proliferation much of it was forced underground into the clandestine clubs and enjoyed by the *Swingjugend*, Germany's 'swing kids', who opposed the National Socialist ideology.

If you are choosing to have live musicians rather than use recorded archive music select your instruments carefully and aim to make them authentic to the era. Experiment with what instruments will best support the song (e.g. piano and bass) and those that risk interfering with the voice (e.g. accordion and violin).

The first use of music, the Hitlerjugend's anthem 'Vorwarts', may not need musical accompaniment at all; it's a marching song and has a strong definite tempo. Tom Brady suggested if you wanted to make it more 'interesting' you might want to consider a harmony but nothing too elaborate: don't forget its context. The recording played at the workshop was of an adult singing the song; what might be the effect of hearing children's voices not long after Hitler at the Nuremberg rally? There was also some discussion about the sound quality of the recordings of the era; there is software available to 'clean up' crackling recordings but what might be the effects of using less than perfect quality sound? Were the recordings ever pristine? If you do choose to use recorded music try to be consistent with the sound type and quality throughout.

When considering the next music choice, 'Hitler's Favourite Flower', weigh up why it may have been placed here and the role of juxtaposition that continues throughout the play. This song was most likely written for Hitler and was something of an Aryan drinking song; what are its effects when sandwiched between the Hitlerjugend's march and talk of concentration camps?

The next piece is a bright, happy and bouncy number, Rudi Schuricke singing 'Traumorchester' to Willy Berking's

Orchestra, and is in stark contrast to Klaus's monologue about his parents' arrest that ends, 'They were both shot in Dachau'. How would you choose to introduce this music? Could it fade in under the end of the monologue or would you choose silence after the last line and then bring in the music? How much of it will you use before introducing the sound effects of the humming of the bombers? Do you want silence this early in the production? Maybe play around with cross-fading? Be judicious and experiment with how you can use the energy of the music to sustain the momentum and fluidity of your production; try to avoid using the music as too much of a break or breather.

The next music is Ilse Werner singing 'Wann wirst du wieder bei mir sein'. It is some months later and this music could help to show the transition of time; again it is in contrast to Petra's curse on the Nazis. Here an interesting choice would be where and how to take the sound out? It was suggested that perhaps the music starts *outside* and beyond the action of the scene and then is gradually focused as if it were coming from the onstage radio which could then be switched off, onstage, at a relevant moment, when the bomb drops and Dieter is about to take out the leaflets – an example of a change strong enough to justify taking the music out.

When using 'Bei mir bist du schön' be sure you understand the words of the song in English translation. What is the connection or antithesis between the lyrics and the narrator's lines? If using live music, an option might be to use the song's melody without words, maybe using humming or sustained vowels, to avoid clashing too many voices. If you were to use a recorded version then carefully monitor the volume of the underscore.

For 'Ja, das ist meine Melodie', Ayub has suggested how this could be incorporated into the scene by the Narrator becoming 'part' of the music. Again be wary of your music's volume levels – don't let it conflict with the dialogue. This piece shifts into a waltz cadence and the rhythm changes; how might you be able to use this accessible and evocative dance tempo? It becomes ballroom, imperial, Strauss, grand, Prussian, ebullient, colourful, buoyant. How could this drive the imagery and movement of the chorus scene and then how could you sustain it when moving into the next scene to the stage direction *'The radio continues to play the song'*? The next question will be how and when to take the sound out. How much would you like it to be part of the subsequent scene – as underscore, or as continuing a motif of a monitored and controllable sound commanded by the Narrator? Or is it part of the onstage world, and so could be turned off by a scene character?

Gideon Klein's 'Trio for Strings' offers an ideal opportunity for a company to discuss, wrestle and experiment with these musical documents and Ayub's music choices. Klein was a Jewish composer who was imprisoned in the Theresienstadt concentration camp, discussed in the script, where he was 'an organiser of cultural life'. Klein wrote his Trios while imprisoned. He was moved between a number of concentration camps, including Auschwitz, and died in the Furstengrube camp in 1945. Such experimental and *contemporary* music was vilified by the Nazis, Hitler himself preferring the fiercer strains of Wagner and the work of Bruckner, whom Hitler saw as 'a farm boy who conquered the world with his music'.

Klein's first movement is busy and agile, suggesting chase, motion and travel: how could you use this to augment and develop the staging of the Chorus's story of the streets, the train, the shouting, the screaming, the families, the goodbyes, the inhumanity, the winter and the silence?

The second movement of the 'Trio for Strings' is composed of comparatively shorter, more condensed passages and chapters; it is more episodic, more unpredictable and spasmodic, with definite silences, suspensions and pauses for thought, reflection or re-composure. How could you 'score' your performances accordingly? Here the script is punchy, broken, chaotic, urgent; full of ellipses and unspoken thoughts. Consider the tones, tempos and imagery of Klein's

unpredictable second movement and experiment with how
the music could 'conduct' your interpretation of this scene.

Ilse Werner singing 'Das wird ein Frühling ohne Ende'
(literally, 'This will be a spring without end') is another
example of a striking contrast of tone between the music and
script. The song is bright as a soap advert or an escapist
Disney fairy tale, honeyed with the fantastical vibraphone
motif suggestive of optimism and consumerism (the 'new'
clothes) sharply at variance with the tone of the tragic
revelation preceding it and the Chorus's similarly grim
realisation by the end of the story of the 'yellow Jew stars'.
The lyrics of the song suggest a desire to forget, to dream, to
enjoy and indulge without fear of loss or consequence, to be
insulated from anything like the brutal denouement of the
carpet of stars. 'Humankind cannot bear very much reality.'

The final piece of music, Rudi Schuricke singing 'Heimat
deine Sterne', similarly contrasts with the script's epitaph for
the Edelweiss Pirates, offering many possibilities for
production: could this be a poignant moment for the Chorus
to recognise the young Pirates as the stars (*Sterne*) and the
diamonds mentioned in the song – symbols of martyrdom,
light and hope? Or, conversely, could this be a macabre
return of the Hitlerjugend, trampling inexorably over the
recent past and the memory of the young dead, and defiantly
extolling the radiant might of their homeland. Translate and
understand the lyrics and investigate the possibilities for your
interpretation.

The directors were encouraged to 'Be brave, be bold and
challenge your audience'.

Follow, Follow

By Katie Douglas

After an Orange Order march through the town where they live, Al, Billy, Stacey, Kelly-Anne and Big Mikey head to the local park with a gaggle of younger kids, ready to drink, flirt and have a laugh. But when one of their group is robbed and the others assume they know who is to blame, a group becomes a gang. Events spiral out of control, ending in an act of violence that some of them can't understand, none of them can handle and all of them will remember for the rest of their lives.

Age suitability: 15+

Cast size: 8
Strong language throughout

Katie Douglas is a prizewinning scriptwriter whose work has spanned drama and comedy both here and in the States. She has a wealth of experience under her belt, both as a writer for hire and adaptor, and has worked on such shows as *Secret Diary of a Call Girl*, *After You've Gone*, *M.I. High*, *Waterloo Road* and *EastEnders*. She currently has several original comedy and drama projects in active development. As a playwright, she has worked with a number of theatres, including Liverpool Everyman, the RSC, Paines Plough, Soho and Southwark Playhouse, and her work has been shortlisted for the Susan Smith Blackburn Prize. Her most recent play, *Dig*, was described by Joyce McMillan as 'a small masterpiece'.

Characters

THE BOYS

Al, *seventeen*
Billy, *sixteen*
Big Mikey, *eighteen*
Graeme, *fourteen*

THE GIRLS

Stacey, *sixteen*
Kelly-Anne, *sixteen*
Kacey, *thirteen*
Annmarie, *twelve*

This play is intended to be performed anywhere in the natural dialects of the actors.

Flute music over black.

A patch of wasteland in a small town. A group of teenagers show up with carrier bags clinking full of bottles.

They're all wearing the uniform of an Orange Order marching band and carrying various instruments – flutes, drums, etc.

The music ends abruptly.

Billy   Telling you, he did.

Big Mikey   Liar.

Billy   Not a liar –

Al   Leave him alone.

Billy   See? He believes me.

Kelly-Anne   Only cos you're bum-chums.

Al *hits* **Kelly-Anne** *on the arm.*

Kelly-Anne   Ah! Hitting a girl. You should be on a register or something.

Stacey *concentrates on unpacking the bottles of booze. Can't be doing with all this talk, this aggravation.*

Stacey   Who bought this shit?

Graeme *snatches the bottle.*

Stacey   Tastes like cough syrup.

Graeme   Beautiful.

Stacey   Tastes like what you give kids when they've got snot running out their nose.

Graeme   I like the taste.

Stacey   Child.

Billy   Oi, I'm talking.

Kelly-Anne   Talking crap none of us are daft enough to believe.

Big Mikey   Your old man hasn't been seen round here in years.

Billy   Didn't say he turned up. Said he rung me up, it's different.

Big Mikey   Last time I saw your father – last time anyone round here saw your father – he was too pissed to use a phone.

Billy (*embarrassed*)   And your mum gave me a ride round the back of the Tesco's but you don't see me going on about it.

Big Mikey*'s face pales. He fixes his sights on* **Billy**.

Al   He didn't mean it.

He pulls **Billy** *away from* **Big Mikey**.

Al   It's him. He's a liar. He didn't mean it. Things just fly out his mouth unbidden, he's got no idea –

Big Mikey   On your knees.

Billy *looks at* **Big Mikey**, *utterly horrified.* **Kelly-Anne** *thinks this is hilarious.*

Kelly-Anne   Oh my God!

She nudges **Stacey**, *amused.*

Kelly-Anne   Are you hearing this?

Big Mikey (*not mucking about*)   On your knees, Billy boy.

Al   Hang on –

Big Mikey   You've got three seconds. One, two –

Kelly-Anne   You sure you don't want one of the girls on her knees instead? Go on, Kacey, you're well good at it.

Stacey   Shut your mouth.

Kelly-Anne *tuts at* **Stacey** − *'What the hell's your problem?'*

Big Mikey   Three.

He grabs **Billy** *by the scruff of the neck and forces him onto his knees.*

Billy   No, no, no! Don't! Mikey − Al, stop him!

Big Mikey   Don't move.

He takes a step back from **Billy**.

Billy   Al − Al, c'mon. Talk to him. Tell him I didn't mean it. I know his mum doesn't give rides round the back of Tesco's −

Al (*to* **Big Mikey**)   See? He's sorry. He didn't mean it.

Billy   Everyone knows it's Sainsbury's she hangs round.

Big Mikey *takes a run and boots* **Billy** *in the back. He goes flying head first into the mud.*

Stacey   Pathetic.

Kacey   What is wrong with your face? You've well been moany since we got here.

Annmarie   Been like that all day. Even when we were marching she was there, face like fizz.

Kelly-Anne (*with a dirty look*)   Moany cow. Ignore her.

Billy *scrambles out of the mud. Looks to* **Al** *for support.*

Al   Last time I try and help you.

Billy   I was joking! He can't take a joke!

Graeme   You don't joke about something like that.

Big Mikey   Not twice, anyway.

Billy   You don't have a sense of humour! None of you!

Al   On your feet and stop moaning. Are we getting pissed or what?

Kelly-Anne   I am. Batter in.

Kelly-Anne *drinks from a five-litre bottle of cider.* **Al** *opens a can. The others also get stuck into the booze.* **Graeme** *clocks* **Annmarie** *drinking some alcopop.*

Graeme   State of her. She shouldn't be out at this time.

Big Mikey   Listen to it. Graeme's all worried.

Graeme   Same age as my wee sister. Should be at home tucked up in bed.

Annmarie   Nothing to do with you.

Kacey   It's only for the one night.

Big Mikey   Course it is. You think I hang about with kids normally? This is a one-night-only deal. Special occasion.

Billy   Dead special. I loved it, man. The drums. When them things pound it gets right in your chest. Gets right deep down.

Stacey (*downbeat*)   Don't think I'll hear right for a week.

Al   Standing too close, that's why.

Stacey   I stand where I'm told to stand.

A look between **Al** *and* **Stacey** – *there's a relationship between these two. They understand each other.*

Billy   I just wish he could've seen it.

All eyes on him.

My old man. That's what he was ringing about. Saying he was gonna come down today. See me march.

There's a beat of silence and then laughter.

Billy   What? What's funny?

Big Mikey   You serious?

Billy   I'm serious.

Big Mikey   The march is over, fanny rag. We been, we marched, we done.

Billy   So?

Kelly-Anne   So where is he then?

Billy   So maybe he's on his way?

Graeme   What kind of idiot would ring up to say he's gonna come then not show until this time?

Annmarie   It's dark and everything.

Kacey   Everyone's in the pub.

Graeme   Everyone except us.

Billy   He'll be here.

He turns to **Al** *and* **Stacey**.

Billy   He will.

Al   I believe you.

Stacey   I couldn't give a shit either way. Just for the record.

Kelly-Anne   You need to buck up!

Stacey   Or what?

Kelly-Anne   I seriously cannot look at your hacked-up mush any longer.

Big Mikey   There's a nice fresh patch of mud over there if you girls want to settle this the old-fashioned way. And by 'old-fashioned' I mean 'sexy'.

Stacey *and* **Kelly-Anne** *unite briefly to give* **Big Mikey** *a withering stare.*

Big Mikey   I'll even tape it on my phone. Shove it on the internet, we'll split the profits.

Stacey   If I had a shovel I'd smash every one of you right in the teeth. Bang, bang, bang.

Billy   Anger issues much?

Stacey *steps to* **Billy** *and he backs off rapidly.*

Kelly-Anne   We're here to have a laugh, Stacey, not put up with your PMT, so rein it in.

Stacey   Rein it in?

Kelly-Anne   Get a hold of it – whatever it is – and rein it in. (*Beat.*) Why's there no vodka in my hand?

Graeme *scrambles to pass* **Kelly-Anne** *the vodka. She drinks.*

Stacey   Keep drinking, why not?

Big Mikey   Your attitude is reeking, by the way.

Billy   You better not be in this sort of mood when my father turns up.

Al (*weary*)   Billy, seriously . . .

Billy   Well, she'd better not be! He'll turn round and walk straight out the town again if he sees her looking like she's chewing a wasp.

Big Mikey   Walking out of town's that bloke's favourite hobby.

It's a low blow. **Billy** *is genuinely hurt.* **Al** *steps between* **Big Mikey** *and* **Billy***.*

Al   He says his father'll be here and he'll be here.

Something in his tone – the authority – says that's the end of the conversation.

Kelly-Anne *looks at* **Stacey***, who's sitting alone, sipping her drink.*

Kelly-Anne   I'm bored. Mikey?

Big Mikey   What?

Kelly-Anne   Make me not be bored.

Big Mikey   Expecting me to whip out a Game Boy or something?

Graeme   Game Boy. You don't even get them any more.

Kelly-Anne   You whip out a Game Boy you better know how to use it.

Kelly-Anne's *giving* **Big Mikey** *the eye. After a beat, he catches on.*

Big Mikey   You mean . . . ?

Kelly-Anne *smiles coyly. Course that's what she means . . .*

Stacey   He really is slower than a week in the jail.

Kelly-Anne   Finish that drink before we get back and you're dead.

She takes **Big Mikey** *by the hand – she's in charge here – and takes him off.*

Stacey   We finish all this drink we literally will be dead.

Kelly-Anne *and* **Big Mikey** *are gone.*

Annmarie   Where they going?

Al   Never you mind.

Billy   Where are they going?

Al *gives* **Billy** *a hard stare.* **Billy** *catches on. He grabs a can of lager out of one of the bags.*

Billy   How many of these do you think we'd have to drink before we died?

Stacey   A brain your size would probably become saturated in a matter of one or two cans.

Billy   Hilarious.

Graeme   Where's your father tonight, Al?

Al   How the fuck should I know?

Kacey   In the lodge with everyone else's father, likely.

Graeme   He still march then?

Annmarie   My father'd cut off his left nut rather than stop marching.

Kacey   Mine and all.

Al   He does the local marches. His knees are fucked, he doesn't travel so much any more.

Graeme   He must be proud, you on the drum and everything.

Al *shrugs, doesn't want to talk about it.*

Graeme   I bet you're a right golden boy for that.

Al (*quiet*)   I'm not his golden boy.

Billy (*deliberate change of subject*)   His nickname's Crater Face not Golden Boy.

Al *looks at* **Billy** *for a beat. Then* **Billy** *takes off at a run and* **Al** *chases him.* **Al** *tackles* **Billy** *to the ground.*

Billy   Mercy, mercy!

Al *gets off* **Billy** *and holds out his hand.* **Billy** *takes it and* **Al** *helps him to his feet.*

A quiet moment.

Graeme (*to* **Stacey**)   Who's your father again?

Stacey   None of your business.

Billy   Don't be shy. I thought your mum drew straws a few years back to sort that one out?

Stacey *glares at* **Billy**.

Al   I'll hold him for you.

Stacey *goes over and gives* **Billy** *a dead arm.*

Billy   Will everyone stop beating me up?!

Al   Stop running your gob then.

Graeme (*to* **Stacey**)   Is your pal really into everything they say she is?

Stacey *throws an empty can of alcopop into the mud, then goes to a carrier bag for another.*

Graeme   What did I say?

Stacey *can't even look at* **Graeme**. **Kacey** *nudges him.*

Kacey   You should hear what she got up to at this party the other night . . .

Stacey *turns her laser-like glare on* **Kacey**. *She shuts up and moves away from* **Graeme**.

Billy   I need a piss.

He turns his back on the group.

Stacey   Don't even think about it!

Billy   I'm not thinking, I'm unzipping . . .

Stacey   Al!

Al   I'm not in charge of where he pisses!

Billy   There's only one man in charge of where this man pisses and that man is me.

Kacey *and* **Annmarie** *lean back to see* **Billy**'s *manhood.*

Kacey   There, see it?

Annmarie   Is that it?

Stacey (*to* **Billy**)   Have a bit of respect?

Billy *looks at* **Stacey**, *confused.*

Stacey   Go in the bushes, you animal!

Billy   The bushes are occupied.

Stacey   There's more than one bush.

Graeme   You know when you say a word and it loses all meaning? Bush, bush, bush, bush –

Kacey *and* **Annmarie**   Bush, bush, bush, bush –

Billy   Alright!

He zips himself up and turns back round.

If you lot shut your yaps, I'll go in the bushes.

Stacey   Thank you.

Billy   Considering where you live I'm surprised you're not more used to rivers of piss running next to your feet.

Stacey*'s unimpressed.*

Stacey   Move.

Billy   I will. But only cos I don't want to embarrass everyone when my dick hits the ground like a coiled snake. Not cos you told me to.

He moves off a little.

Stacey   Further!

Billy   How much further?

Stacey   Imagine the only appropriate place for you to have a piss is the moon.

Annmarie   And we already saw it, by the way.

Kacey   Coiled snake, my arse.

Annmarie   Runt of the tadpole litter, more like.

She and **Kacey** *laugh and high-five.*

Billy *tuts and moves offstage, in search of an appropriate bush.*

Al *moves to sit next to* **Stacey**. *She passes him a can of lager from one of the carrier bags.*

Stacey   Do you really think he'll turn up?

Al *shrugs. Opens his can.*

Stacey   You don't think it's just a tiny bit cruel? Letting him believe something which is probably never going to happen?

Al   He could come round that corner in two seconds for all we know. All 'sorry I'm late'.

Stacey   He won't! Will you please just stop and admit what's going on here!

Al *lets* **Stacey** *calm down for a beat.*

Al   What is going on here?

Stacey *knows he's asking her what's wrong. She doesn't want to tell him.*

Stacey   It's worse. Living in cloud cuckoo land, believing the hype, having some dream in your hand that everyone else knows is smoke but to you feels solid. When that goes, when you catch on to what everyone else has known the whole time. It's worse. Having that hope. Losing it. It's worse than the truth. It's worse – ten times worse.

Al *doesn't know what to say.*

Stacey   He's your best friend.

Stacey *grips* **Al**'s *arm.*

Stacey   Tell him. Tell him there are no happy endings.

After a long beat, **Al** *reaches out and tucks a strand of hair behind* **Stacey**'s *ear. Gentle.*

The moment is broken by the return of **Big Mikey** *and* **Kelly-Anne**.

Graeme   Mikey, did you pump her?

Stacey   Jesus Christ.

She moves away from **Al**.

Kelly-Anne   Like he's gonna tell you what happened, you paedo.

Stacey   Someone tell her what paedo means before I have to shoot myself in the face.

Kelly-Anne (*grabbing the vodka*)   If you're not careful that grumpy-boot impression you're doing is going to end up permanent.

Kacey   Did you really do it in a bush?

Kelly-Anne *grins at* **Kacey** *and* **Annmarie** *coyly – telling them all they need to know.*

Annmarie   Rank!

Big Mikey *guzzles half a can of lager then lets out a massive belch.*

Al *can't take his eyes off* **Stacey**, *who seems increasingly uncomfortable at being here.*

Al   Maybe we should just call it a night, eh?

Big Mikey   It's not even half-nine yet.

Al   I know, just –

Kelly-Anne   Daddy wanting you home before dark, is he?

Al   Course not.

Kelly-Anne   Belt up then and try and enjoy yourself! Unless you want to end up like old mouldy-arse over there.

Al *looks at the group for a beat. Locks eyes with* **Stacey**. *He puts his beer down.*

Al   I'm done.

Stacey (*quick*)   Me too.

Graeme   No way! Special night, you said.

Kacey   This is meant to be us having a laugh.

Kelly-Anne   Not slinking off to bed early doors.

Big Mikey   Man up.

Al   I said it's done.

He holds his hand towards **Stacey**. *She joins him and they make to go until –*

Billy (*offstage*)   Al!

Al *looks sharply towards the direction of the shouting.*

Billy (*offstage*)   Al, help me!

Billy *staggers into view. He's been beaten up and his uniform has been stolen.* **Al**'s *right next to him in a flash.*

Al   What happened?

Billy   My uniform – they nicked it –

Al   Who? Who did?

Billy   Them – I dunno –

Big Mikey   Have a guess who it was!

Al   Was it them?

After a beat, **Billy** *nods.*

Billy   I think so.

Stacey   'Think', he says.

Big Mikey   Belt up, we're dealing with this.

Stacey   Jumping to conclusions, more like.

Al *rounds on* **Stacey**.

Al   Look at the state of him!

Billy   My uniform. They nicked my uniform and my dad's gonna be here soon. He's gonna be here soon, Al. He's gonna be here and he's gonna want to see me in my uniform.

He starts to cry. **Al** *puts his arm around his friend.*

Kacey   Look at him crying . . .

Stacey   Shut the fuck up, Kacey.

Kacey *rapidly belts up.*

Big Mikey   Stating the obvious, but we're not just gonna sit here and take this?

Kelly-Anne   Fanny-face has got a point.

Stacey   Charming.

Kelly-Anne   You don't even know it is them.

Big Mikey   Who else would it be?!

Stacey   The whole town's either in the pubs or on the streets tonight. And every single one of them's got a drink in their hand.

Kelly-Anne   If I saw a pleb like him wandering about with his dick hanging out I might be tempted to give him a punch.

Stacey   Maybe it's just someone's idea of a joke?

She and **Kelly-Anne** *exchange a look, a bit disturbed to find themselves on the same side of this argument.*

Al*'s thinking this over.*

Al   You're definitely sure it was him?

Billy   He's lived across the road from me my whole life, I know what he looks like.

Al   Big ears? Fat moon face?

Big Mikey   He said he's sure.

Al   It's dark.

Graeme   He was probably draped in green, knowing him.

Big Mikey   We spent today marching. Marching through town, banging the drums, letting folk know who we are. And now what? We forget all that? What's the point if we sit back now and let them walk all over us?

Stacey   It's supposed to be about more than that.

Big Mikey   There is nothing more than that. We are here –
this is us – this is our town.

Al   How many was there? Just him?

Graeme   What about all those mates he hangs around
with?

Al   That's what I'm asking.

Kacey   They're always round the back of the Spar. They
tried to get my father to buy them drink the other night.

Al *focuses on* **Billy**.

Al   How many was there? Just him or him and his cronies?

Billy   There was a few cronies standing behind him.

Big Mikey   But it was him did it? Him that smashed
you up?

After a beat, **Billy** *nods.*

Billy   I'm sure.

Big Mikey   Done deal.

He turns to **Al**.

Big Mikey   Let's roll.

Stacey   You seriously did not just say that.

Big Mikey   This isn't a joke!

Something in his tone puts both **Stacey** *and* **Kelly-Anne** *on the back
foot. The atmosphere has taken a turn for the serious.*

Big Mikey   Billy boy might be a turd in human form –

Billy   Nice.

Big Mikey   But he's one of us. These folk think they can
come here? Disobey our rules? Hit out at our people?

Annmarie   Think again.

Big Mikey   See, she gets it.

Al   We all get it.

Big Mikey   Then why we still standing here?

He makes to go.

Billy   What you gonna do?

Big Mikey   Me?

Billy   Cos, I mean – I just want to find my uniform –

Big Mikey   This isn't 'me'. This is 'we'.

Billy   And we'll just, what? Have a look about for it?

Big Mikey   We can get you another uniform. This is what matters.

Billy   I don't know what this is.

He looks to **Al**.

Billy   What's he saying?

Al   He's saying he doesn't care about the uniform.

Billy   But –

Al   He's saying – if you want us to – we can find him.

Billy   But not get the jacket back.

Al   Not care about getting the jacket back. Not go there for that. Make it clear when we're there that our purpose isn't the jacket. If we go – if you want us to go –

Big Mikey   Course he does!

Al   We might have you here all tidied up for when your old man arrives.

Kacey   Well, there you go, that's what he wants.

Al   Or – or – we might not. And there's other stuff that will almost definitely happen if we go. If we find him. If we track him down and we find him.

Billy   Violence.

Big Mikey   Education dealt out. Lessons learned.

Billy   Blood on collars and knuckles.

Al   Mine and yours.

Billy   His face.

Al   His face. Our knuckles.

Billy   His face. Our knuckles. These streets.

He looks at the faces surrounding him.

Not sure.

Big Mikey*'s getting sick of this. He gets in* **Billy***'s face.*

Big Mikey   Then get sure! Think back. What have you been taught? Them and us. Band of brothers. They put one of ours in the hospital – we put one of theirs in the morgue.

Stacey   No one's in hospital. It's some daft uniform. A cut on his face.

Kelly-Anne   I thought we were meant to be here for a laugh?

Big Mikey   A man wouldn't hesitate. Are you a man?

All eyes on **Billy***.*

Annmarie   Look at him. Shaking.

Graeme   Snivelling like a weasel.

Kacey   He wouldn't know a proper man if he got smacked in the face by one.

Big Mikey   What would Wayne Rooney do?

Graeme   Simon Cowell.

Kacey   Danny Dyer.

Annmarie   Real men, real men, real men, real men, real men, real men –

Billy   Alright!

A beat of silence.

Okay. Let's do it.

A smile appears on **Big Mikey***'s face.*

Big Mikey   Lead the way.

He pushes **Billy** *in front of him.*

Big Mikey   The rest of you follow on.

Graeme, **Kacey**, **Annmarie** *all line up behind* **Big Mikey** *as instructed.* **Stacey**, **Kelly-Anne** *and* **Al** *hang back.*

Stacey (*to* **Al**)   Put an end to this. Step up. Draw a line.

Kelly-Anne   Tonight was supposed to be a laugh.

Annmarie   Real men, real men, real men –

Stacey   Al!

Big Mikey   Let's get this show on the road, c'mon.

He shoves **Billy** *in the back, hard.*

Stacey   Al!

Big Mikey *shoves* **Billy** *again.* **Al**, *still hanging back, doesn't know what to do.*

Big Mikey *shoves* **Billy** *again.*

And again.

And again.

Until finally –

Billy   No!

He breaks formation.

Big Mikey   'No'?

Billy   I just want my old man to see me march.

Big Mikey   What do you mean, 'no'?

Billy   You're gonna go there and not even get my uniform back.

Big Mikey *looks at* **Billy** *for a beat then slaps him hard across the face.*

Big Mikey (*dark*)   Remember whose side you're on.

Billy *is reeling. Gutted. The thought of what's about to happen – what he might be made to do – churning him up inside. In desperation, he looks at* **Al** *for support.*

A long, tense beat.

Al   I'll go.

Stacey   What?

Al   I'll lead the way. Ram the front of this guy's skull out the back of his head.

Big Mikey   Bring it!

Al   Pull his jaws apart. Piss down his throat.

Big Mikey   And the rest!

Al   Teach him a lesson.

Big Mikey   Education, education, education.

Al *marches to the front of the pack, shoving* **Billy** *unceremoniously out the way as he does.*

Al   Let's fucking roll.

Billy *is left standing there as* **Al**, **Big Mikey**, **Graeme**, **Kacey** *and* **Annmarie** *move off, excited.*

Billy (*pathetic*)   If you see my uniform . . .

Kelly-Anne *hangs back. Gropes* **Billy***.*

Kelly-Anne   Don't worry. I'll keep you company while they're gone.

Billy *looks terrified. Can't say no.*

Al *looks back at* **Stacey***. They lock eyes for a beat then he focuses ahead, goes with the rest.*

Stacey   What is happening here?

The stage grows quiet. **Stacey** *looks to* **Kelly-Anne** *and* **Billy***. Neither has any answers.*

Stacey   Fuck this for a game of soldiers.

She storms off in the opposite direction to the others.

A beat of silence.

Billy *and* **Kelly-Anne** *look at each other then slowly make their way to the bag of booze. They sit on the grass, open a bottle of vodka and sit passing it back and forth in silence for a while.*

Kelly-Anne   I'll let you poke me if you like.

Billy   Poke you.

Kelly-Anne   In the fanny?

Billy   Jesus. I get it.

Kelly-Anne   Sorry, you're a bit slow on the uptake sometimes, I thought you might need it spelling out.

Billy   Loud and clear.

A beat of silence.

Kelly-Anne   So – y'know. The offer's on the table if you want it.

Billy *takes a long sip from the vodka, doesn't quite know what to do here.*

Billy   Do you want me to poke you?

Kelly-Anne   I don't understand the question.

Billy   You told me I could poke you if I wanted to. But you didn't say whether you wanted me to or not. So I'm asking. Do you?

Kelly-Anne *looks at* **Billy** *for a beat.*

Kelly-Anne   You're a proper freak, you know that?

Billy   It's a yes-or-no question.

Kelly-Anne *tuts, doesn't want to get into this.*

Billy   It's fine, you don't have to answer. I can tell it's a no.

Kelly-Anne   Hark at you, Mystic Meg.

Billy   I just don't know why you'd offer if you're not even that into it, that's all.

Pause.

Kelly-Anne   Who says I'm not into it?

Billy   I can tell. From your face.

Kelly-Anne   You can't tell anything from my face.

Billy   I can. Trust me.

Kelly-Anne *shakes her head, not believing a word of it.*

Billy   Look at me, I'll prove it.

She doesn't.

Look at me.

Kelly-Anne *sighs and turns to* **Billy**.

Kelly-Anne   Only doing this to shut you up.

Billy   Shhh.

Billy *looks deep into* **Kelly-Anne**'s *eyes.*

Kelly-Anne   You're sick in the head, what are you – (*doing*).

Billy *takes* **Kelly-Anne**'s *hands. It takes her by surprise. He maintains eye contact. She gets more and more uncomfortable the longer it goes on.*

Kelly-Anne   Alright, stop it now.

Billy   Bit longer . . .

Kelly-Anne   Billy –

Billy   Few seconds –

Kelly-Anne   I said stop it!

She tugs her hands out of **Billy**'s *grip and looks away, can't handle this any more.*

A beat of silence.

Billy   Do you want to know what I saw?

Kelly-Anne (*beat*)   Whatever it was – don't tell anyone.

A moment of closeness between them.

Billy   I don't think he's coming, is he? My dad.

Kelly-Anne   It is getting late.

Billy   People don't always do what they say they're gonna do. I know that. I mean he's rung up before. Said – said he wanted to see me. That he missed me. Once, he invited me round to his. He's got this massive new house up in the next town. Four beds or whatever. And he rung me up all like, come over. Have your dinner with us. Us meaning him and his new wife. The new kids. So I went. I stole money out my mum's purse for the bus fare cos she hates him, she'd never have loaned me it, and I got on the bus and I went. I got there and – house was dark. No car in the drive, blinds all pulled. I'm like, what's going on? Worried, y'know. Emergency or something maybe. My phone was out of credit so I sat on the front step and waited. Biting cold. Freezing, it was. Dunno how long I waited. Eventually they turned up, boot full of Tesco shopping. The wife looks at me like she's trod in something. Like there's a bad smell in the air. And he's like full of apologies. Slipped my mind. Something came up. Busy lives. Another time?

Another time. Turn on my heel and go and I'm waiting for him to call me back. Check on me. How you getting home? Need a lift?

He keeps schtum. I keep walking. Last bus has gone so . . . kipped down in the shelter. After a while – you don't even feel the cold.

I know it's daft. I know cos when he was with us he was this useless bag of shit and now he's all sorted and has this life that means he gets to look down on us and I should tell him where to go, I know I should, but –

But the phone rings and I can't help it. A bit of me always believes. This time, this time, this time.

Kelly-Anne *feels for* **Billy**. *She doesn't know how to make him feel better. She slides a hand onto his thigh.*

Kelly-Anne   You sure you don't want to –

Billy *gently moves her hand off him.*

Billy   Don't ask me that again.

Kelly-Anne *looks at* **Billy** *with new eyes.*

Kelly-Anne   Tell me what you saw. When you looked at me. Looked in my eyes. What did you see?

Billy (*beat*)   That everything's going to be okay.

Kelly-Anne's *body sags with relief.*

Kelly-Anne   When?

Stacey *comes back, interrupting.*

Stacey   Where are they?

Billy *and* **Kelly-Anne** *scramble to their feet.*

Kelly-Anne   I thought you'd gone home in a huff?

Stacey   Say they've been back. Say they've come back here and they're not still –

Billy   They're still . . .

Stacey's *face fills with dread.*

Billy   Dial down the panic, c'mon. This is Al we're dealing with here. We've been pals since the year dot. Take it from me, the boy's golden.

Stacey *clocks the intimacy between* **Kelly-Anne** *and* **Billy**.

Stacey   What have I missed?

Kelly-Anne   We've just been sitting here.

Stacey   Just?

Kelly-Anne   If you've got something to say –

Stacey   I've got something to say.

Kelly-Anne's *on her feet. Facing* **Stacey**.

Billy   Woah, ladies –

Stacey   You're a disgrace.

Kelly-Anne   Hark at it.

Stacey   He's not like you. You don't touch him.

Kelly-Anne *laughs.*

Kelly-Anne   He wanted it.

Stacey   What?

Kelly-Anne   I said – he wanted it.

Stacey   So –

Kelly-Anne   So we did. It. We did it.

Stacey *looks at* **Billy**.

Stacey   Is this true?

Kelly-Anne   Course it's true. This is me you're talking to. Like it'd ever not be true.

Stacey   Unbelievable.

Kelly-Anne   That's me.

Billy   Anybody want a drink?

He tries to ease the tension by going for some more cans but the girls don't move.

Kelly-Anne   When are you just gonna admit it?

Stacey   Admit what?

Kelly-Anne   The reason you've got such a problem with me these days. The thing that gets to you. That makes your face shrivel and your nose turn up whenever I'm around.

Stacey   My nose doesn't turn up.

Kelly-Anne   It turns straight up. And it's weird cos me and you –

Stacey   Best mates.

Kelly-Anne   Solid as a rock.

Stacey   Since the year dot.

Kelly-Anne (*beat*)   But not any more.

Stacey   Nope. Not any more.

Billy   Seriously, there's drink going begging over here –

Kelly-Anne   It's alright if you don't want to say. I know why. I've always known.

Stacey   Cos you're so clever. Switched on.

Kelly-Anne   Cos it's so fucking obvious. (*Beat.*) You're jealous.

*Now it's **Stacey**'s turn to laugh.*

Stacey   I don't intend to get up close and personal with a dose of the clap anytime soon so no – not jealous.

Kelly-Anne   You look across rooms at people and they turn their face away. Me, I look and they look back.

Stacey   Because they're after a wet fanny on a dry day.

Kelly-Anne   I'm a laugh. People like me. And you can't stand it.

Stacey *looks at* **Kelly-Anne** *for a long beat.*

Stacey   You really believe I'm jealous.

She steps towards **Kelly-Anne**.

Stacey   You with your parents still together and your house with a garden. Help with your homework and swimming lessons. Dogs and cats and pats on the hea

Kelly-Anne   I don't get you.

Stacey   It's such a *waste.* You look across a room and they look back and the whole time you're worrying what they think when really you should be proud and confident and know that you have the world at your feet and all you need do is reach out a pinky finger and grab it. You can do anything. And you choose this. You give in, every day, to the hole in your soul that believes them when they tell you you're not good enough. It's a waste. It's tragic. It makes me want to sit down on this stinking patch of grass and cry.

You and me have been you and me since the year dot. Then we get here. This year. This age. And the rest of them step in and ruin you and make me watch.

Kelly-Anne *has tears in her eyes.*

Stacey   I can't watch any more.

Kelly-Anne *sits down on the grass, struggling to take in what she's just heard.*

Billy   There's some vodka left.

Billy *holds the bottle towards* **Kelly-Anne** *and she waves it away. He turns to* **Stacey**.

Billy   We just talked. When you were away. We just sat on the grass and talked.

Stacey *looks over at* **Kelly-Anne** *for a beat, then back at* **Billy**. **Stacey** *reaches out and squeezes* **Billy**'*s hand.*

After a beat, **Big Mikey**, **Graeme**, **Kacey** *and* **Annmarie** *rock up.*

Stacey   Al –

Big Mikey   He's not here?

Stacey   We've been waiting –

Billy   You got separated?

Graeme   Deliberate. Cover more ground.

Billy   So you didn't find him then?

All eyes on **Billy**.

Big Mikey   Your lucky day, arse bandit. They got away with it just like you wanted.

Billy   I never said that's what I wanted. I just didn't want –

Stacey   Don't rise to the bait, Billy. You did the right thing.

Big Mikey   Since when is sitting on your hands the right thing?

Stacey   No, you're right. Stamping your foot on someone's face. Much better.

Big Mikey   If they deserve it.

Annmarie   Can I have a drink now? We've been traipsing round like idiots.

Kacey   Pointless idiots.

Annmarie *grabs the bottle of vodka.* **Stacey** *snatches it off her.*

Stacey   You've had enough. You're twelve. Go home.

Big Mikey *takes the vodka from* **Stacey** *and hands it to* **Annmarie**. *He smirks at* **Stacey**. *After a beat,* **Kelly-Anne** *stands and grabs the bottle from* **Annmarie**.

Kelly-Anne   Go home, both of you. (*To* **Graeme**.) And you.

Graeme *laughs.*

Kelly-Anne   I said go!

Billy   Al should be back by now. If he couldn't find these guys, if he couldn't get my uniform back, he'd be here. He'd be back.

Stacey *puts a hand on* **Billy**'s *arm.*

Stacey   This is Al we're talking about. The boy's golden.

Billy *smiles, comforted.*

Al *comes running on stage. He stops and bends double, catching his breath.*

Billy   You're back!

Big Mikey   I take it the scum were nowhere to be found?

Graeme   Gone to ground.

Kacey   Run off –

Annmarie   Tails between their legs!

Kelly-Anne   You don't know what the fuck you're talking about, any of you.

She and **Stacey** *exchange a look. The old* **Kelly-Anne** *is re-emerging.*

Billy   Al?

Stacey   What happened?

Billy   Al?

Al *straightens up. He has blood on his hands and in his hair and on his face.*

The others look at him with shock.

Al   They were there. The back of the Spar. Hanging round in the car park.

After a beat, **Stacey** *goes for* **Al***, beating him around the body with her fists.*

Stacey   You stupid – stupid – stupid –

Billy   Back off!

He grabs **Stacey** *and pulls her away from* **Al***.*

Billy   Back off. Let him speak. He'll tell us. He'll explain.

He looks at **Al***, absolute trust.*

Al   I found them. Back of the Spar. The car park –

Billy   And then?

Al   The Spar – the car park –

Billy   You talked to them. You – settled things? You didn't. Didn't go in all guns blazing cos – You wouldn't. Stupid. Dumb, that's not you, that's not –

Al *looks* **Billy** *in the eye.* **Billy** *realises that* **Al** *has done something terrible.*

Billy   We need to get this off you.

He starts wiping at the blood with his sleeve.

We'll get it off and it'll be gone and we'll say no more about it.

Stacey   I don't think that's going to work.

Billy   Shut up! Just – shut up.

He continues wiping at the blood.

Big Mikey   I hope you gave them a right kicking.

Billy *stops what he's doing. A beat and then he runs at* **Big Mikey**, *knocking him off his feet.*

Billy *starts hitting* **Big Mikey** *round the head.*

Billy   Is this what a real man does, is it? Is this what we're marching for? To be like you? To belong to this bullshit?

Graeme, **Kacey**, **Annmarie**, **Kacey** *and* **Kelly-Anne** *struggle to separate* **Billy** *and* **Big Mikey**.

Stacey *goes to* **Al**. *He's staring straight ahead. Not looking at her.*

Everything is descending into chaos until –

Al   I found them in the car park at the Spar. They were drinking bottles of beer. Laughing. Had his uniform on the ground and they were pissing on it.

Everyone's stopped to listen now.

They saw me. Knew who I was and why I was there. They laughed a bit, threw some bottles. Pushed me down.

He shows the others his bloodied hands.

Cut me.

Graeme   So you didn't –

Annmarie   Nothing –

Big Mikey   You let them push you down?

Al   They pushed me down. I cut myself. On the broken bottle and – I ran.

Stacey *and* **Billy** *exchange a worried look.*

Big Mikey   I don't believe what I'm hearing here.

Graeme   He did his best.

Big Mikey   They got away with it!

Al   They did. They got away with it. I – I couldn't do anything.

Big Mikey *shakes his head, disappointed.*

Big Mikey   Y'know today, us all out there, filling the streets with our flutes and drums and the songs vibrating off every building. I was proud. It filled me up. But now?

This is a bust. All of this.

Graeme   We know where they are now. We could go back. Find them and –

Big Mikey   It's done, over with. He's fucked it.

Graeme   But –

Big Mikey   This was supposed to be a laugh.

He stands, grabs one of the carrier bags and goes.

Stacey   The rest of you get your stuff and go.

Annmarie   No way.

Kacey   We're not just going slinking off home for no reason, we haven't even –

Stacey   Get out of here!

Kacey *and* **Annmarie** *look to* **Kelly-Anne**.

Kelly-Anne   You heard her.

Kacey *and* **Annmarie** *get the message. They gather their things and go.* **Graeme** *looks at* **Al**, **Billy**, **Kelly-Anne** *and* **Stacey**. *It's clear none of them want him there.*

Graeme   Fuck this.

He heads off.

Silence for a long time.

Stacey   So what really happened?

Al *sits down. Takes his time.*

Al   He was on his own.

Slowly the others sit down around **Al**, *ready to listen.*

I ran up and I punched him in the face. He dropped the carrier bag he was holding. There was a bottle inside, some kind of sauce and – it smashed. On the ground and I did cut my hand. I did, I – I bent down and picked it up and I cut my hand.

Stacey   You picked it up.

Al   It seemed like the thing to do. I could hear everyone in the pub round the corner. Singing. Laughing and singing the same songs we've been singing all day. And he's cowering by now, he wants to run but he's thinking that he knows me. We've lived on the same street our whole lives. He doesn't think he should run. Doesn't think he needs to but – I've got the bottle in my hand and we're eyeing each other. Eyeing each other and circling and I want to run too. I don't want to be here, can't remember how I ended up here, why. All I can see is him and all I can feel is the bottle in my hand and all I can hear is the songs and the drums, drums, drums.

He bled a lot. When I slashed him. Grabbed himself here.

Al *grabs his throat.*

But it's gushing through the cracks in his fingers and there's nothing he can do. I know it. He knows it. So he lets go and –

Silence.

Billy   I'm gonna be sick.

He runs to the bushes and throws up. **Kelly-Anne** *is shaking.*

Kelly-Anne   So what really happened?

Al *looks at* **Kelly-Anne**.

Kelly-Anne   Tell us. Please. Tell us what really happened.

Stacey *tries to comfort* **Kelly-Anne**, *but she's scared and this is horrible and she won't let her.*

Kelly-Anne   Tell me!

Billy *returns.*

Kelly-Anne (*to* **Al**)   I know that didn't happen – couldn't happen – so tell me the truth. The truth!

Al   I found him in the car park at the back of the Spar. He had a carrier bag in his hand. Light, just – bits and bobs. Taking them home to his mum.

Kelly-Anne   And then what?

Al   And we looked at each other and we recognised each other cos we've lived across the road from each other for years.

Kelly-Anne   And then? And then?

Al   And then he walked right past me. And I let him go. He went home to his mum and I came here. I fell over on the way, must've cut myself on something.

Long beat.

Kelly-Anne   And that's the truth?

Al *nods.*

Billy *smiles.*

Billy   I knew it.

He punches **Al** *on the shoulder, friendly.*

Billy   Solid as a rock, you are.

Al *smiles at* **Billy**. *There's real love there.*

Al   Maybe your old man'll be waiting at home for you, eh? I mean no reason he'd think to come all the way down here.

Billy   He could be sitting waiting on the doorstep right now!

His hope restored, he's itching to leave.

Stacey (*to* **Billy**)   Walk her home first?

Billy nods. *He goes to* **Al**, *grateful.*

Al   Haven't I always got out in front of trouble when you needed me?

Billy   Since the year dot.

He holds out a hand towards **Kelly-Anne**, *she takes it and they move off.* **Al** *and* **Stacey** *watch them go.*

Stacey   One more drink?

Al   For the road.

They crack open cans of lager and sit side by side.

Stacey   It's weird, innit. My stepdad has the news on – six o'clock every single day. And they're always on about young people.

Beat.

I never thought I'd feel this old.

Al *completely understands what she's saying.*

Stacey   I could go to the pub. Get your father. Tell him . . .

Al *shakes his head.*

Al   You can go home if you like?

Stacey *thinks about that for a second – she doesn't move.*

Al   Do you think the police'll be able to find me here?

Stacey *looks at* **Al** *and nods.*

Stacey   I'll wait with you.

She takes **Al**'s *hand and they sit in silence, drinking, for a long time.*

Fade to black.

Follow, Follow

BY KATIE DOUGLAS

*Notes on rehearsal and staging drawn from a workshop
with the writer held at the National Theatre, October 2014.
Workshop led by Róisín McBrinn, with notes by Drew Mulligan.*

Reasons for writing the play

Katie had wanted to write this play for a long time. She felt
that this was a community that wasn't widely known about or
understood. She didn't want to make a political point but to
explore the dynamics of a closed community. She felt that
children were being taught things that they needed to be
un-taught. She wanted to convey the message that being
individual means thinking for yourself, and not only about
nonconformity and anti-social behaviour. She wanted the
young people staging this play and watching it to be reminded
that they have a choice and must think for themselves.

She wanted the style of the play to be naturalistic, something
that would immediately speak to them and be a bit rough
round the edges – something that wouldn't feel like 'work'.
The characters are not so far from most kids, so it should be
easy for a young company to access these characters.

The play offers an opportunity for the actors to explore
religion and how it affects their lives. They may not have
direct experience of the Orange Order but it could be
interesting to explore what parallels they can find in their
own lives.

There is a good balance of comedy, and Katie encourages
you to bring out the humour as much as possible as this will
help you earn the serious moments.

Approaching the play

Facilitating director Róisín McBrinn pointed out that the
stakes in this play are very high. Why is the play set on this
night? Some of the characters are at points in their lives when

they have to make a decision: do they become their parents? What happens tonight will affect the rest of their lives. This night represents a turning point where they will either be okay or not.

The march

EXERCISE

It could be useful to begin rehearsals with an exercise based around a march.

- Divide the group into three, with one other person providing the bass rhythm by stamping their feet. The first group then sets a rhythm on top of that, clapping, stamping, etc. The second group then joins in with another rhythm, and then the third.

- Name each group: A, B, C. One person becomes the conductor and stands in the middle. When they call out the group's name that group starts to walk around the room still playing their rhythm. Once they are all moving the conductor can choose to start and stop groups. When they stop the rhythm stops too. The conductor can also gesture for the rhythms to be louder or softer, quicker or slower. Play around with this and keep layering on instructions. The more complex your game becomes the better.

This exercise is a practical way to get the group to focus, work together and listen. The play is an ensemble piece; the cast need to be alive and multitasking throughout the play.

Katie emphasised that it is very important that all the actors are engaged in the play and alive even when they are not speaking. They may have their own tasks and not be part of the primary conversation but they need to be listening. This is a group that knows each other really well: they can jump in and out of each other's conversations, and they can finish each other's thoughts. This gang are deeply connected to each other through their community and place: they went to school together and they share the same specific cultural background. So, how do you create a family out of the gang? The march exercise is one example of how to achieve this.

Research: the Orange Order

There is a lot of information available about the Orange marches and one of your first tasks in rehearsals could be to get the group to research the Orange Order. For some individuals, taking part in the marches was like being a member of a youth club – it was the thing they did and was not necessarily ideologically driven. They are part of a very close-knit community; they rehearse hard with practice marches in January and the real marches in July. Generations of families frequently take part, often playing the same instrument.

It could be interesting to look to your own community, to any tight-knit groups that exist around you. Do you have experience of one set of people set up against another? Often schools will have rivalries with other schools where the actual meaning behind the rivalry has been lost and it becomes about 'us' and 'them'. Katie mentioned that in her town the green Asda sign was vandalised because it was green – green representing the Catholics as opposed to blue, one of the colours of the Protestants. In Scotland this division is reflected in the rivalry between Glasgow Celtic and Rangers football clubs, the Catholics and Protestants. In England this is no longer an issue when supporting a club but many big cities still have clubs that were originally aligned to Catholics or Protestants – Liverpool and Everton, for example.

Themes

PUBLIC VERSUS PRIVATE

When are the characters speaking privately and when publicly? The private moments need to be earned. At the same time you should challenge the idea that public statements need to be over-weighted – they can be throwaway too.

RITUALS

Róisín asked the group what they thought when they heard the word 'ritual'? She defined it as, 'a solemn ceremony consisting of a series of actions that follow a prescribed order'.

She encouraged the group to explore the idea of rituals. They exist on different scales. What are the rituals that take place that bind your group together? These annual rituals could be some event at school, or some yearly ceremony – Bonfire Night or Halloween or something around Christmas.

What are the rituals that you perform within your family? Could they be a family meal on the same day each year, for example?

Now, look for the rituals you perform daily. For example; setting the table for breakfast, brushing your teeth, putting your clothes on in a certain order.

EXERCISE: DAILY RITUALS

- Enact these daily rituals as a simple set of mimed repeatable actions. Be precise, minimal. Try teaching them to others or swapping them with others in the group. Ask the group to perform these together. Distil the ritual into two actions and ask the group to repeat them. Ask them to move these around the space and be aware of the others. Move the actions within a circle. Then ask four people to perform these actions in a square moving on the diagonals. Can these actions be developed into a march? Perhaps you can set them to music?

The march is an expression of conformity. It is not questioned. The characters have been doing this for so long that it has become a ritual that is familiar to them. Find a parallel within your group, something that you can do almost unconsciously. Where is the conformity in their lives? For example, what changes in a classroom when you hear the school bell? Everyone knows where they are going, what desk they sit at. Look at what happens when you don't conform to this regular set of moves, when you go against it. Only by doing the opposite do you start to recognise the ritualism in your habitual daily actions. For example, what happens if you don't clap at the end of a performance when everyone else is doing so? Ask your group: when do they follow what everyone else is doing and not question it?

The march: the fuel for the play

This event is not seen onstage but has an enormous effect: it provides the fuel for the play. Think about when preparations started, how long characters have been up and what time the march started. The anticipation for this day and this party would have been building for months. The march itself would be a glorious celebration and they would be full of adrenaline from the performance. They have been practising for months and have probably become highly skilled in their musicianship.

You could tie this idea into rehearsals by inviting the company to develop a call-and-response game that starts simply and become more intricate as rehearsals go on, so that eventually performing it perfectly gives them a sense of real achievement. This can then feed into the energy of the play.

It could also be a good idea to play some trust games with your company to help build the group cohesion and strengthen the ensemble dynamic.

Think about what has happened before the play begins. The parents are all together in the pub and it's time for the kids to gather for their party. They might have either been to the off-licence or have stolen alcohol from their homes, or perhaps have been hoarding it for months in anticipation. All this leads to them being on a high. They have received praise and are not used to it. The play starts at a peak from which they are coming down. The party is their way to create another peak. There are huge expectations for it. There is a fast-paced, excited energy at the start of the play, a feeling of 'let's get on this'.

The enemy

Are the enemy 'present' at the top of the show? Perhaps it is more theatrical if they are initially nowhere to be seen. This has been their day, the enemy are not present in their minds, and they are not looking over their shoulders or anticipating any trouble. These two communities exist alongside each other but they don't mix. They ignore each other but they live in the same street.

Rehearsal exercises

EXERCISE: CREATING A SYSTEM

This is good for creating and developing the ensemble.

- Stand the group in a circle. Pass a juggling ball from one person to another across the circle until everyone has had the ball and it returns to the first person. Repeat this exactly so that everyone remembers who they received the ball from and who they are passing it to.

- Give a second ball to someone else to start a new route and remember this one. Now play both routes at the same time; the second one could be started five passes after the first.

- Keep adding to this game the whole way through the rehearsal and performance process. Try moving the ball between characters who are speaking. Notice who the ball always goes back to or who is in control of the ball.

Róisín suggested that this game is great for group awareness. Look at scenes between characters where others are watching. This level of concentration will help keep them in character. This helps to emphasise that the actors are always present in the scene, always ready to give and receive.

GAME: ZIP ZAP BOING (VARIATION)

- Stand in a circle.
- ZIP – To pass the ZIP around the circle, gesture with your palm open to the person next to you; the left hand for the person on the left. To reverse the movement of the ZIP

anyone can send it the other way by gesturing with the other hand, the right hand to move it back round the circle anticlockwise.

- ZAP – Both hands gesture across the circle.

- BOING – Sends the ZAP back to the person who sent it. They can then ZAP again or return to the ZIP around the circle. You can only BOING a ZAP!

- CHING – Throw your hand up to either left or right. This sends the move over to the person next to you and the person after that continues. You can't CHING a ZIP!

- Competitive ZIP ZAP BOING: if there is any hesitation or mistake the person has to sit down. When there are more than three people sitting down they start their own game between them. The standing game continues but missing out the people that are sitting. When someone makes a mistake or hesitates in the sitting game they stand up and join the standing game. So, both games are changing players constantly and working together.

You can change the words of the game to something that is relevant to the play.

Structure: finding the events

Róisín asked the group to look for the moments where the rhythm changes for all the characters on stage. These moments are *events*. Once you have identified these changes the best way to test them is to read the extract to see if it feels right. The aim is to try and find the 'gear shifts': who instigates them or is in control of them? Between the *events* there are *units*. These units are useful, smaller chunks to rehearse. By identifying the events and units you can start to understand the rhythm of the play and find the motor of each scene and what makes it dynamic.

Below are some initial suggestions of *events* or moments of change that were identified in the workshop:

1 p. 260 – Change happens at the end of Billy's line 'don't see me going on about it'.

2   p. 261 – Big Mikey boots Billy in the back.

3   p. 261 – Al says, 'Are we getting pissed or what?'

4   p. 262 – Billy says, 'See me march.'

5   p. 263 – Stacey says, 'I couldn't give a shit either way. Just for the record.'

6   p. 264 – Stage direction: *'Something in his [Al's] tone – the authority – says that's the end of the conversation.'*

7   p. 265 – Starts with Billy grabbing a can of lager.

8   p. 266 – Stage direction: *'A quiet moment.'*

9   p. 267 – Stage direction: *'**Stacey** turns her laser-like glare on **Kacey**. She shuts up and moves away from **Graeme**.'*

10   p. 268 – Stage direction: *'**Al** moves to sit next to **Stacey**.'*

11   p. 269 – Stage direction: *'The moment is broken by the return of **Big Mikey** and **Kelly-Anne**.'*

12   p. 271 – Billy's shout from offstage and his return.

13   p. 273 – Big Mikey says, 'Done deal.'

14   p. 276 – Billy says, 'Okay. Let's do it.'

15   p. 277 – Stage direction: *'He [**Billy**] breaks formation.'*

16   p. 277 – Al says, 'I'll go.'

17   p. 277 – The group *'move off, excited'*.

18   p. 278 – Stage direction: *'The stage grows quiet.'*

19   p. 278 – Stage direction: *'She [**Stacey**] storms off in the opposite direction to the others.'*

20   p. 281 – Stage direction: *'**Stacey** comes back, interrupting.'*

21   p. 282 – Stage Direction: **Stacey** *clocks the intimacy between* **Kelly-Anne** *and* **Billy**.'

22   p. 284 – Stacey says, 'I can't watch any more.'

These events have different levels of significance within the narrative. Look for the big moments. Identifying these will help you tell the story.

KEY EVENTS: SOME THINGS TO CONSIDER

EVENT 7 – This moment establishes the relationship between Al and Billy. Al gives Billy a hard stare and Billy catches on. This is done privately and it is a kind of private moment between two people who know each other really well.

EVENT 10 – After this we see the first private moment between Al and Stacey. This is the first time that the characters drop their public masks. Stacey's speech encapsulates the world of the play and is an 'in' to what the play is about.

EVENT 12 – When Billy comes back the whole play changes. Before this there should be no anticipation of a problem; they are having a party and they are all together. After this event the group start to split up as they have differing opinions as to how to react. As an exercise, you could set up a debate with the characters and put Billy in the middle. Get the actors to work hard to persuade him onto their side. Billy wants his uniform back so that his dad doesn't see him without it. Before Billy's return they were a unit, now we really start to understand who they are. It could be interesting to discuss their world-view in which they have been taught that violence is the answer.

What happened to Billy? He has no uniform, he has been kicked and beaten. It is important to show in the other characters' reactions that this kind of event has never happened before, and that they are terrified by it.

EVENT 16 – Al steps in to keep the group together and to protect Billy. He didn't want to go, but something happened and he had to step in. By taking the lead Al deflects the anger of Big Mikey towards Billy. This is a moment where the stakes are very high.

EVENT 19 – Where does Stacey storm off to? Why does she come back? For her the evening was going well, she was going to go off with Al. Now the evening has taken a completely different turn. Is she coming back to see if everything is all right?

Stacey's speech to Kelly-Anne on p. 284 is about Kelly-Anne but it could also be about Al. It could be useful to explore what might have happened in the year mentioned in the speech. How have things changed? What has happened?

Characters and characterisation

All the kids in the group are different. They have no one else to rely on and don't know who to follow: they have one another and nothing else. There is a rawness and a desire to belong. There is a hierarchy within the group but in this society they are all on the same level. There is also the chance to explore the back story of each character; there is clearly something in the past of many of them that can be developed.

THE RELATIONSHIP BETWEEN AL AND HIS DAD

Al doesn't want to become his father. Katie has left it deliberately ambiguous as to what the problem is. All we know is that Al's dad is disappointed in him but it is up to you and your company to decide on the reason. Maybe Al feels he can never be good enough for his father or doesn't want what his father wants for him. His dad has high status, he is a community figure. Could Al's dad be the enforcer of the Orange Order, could he be violent? There is a feeling that Al's dad might be proud of what Al does at the end of the play and that this would be the worst thing for him. Katie definitely wanted us to feel that Al's dad is the 'baddie' of the play.

BIG MIKEY

He quotes from films. This could mean that he doesn't have any language of his own to express himself. He thinks he is an action hero. This is his mask. His name might be a description of him rather than something that he has earned. He may have had to grow into his name, it may have made him. In unit 12, he asks a lot of questions. Why? Perhaps he wants reassurance? Or perhaps he wants to persuade the others to join him? Has he heard this type of speech before? It could be useful to read his lines only from after Billy's return until he leaves. Hearing his words in isolation might help the company really pay attention to the tactics he is using to manipulate the group.

The stakes

The *stakes* are what you have to win or lose out of a situation, what really matters to you. Usually it is to do with your own life, your family and friends. In the play, Al is saving his friend Billy, but he is also forced into making a choice that will have a profound effect on his life. He doesn't know the outcome of this but he has been forced to make a choice to save his friend. The stakes are very high here: the threat to his friend is huge, his love for his friend is strong, and this leads him to sacrifice himself. The stakes are so high in this moment because he has to make a very difficult choice.

Language

Katie is happy for companies to change any language that seems very Scottish and might not work in other locations. For example, 'wee' could be changed to 'little'. Ask the cast to say the words before changing them so they find an alternative that is meaningful and idiomatic to them.

Rehearsal techniques

ARCHETYPES

Róisín asked the group to identify the *archetypes* for the characters in the play. She described these as the two-dimensional, cartoon versions of the characters. Here is what the group came up with:

Al – The golden boy, the big brother, the hero, the prince.

Big Mikey – The brawler, the warrior, brawn.

Kelly-Anne – The tart, the slut – initially 'the tart with a heart' was suggested, but Róisín wanted to find the simple basic archetype as this is to do with public masks and not initially what is behind them.

Billy – The baby, the underdog.

Graeme – The dope, the idiot.

Anne-Marie – Tough girl.

Kacey – Shit-stirrer, gobbie, gossip girl.

Stacey – Boss girl, the king.

With your company, find the strongest archetype to play with. (Billy and Stacey are the most complex characters so more archetypes could be applied to them.)

EXERCISES

- Ask members of your company to represent each character archetype and ask them to stand in a line in front of the rest of the group. Imagine that they are in a photo booth, separately. They have to strike poses that reflect their archetypes as the photos are taken. Ask them to do it all together.

- Take a snapshot of the gang to reflect their hierarchy. The first snapshot could be the obvious public status. The second could be the true status, taking into account morality, strength but not respect. The third snapshot could reflect life opportunity. Katie suggested that Kerry-Anne has the greatest opportunities and a family that support her. What about the others? Róisín suggested Al might be at the top – he has the potential to be a winner?

The point of these exercises is to provoke debate and not to set the dynamics of the group. There are no right or wrong answers. You could choose to extend the above exercises by focusing in on certain characters. Examples:

- FOCUS ON KELLY-ANNE ARCHETYPE. Ask the actress playing Kelly-Anne to move like she is in a pop video, dancing, using her archetype of the tart. As she does this ask another actor to read out Stacey's speech to Kelly-Anne from p. 284. Kelly-Anne should try and block out the speech as much as she can with her movements. She should push the archetype 'mask' to the extreme.

- FOCUS ON BIG MIKEY'S ARCHETYPE. Ask the actor playing Big Mikey to strike some poses that represent his archetype as the brawler. Ask the actor playing Al to improvise lines that challenge Mikey, that look beyond this mask. Mikey has to fight against this with his moves.

This work can really help develop the public mask of the character and shows the actor the level they will have to work to maintain it. How much energy are characters putting in to hiding their fears and insecurities? It also really helps to develop that layer underneath. See how far you can go with these exercises. Use the lines from the script as much as you can so that there is not a disconnection between the exercise and the play itself. It is also useful to note that the characters are not showing their inner fears, their 'ghosts' as Róisín describes them, the whole time. These exercises are about finding out their masks, what they show to others, but by doing it you discover too what they are hiding.

Casting

Gender. Katie felt that the main characters of Al, Billy, Stacey and Kelly-Anne were gender-specific but that for the younger characters the gender was interchangeable. If changing the gender, feel free to change the names to something appropriate. Katie suggested it was better to change the gender of the character than ask an actor to play a different gender.

Cast size. Katie suggested creating an understudy company rather than expanding the size of the gang.

Age. If you have actors that are different ages to those mentioned in the script let the characterisation lead you, don't consciously play the age.

Production, staging and design

LOCATION

Does the play have to be set on the West Coast of Scotland?

Katie wants the show to be applicable to all regions but also for it to be specific. This is a play about a group of people embedded within the Orange Order. But it can be set anywhere in the UK. The location is just a small patch of waste land in any small town. The key factors to explore are the tribalism of the group and the small-town setting.

The play takes place on a small piece of waste land in a park. It is a place where no one else would go.

PHYSICALITY/STAGE FIGHTING

Katie wants the violence in the play to be physically believable and not impressionistic. It has to reflect rawness but be safe. If it is not a slap, then what action can you replace it with that has the same sudden impact? What will produce the same effect?

COSTUME

There are many different types of Orange Order costume, look online for examples. It is important that the uniform is clearly established even if characters subsequently discard it or accessorise it. Accessorising could also be a helpful way to define them as individual but within a group. Jackets and sashes are probably a good place to start.

Online research

Róisín suggested watching a YouTube video of two American news anchors who had developed a complex dance that they did during advert breaks. You can find them by typing 'WGN TV Anchors' into YouTube. This complex routine could provide inspiration for the movement in the play.

There is a great deal to be found online about the Orange Order and the marches which could provide valuable research to feed into rehearsals.

The Accordion Shop

By Cush Jumbo

Mister Ellody has quietly kept his accordion shop going on his local high street for generations.

One day, he steps out of his door and witnesses an extraordinary incident: hundreds of young people are surging on to the street, and they've all received the same text message on their phones which simply says:

'RIOT — THE ROAD — 7 PM TONIGHT'

Age suitability: 15+

Cast size:
an ensemble piece

Cush Jumbo is an award-winning actress and writer. She was nominated for an Olivier Award in 2014 for Outstanding Achievement in an Affiliate Theatre for *Josephine and I*, which she wrote and performed to rave reviews at the Bush Theatre.

Cush won the award for Best Actress at the Manchester Theatre Awards 2014 for her performance as Nora in *A Doll's House* at the Royal Exchange Theatre, Manchester. Prior to this Cush was nominated for an Olivier Award for her performance as Mark Antony in *Julius Caesar* at the Donmar Warehouse, and the prestigious Ian Charleson Award 2012 for her performance as Shakespeare's heroine Rosalind in Greg Hersov's production of *As You Like It* at the Royal Exchange.

Characters

Boy *can be played by multiple actors*
Police Officer *should be played by one actor*
Older Lady *should be played by one actor*
Mister Ellody *should be played by one actor*
News Reporter *should be played by one actor*
Girl *can be played by multiple actors*
Teacher *should be played by one actor*

Notes

Directors can use as much set and costume as they require, but should be aware that this play can be done very effectively in a black-box space with minimal set and costume.

The play is written to be performed at pace. This doesn't mean it needs to be rushed or gabbled or that certain moments can't be allowed to breathe, but the key is to make sure actors pick up their cues very promptly.

Lights up.

Boy Everybody knows 'The Road'. If you're from round here you know it and if you're not from round here you still know it. It's one of those roads where the sign always gets stolen so no one really knows what it's actually called. It's always busy and –

Boy Like an A-road –

Boy Yeah . . . wait, nah, it's not an A-road –

Boy Yeah it is –

Boy Nah it ain't – it's just like a busy high street –

Boy It don't really have enough shops to be a high street –

Boy And *precisely* how many shops does a road need to have to be a high street?

Boy I dunno!

*

Police Officer Yes I suppose you are trained to expect it . . . but that doesn't mean it's ever something you get used to. If you got used to it you'd become completely desensitised. It's hard sometimes of course. Part of you wants to be numb, to feel nothing, it would make the job easier . . . but I've never wanted to be that kind of officer. I grew up round here, I've lived here my whole life, I know The Road like the back of my hand, I know the people by name.

*

Boy It's not a high street.

Boy Then it's an A-road –

Boy Shut up, you're ruining the interview.

Boy   *You're* ruining the interview.

Boy   If you don't shut up they won't show it on TV.

Boy   Fine.

Boy   Anyway. Whatever 'The Road' is, people just know it, it's just a road everyone knows but no one ever knows the name so we always just called it – The Road.

Boy   Yeah.

*

Older Lady   Butcher, baker, candlestick maker . . . that used to be the rhyme when I was a child although I don't think I ever saw a candlestick maker's shop on The Road . . . but there was definitely always a butcher and a baker . . .

*

Police Officer   Some people are part of the fabric of The Road, they've been here for ever like Mister Ellody. I can't remember Mister Ellody's shop ever not being there. It was run by his dad originally, a lovely old geezer, used to give us pear drops on Saturdays and play his accordion outside the shop for us in the afternoon. Then his son, Mister Ellody Junior, took over and he was a nice bloke too. Quieter than his dad but he loved those accordions just as much.

*

Older Lady   Do you know I can't think for the life of me what its real name is to be honest, it's been The Road for as long as I can remember – people say the signs keep getting stolen but I don't remember it ever having one in the first place, not even when I was a girl. The Road just stuck. It was nice . . . a nice road. I don't mean posh, oh it was never posh, but it was nice, you know, nice people, nice shops.

*

Mister Ellody   When my father came here from Italy seventy years ago and moved to The Road the local people had never seen or heard anything like him before. He was the only Italian living round here and he was a very likable man. My father could play the accordion like no one else, he was the most skilled accordion player in the whole country. My father took all the money he made from playing the accordion, married my mother who lived in the next street along and opened the very first accordion shop for miles around. Everybody knew 'Ellody's Accordions'. My father bought them and sold them and mended them for fifty years. He sent me to a good school and put me through university and when I graduated he taught me everything he knew about the magic of accordions . . . and then he died. I took over the shop and I've been here ever since.

*

News Reporter   When? Now? How long? Five?

The reporter counts down 4, 3, 2, 1 in silence.

Thanks, John, I'm here on the street known affectionately by its nickname of 'The Road' in the aftermath of what has been the most disturbingly violent scenes that this area has seen in years. The police are still trying to piece together what happened here and many are asking the question why? Why at 7 p.m. last night over five hundred school children aged between twelve and eighteen descended on this road and wreaked havoc for the next six hours. Businesses have been destroyed, cars have been set on fire, homes have been broken into. This is a community shaken to its core and still in shock. I've been speaking to local people to find out what exactly happened here and why. Marilyn Belvoir for Eye Witness News.

*

Girl   I got the text at like two in the morning and it was like proper loud so it like woke me up didn't it?

Girl   Yeah – I was staying over so I was there and it was like proper loud –

Girl   Yeah, she was staying over and I get this text and I'm like, what? Who is like texting me at like two in the morning?

Girl   Yeah – she was like what? 'Cause we are really not those kind of girls that receive texts at like two in the morning do you know what I mean?

Girl   Yeah, we are really not. So I wasn't gonna answer it 'cause I thought it was gonna be like the wrong number or something but then I started thinking –

Girl   Then she started thinking what if it's an emergency –

Girl   Yeah, like what if it's my mum and like she's lost her phone or got locked out –

Girl   Or been kidnapped and the kidnappers are only giving her like *one* text to contact someone –

Girl   Yeah, and I ignore it? So I get out of bed and get my phone and look at it –

Girl   And it weren't her mum

Girl   Nah, it was a number I didn't know which I thought might be like dodgy? But then I thought –

Girl   What if that's the kidnapper's phone number –

Girl   In which case it would be fair enough –

Girl   Yeah.

*

Older Lady   Are the kids different now? Well they're not nasty or scary despite what all the news reports say on the telly, I'm certainly not scared of them. I sit on my bench and watch them every day. They see things in a different way from how we did. They live in a different world. It's all tweeting a bit of this and Facebooking a bit of that but they're not bad kids . . . just very loud and very overexcited and we all remember what that was like, don't we . . . but our energy had somewhere to escape to, they just seem to carry it round with them like fully charged batteries. If I had grandchildren I'd plug them into my flat, electricity is so expensive now, that's why I spend so much of my time outside on the bench.

*

Girl   So I open this text and it ain't my mum, it's just this weird message that I don't get, so I read it again –

Girl   And then *I* read it twice –

Girl   But neither of us understand it? And then *her* phone gets a text –

Girl   Mine was proper loud too –

Girl   And the message said exactly the same thing,

Girl   RIOT –

THE ROAD –

7 PM TONIGHT.

Girl   It was so weird.

Girl   Yeah and we didn't know what it meant –

Girl   Nope –

Girl   So we forwarded it to everyone in our phonebooks to see if they knew what it meant?

Girl   And that's when we found out that everyone we knew had got the same message.

Girl   Freaky.

Girl   Yeah. But at least your mum hadn't been kidnapped.

Girl   Yeah.

Girl   Will this go on iPlayer?

*

News Reporter   Marilyn Belvoir for Eye Witness News.

The reporter holds her position for a few moments and then relaxes.

Now? Are we out? Great.

Really? The community is 'shocked', are you kidding me? My God have you seen this street? Boarded-up shops, crazy people, overflowing bins, it's not exactly 'shocking', is it? I don't even feel comfortable standing here and we're yards from the car. My husband told me this morning that the children round here can steal your watch without you even realising. It's like *Oliver Twist*. This would never happen in Ramsbottom Park. What? Yep, okay. How long? Four?

The reporter counts down 3,2,1 in silence.

Hello again, John, yes I'm still here on the 'The Road' right in the heart of what can only be described as utter devastation. Looking around at these warm-hearted people it's difficult to imagine how such an act could have possibly been committed. Earlier I spoke to one such warm-hearted resident, a teacher at the local secondary school.

*

Teacher   Three years I've been teaching here. Three years and I won't lie to you, I had friends who laughed at me when I told them I'd decided to stay on here after qualifying. 'Now's your chance to get out!' they said. Most of my university friends went into other careers, Finance, advertising, jobs that make money and buy houses in the suburbs. Sometimes I think I should have done that too.

*

Boy   RIOT –

THE ROAD –

7 PM TONIGHT.

Everyone got the same text.

Boy   Everyone – the year sevens, the year eights –

Girl   And sixth form, I heard sixth form got it –

Girl   Yeah, they did, my cousin's in sixth form –

Boy   Everyone got it –

Girl   And then everyone was like, who sent it?

Boy   Everyone was asking – the year nines, the year tens –

Girl   My cousin said it was someone in sixth form –

Boy   Someone in year eleven said it was someone from another school –

Girl   But in the end it didn't actually matter who sent it because everyone was going –

Boy   Everyone – the year sevens –

Girl   EVERYONE.

*

Teacher   The first year was hard and I felt frustrated. I went home in utter depression on Friday feeling like I'd achieved nothing and ended the weekend sick with anxiety at the thought of returning on Monday. But slowly, very slowly, things began to change. The students, even the difficult ones, began to listen to me. They began to respect me. I found out that I was the longest-serving member of the faculty that the school had ever had. Can you believe that? I began to enjoy it actually, I looked forward to Mondays, I liked the kids. They all have potential, every single one of them, they're just easily led. Very easily led.

*

Boy   We weren't going down there to start trouble – it's The Road, you don't start trouble in your own area –

Girl   We just wanted to know what was gonna happen –

Boy   We didn't wanna miss it even if we didn't know what 'it' was.

Girl   What if it was the biggest flash mob in history, or Ant and Dec were down there . . . or it was a secret Beyoncé concert?

Boy   There was no way we were missing it.

Girl   No way.

*

Mister Ellody   Children used to be so excited by the mystery of things, I know I was. Watching my dad build an accordion was like watching a wizard cast a spell. He'd make the bellows by intricately pleating layer after layer of cloth and cardboard, cloth and cardboard. I'd never take my eyes off his hands as he closed up the wooden body for the last time because I knew I'd probably never see the inside of that accordion again. What I'd seen was a one-off. It made me feel special. I wanted to pass that on to someone else but unfortunately I don't have any children.

*

Boy   Yeah, we know Mister Ellody, he's across the road from the chicken shop –

Girl   He's always cleaning his windows –

Boy   Which is jokes because no one ever goes in there, no one from The Road anyway –

Girl   He cleans them at lunchtime, we've seen him 'cause we sit on that bench opposite –

Boy   Where the old lady sits –

Girl   She's alright –

Boy   She's funny –

Girl   One time she gave me 20p 'cause I didn't have enough for the bus –

Boy   Did she?

Girl   What does he sell?

Boy   Who? Oh, Mister Ellody? I dunno –

Girl   I think it's Hoovers.

*

Mister Ellody   It's not the money, I make enough of that. I repair accordions from all over the world, I have a waiting list of two years. But sometimes . . . when my dad was alive the shop was full of life. People would come in just to see and touch and hear the music, otherwise what's the point? The only person that seems to show any interest now is the lady across the road, she brings me a cup of tea every day and I don't even know her name. I'd never leave The Road, but sometimes when those kids chuck their chicken boxes in my doorway, or graffiti on my window, or pass by without even noticing the beautiful instruments inside, yes I do feel like leaving. I feel like giving up. I get angry and this hot scratchy air fills up my throat until I can't breathe and it's trapped in there and I don't know what to do.

*

Teacher   It started pretty much as soon as school finished. All of them were completely buzzing with it. They'd been like that all day but none of us had known what it was all about, we had no warning. It was only when we saw them all walking off down the street in the same direction, all heading for The Road, that we realised what was going on.

*

Older Lady   I sit on the bench outside my flat and watch Mister Ellody come out of his accordion shop three times a day. Once in the morning to give his window a wipe – that's when he usually turns and gives me a wave, you know, to say good morning. Once in the afternoon when he comes out to eat his sandwiches – that's when I sometimes take him across a mug of tea. I'm usually making myself one anyway so it's a waste of the kettle otherwise and I think he's quite lonely so I always think it's nice to pop over and say hello.

*

Teacher   It was the strangest thing to look at. You see we find it impossible to get the kids to walk in the same direction

within the school building and yet here they were doing it all
by themselves.

*

Older Lady   The last time I usually see Mister Ellody is in
the evening just before he locks up around six forty-five. I'm
always just about finishing my magazine at that time before
I head into my flat so he usually gives me another wave, you
know, just to say goodnight, and that's what we do every day.

*

Teacher   The thing is it was after 3.30 p.m. and they'd left
the school premises. We *couldn't* have stopped them, but it was
more than that. Trying to stop them would have been like
trying to stop the sea from flooding a coastal town. We all
would have drowned.

*

Girl   RIOT —

THE ROAD —

7 PM TONIGHT.

Girl   And we're all walking down towards The Road from
school and there are more and more and more of us joining,
there are so many of us, it's like an army. Like I've never
been in the army but I bet this is what it's like.

Girl   Yeah.

*

News Reporter   Some say it was five hundred, some say a thousand, what we know for sure is that this time yesterday The Road was completely overrun, private property was destroyed and one local resident tragically lost their life.

*

Boy RIOT –

THE ROAD –

7 PM TONIGHT.

Boy   We got to the top of The Road and nobody could see anything. Everything looked the same. Nothing looked any different, the only difference was us –

Boy   We filled up the whole of The Road. The traffic had to stop. The cars starting beeping at us, people were looking out of their windows at us, everybody was watching –

*

Teacher   Yes, we have a responsibility as teachers to our students and to the community. Yes, we should have done something. Yes, we shouldn't have cared if we drowned or not. But that's easier said than done, that day even I was scared, even *I* didn't want to leave the safety of the school because this had never happened before. But now I know we should have. I should have.

*

Older Lady   When Mister Ellody gives me that last wave of the day I know it's time to go in. I can set my watch by it, I like that, the regularity . . . but he just stood there, he didn't

wave, he didn't smile. He was staring down the road at
something and he had the strangest look on his face –

*

Mister Ellody   They were organised and enthusiastic and
full of energy and that's how I knew something was wrong.
Why can't they be like that about the right things instead
of the wrong ones? If they showed that much dedication to
the right things can you imagine how wonderful our world
would be?

*

News Reporter   The police are at a loss as to what
happened here last night. Some say they reacted too late,
others say they were always five steps behind because of
mobile-phone-messaging networks that the children were
using. Is this a case of technology committing murder?

*

Police Officer   It's like banging your head against a brick
wall! I've been telling my superiors for years that we need to
engage, that we need to stay on the beat, that we need to get
to know the kids. How else are we supposed to know what's
going on? That thousands of dangerous messages are flying
around on a network that we know nothing about? We need
to win back their respect, the respect we lost from their
parents, but my superiors don't listen. My superiors didn't
grow up around here, my superiors don't know The Road
and they don't respect the people . . . I'm sorry, I shouldn't
have said that . . . but they don't.

*

All   RIOT –

THE ROAD –

7 PM TONIGHT.

Boy   And we're walking faster, we're all walking faster down The Road, swarming down there –

Boy   Covering everything, the road, the pavement, some people start climbing lamp posts so they can see what's going on –

Girl   And people keep yelling that 'It's over there!' or 'It's over there!' and we're all saying 'What is?' –

Girl   And there's more and more and more of us, some of the kids I don't even recognise from our school and it's getting packed and everyone's moving in different directions 'cause no one knows what's going on –

Boy   But then suddenly people start running –

Boy   'Cause there's something going on down the other end of The Road and we're gonna miss it if we don't hurry up and it's exciting –

Girl   We're gonna miss it! Hurry up!

Girl   Where?

Boy   Down that way I can see something next to the electronics shop!

Boy   Where?

Girl   Next to the sports shop!

Girl   I can't see!

Boy   Next to that shop with the erm – the erm – you know, the shop with that old guy –

Boy   What shop? What old guy?

Girl   The shop with all them old shitty instruments in the window!

Girl   Go!

Boy   Get out my fucking way! I don't wanna miss it!

All   GO!

*

Mister Ellody   They had bricks and stones and sticks. I don't even know where they got sticks from . . . there are barely any trees around here –

*

Older Lady   The kids came from nowhere so fast, running and yelling and suddenly they were kicking in the windows of the shops either side of Mister Ellody's shop and they were climbing inside and actually taking things away, trainers and TVs. But they weren't touching his shop, they didn't even seem interested in it. Poor Mister Ellody was frozen with this look on his face, but he wasn't scared or angry, he was . . . well, he was disappointed.

*

Mister Ellody   Do you have any idea what an accordion is worth? I sell the most expensive items on the whole of The Road. Beautiful, hand-made, antique, one-of-a-kind instruments and they weren't even looking twice, they didn't care. I saw one boy running away with a mismatched pair of Adidas trainers. Idiot, I thought. You bloody idiot. One of these accordions would buy you five hundred pairs of those.

*

Police Officer   We couldn't get the squad car down the street and when we got out we could barely move, there were so many people. Further down the road Mister Ellody surrounded by kids running in every direction but I couldn't get to him. We'd come unprepared, there were only four of us, so we called for back-up –

*

Older Lady   I could see in Mister Ellody's eyes that he was getting angry, very, very angry. The more kids that ran past him and bashed into him and ignored him, the angrier he got –

*

Teacher   Of course we discussed going down there! Well, I tried to, but the other teachers weren't keen, they said it was out of our hands now –

*

Older Lady   Mister Ellody! Mister Ellody!

Mister Ellody   Stupid bloody kids!

Police Officer   What do you mean, the request wasn't received? Hello?

Older Lady   Mister Ellody!

Boy   Run! Just run! Do what you want!

Boy   Smash it up! Smash it up!

Girl   Oh my God!

Girl   Fucking hell!

Boy   Kick it in!

Boy   Smash it up!

Girl   Run!

Older Lady   Mister Ellody! Come over here! Come to this side!

Police Officer   We requested back-up twenty minutes ago! Hello? We need it now! Can you hear me? This is a riot! A RIOT!

Teacher   We can't be expected to do everything. We aren't jailers. We couldn't have locked them in, who'd get it in the neck then? Us, it's always us, I mean where are their parents?

Boy   Oh my God!

Girl   Fuck!

Girl   Kick it!

Police Officer   Mister Ellody! Put that brick down! Put it down!

Mister Ellody   Idiot kids! Idiots!

Boy   Dudes nuts!

Girl   Run!

Police Officer   Mister Ellody! Put it down! Can you hear me!

Older Lady   Mister Ellody! I'm coming over! I'm coming over to you!

Police Officer   Madam! Stay where you are! Madam! Hello? Base? I'm too far away I can't get down there! Madam!

Older Lady   I'm coming, Mister Ellody don't you worry! Mister –

*

Boy   There were so many people, the whole of our school −

Boy   And other schools, people I'd never seen before −

Boy   And we were all proper crushed in and we didn't . . . see her −

Boy   . . . We just didn't see her.

*

News Reporter   The death of Mrs Rosemary Greaves has hit this close-knit community incredibly hard. The seventy-five-year-old was a resident known well to the people who lived here. The cause of her death still remains to be ascertained but early reports suggest Mrs Greaves was trying to make her way across The Road during the riot to aid another resident and shopkeeper Mister Ellody. It's believed she was knocked to the ground by a crowd of children and crushed to death. A collection has been taken up in her memory and residents hope to install a plaque on the bench where she enjoyed sitting every day. Marilyn Belvoir, Eye Witness News.

She pauses for a couple of seconds.

Yes? Are we done? Great, let's get out of here.

*

Older Lady   Becoming invisible is something you get used to as you get older. You begin to watch others instead. Families moving in, families moving out, the area changes, but other things never do. The world we live in might be different but kids don't change, not really. People like to pretend that the things they do now weren't the things we did then but they just don't want to admit the truth. The kids today still need the same things we needed then − someone to cross the road and help them.

Girl RIOT –
THE ROAD –
7 PM TONIGHT.

Girl I wish I'd never read it in the first place.

Lights down.

End.

The Accordion Shop

BY CUSH JUMBO

*Notes on rehearsal and staging drawn from a workshop
held at the National Theatre, October 2014. Workshop led
by Phyllida Lloyd and Ann Yee, with notes by Tom Hughes
and Kirsty Patrick Ward.*

Cush Jumbo was rehearsing in New York and unable to attend
the workshop. Her comments are derived from a Q&A session
with the group on Skype. Both workshop leaders – Phyllida
Lloyd (director) and Ann Yee (choreographer) – have
collaborated closely with Cush.

Cush's comments about the play

The Accordion Shop contains a lot of hope for young people and
the future. Cush said that, other than the fact that Mrs
Greaves is killed, it is very possible to end the play on a
positive note. The young people in the play do not go down
to The Road with the intention of starting trouble. The play
therefore investigates the question: how do they get involved
in such violence? Cush noted that it is important to look at
each child individually, because the majority of the group do
get involved in the violence in some way.

The final Mrs Greaves speech, Cush suggested, is crucial
to achieving the hope that she'd like the audience to feel.
The speech reminds the audience that modern riots are not
Armageddon, and that a clash between the old and new is
definitely nothing new. The speech illustrates that this is a
cycle: Mr Ellody will become the old woman, and the kids
will become the Mr Ellody. The play is about rationalising
the recent outbreaks of youth violence, and suggesting to the
audience that we must change the way we think before these
things will improve.

Themes

Phyllida stated that the very first thing she does when working
on a play is to analyse the themes. A theme is something that

the play is *about*. The themes should be concise and specific, and they should be based on your response to the play. When you are preparing a production, read the play slowly and constantly ask yourself, 'What is this about?'

Phyllida asked the group to identify the play's core themes. Note that there is no 'correct' answer to this exercise. The themes suggested by the workshop participants included:

- Loss of community and the desire to belong.
- Alienation and disconnect: characters talk about the events, but do not talk to each other.
- Fame and notoriety: 'Is this going to be on iPlayer?'
- Respect and disrespect: are Mr Ellody's accordions ignored in the looting and therefore disrespected, or are they respected and therefore not touched?
- Anarchy: mob culture and mob mentality, authority figures losing their authority.
- Choice and consequence.
- Prejudice.
- Stereotypes and labels.
- Individual vs the group.
- Apathy/boredom.
- Modernity vs tradition.
- Rituals.
- Agency and anonymity: who sent the text and who is responsible?
- Neglect – not just for the community but also for each other.
- Peer pressure.
- Responsibility.
- The power of social media.
- Cycle of youth.
- Competing ideas of value.
- Loneliness and loss.

Phyllida noted that discussing the themes can feel a little intellectual and academic. You should steer the discussion away from feeling like a classroom, but it makes you think about how you are going to show each theme to the audience. She urged directors to consider how a theme could be encapsulated physically within the theatre space and create an image that would clearly communicate a play's theme to an audience. For example, if a director felt that the play's core theme was 'individual vs the group', you could create an image depicting an individual character caught up in a mob.

Phyllida described this process as 'boiling down': what is the pearl/theme at the centre of the play that can be boiled down to a single image? During your rehearsal process, keep asking yourself what on stage is manifesting those core themes in your production.

The themes could be a starting-off point for a director or company's own research. One potential avenue of research is for the company to go out into their own community and meet people. They could have conversations with real people about the play's themes, and this work would feed the imagination in rehearsal.

EXERCISE: THEMES AND THE CAST

- Divide your company into pairs. Directors should ask the cast early in rehearsal whether there is anything in this play that reflects their own life experiences. For example, 'Have you ever done anything because the group wanted to do it?' The participants would then tell their relevant story to their partner. The partner would then re-tell the story to the rest of the group, as if it were their own story (e.g. changing 'They did this' to 'I did this' throughout the narration).

This exercise helps the cast to practise telling stories in an authentic way. The storyteller has to focus in on the content and on the telling of the story rather than on trying to impress other members of the group or make themselves look good.

Structure

Phyllida asked the group to divide the play into 'units' in order to break the script down into smaller sections, using the action within the play as a guide to the divisions. A palpable change in focus or action signifies the ending of a unit, and the beginning of the next.

You should be very specific about where the units begin and where they end. Phyllida suggested that one way to help identify a new unit would be to consider whether, if this were a film, the music would change at this point in the action. These units fit together to form the whole play, like the different movements of a symphony.

It is important to give each individual unit its own title that describes the action in that unit and is applicable for all the characters involved. 'Uniting' encourages specificity within rehearsals, as it allows the play to be worked on in smaller and more accessible sections.

The structure of the play jumps around between character, time and place, which could make breaking it down into units a challenging task. One potential approach to this problem is to treat the units in terms of tone rather than action.

UNITING
example of where and how the script could be divided

As with the themes, there is no correct answer to this and it will be individual to each director. The most important thing is that your selection has a precise beginning and a precise endpoint – points that can be marked by a straight line ruled across the page.

1 WELCOME TO THE ROAD (beginning on p. 311, 'Everybody knows The Road', up to p. 313, 'I took over the shop and I've been here ever since').

2 INTRODUCING THE EVENT (the News Reporter's speech 'When? Now? How long?' – a self-contained unit, on p. 313).

3 INTERGENERATIONAL RELATIONS IN A TECHNOLOGICAL AGE (beginning at p. 314, 'I got the text at like two in the morning', up to p. 316, 'Will this go on iPlayer?').

4   TWO FACES OF THE MEDIA (News Reporter's speeches
     'Marilyn Belvoir for Eye Witness News', on and off
     camera – p. 316).

5   THE SCHOOL GROUND (starting on the last line of the
     News Reporter's speech on p. 316, 'Earlier I spoke to one
     such warm-hearted resident, a teacher at the local
     secondary school', to p. 318, 'No Way').

6   MEET MISTER ELLODY (speech starting on p. 319 and
     ending on Mister Ellody saying 'I don't know what to do'
     on p. 320).

7   TO THE ROAD (from p. 320, 'It started pretty much as
     school finished', to 'He was staring down the road at
     something and he had the strangest look on his face',
     p. 323).

8   WHO IS TO BLAME? (from Mister Ellody on p. 323, 'They
     were organised and enthusiastic' to the Police Officer on
     p. 323, 'I'm sorry I shouldn't have said that . . . but they
     don't').

9   THE RIOT BEGINS (from 'RIOT – THE ROAD – 7 PM
     TONIGHT' on p. 324, to 'Go!', p. 325.

10   ADULTS PAUSE FOR THOUGHT (from 'They had bricks'
     on p. 325, to 'it was out of our hands now' on p. 326).

11   RIOT RECOMMENCES (p. 326, 'Mister Ellody!', to
     'Mister – ' on p. 327).

12   FALL-OUT (from 'There were so many people', p. 328, to
     the end of the play.

Phyllida said that once that you have located the precise units
in your script, your production should commit to these units.
You can show a new unit of action in your production by a
change of music, change of staging, change of physical picture,
change of tone, change of rhythm. All your decisions about
the action in your production should be orientated around
the structure of the play as decided here.

Staging

Cush outlined that she wrote the first part of the play as if the characters were being interviewed for a television news programme. She suggested that it could be helpful to encompass this in the staging.

Phyllida and Ann worked with the whole group to explore staging possibilities. The group were asked to focus on one short section of text and sketch an image for that sequence as if they were completing the storyboard for a film. This could be done in a director's preparation for a show, because it forces you to think about what, visually, can help tell the story to an audience on stage. One suggestion for this was from the line 'And we're walking faster, we're all walking faster down The Road, swarming down there,' to the end of the play.

Phyllida and Ann then asked the groups to make static tableaux of their storyboard image. Working with static tableaux forces you to be as specific as possible with one image. All the stage images in your production should be this precise, as far as possible – the audience should be able to understand what is going on from a single freeze frame. Once these still tableaux are generated, participants incorporate lines of text, while still keeping the image static. Finally slow-motion movement was used to animate the scenes.

Ann suggested that even with a limited budget, peppering the space with chairs could be invaluable in a riot scene – providing, not just different levels, but also great sound when they fall, and great obstacles to climb over. The dynamism of 'traverse' staging (when audiences are seated either side of the stage facing one another, with the action being played out between them) was also emphasised.

Music

This play could contain a clash between old and new music at its centre. Cush recommended that groups staging this play consider using an accordion, or recordings of accordion music (there does not have to be an accordion on stage if this is difficult to achieve). She described how the accordion is a very rich instrument, and how its music sounds ancient, rich and ridiculous. She suggested that listening to Woodkid could be one way to imagine her vision for the play, because parts of his music feel epic and huge. Find contrasting styles – perhaps by consulting the company about potential music or perhaps by creating playlists for each character (see below).

Characters

This play poses many challenges in characterisation, because the young actors must play a wide variety of characters of differing ages. Cush is perfectly happy for the gender of all the characters to be adapted to the individual casting needs of a company. The only roles to which gender is especially important is the Boy and the Girl. Phyllida suggested that an actor's personal qualities should be most important when casting this show. Cush agreed that the swearing could be removed from the play if necessary for a young company or audience.

Phyllida suggested that young actors (depending on which characters they are playing) could be put in contact with an older person, a police officer, a teacher. The actors should be encouraged to interview these people: get them to talk about their childhood, their home life, their personal life, etc., and to observe the way they move, the way they speak and their body language.

This information can help the actors to build well-rounded characters, and it can also be a social mission to get the young people interested in 'invisible' people's lives, and to imagine their past and their humanity. Cush had already described how the play offers an audience the opportunity to view the world from many different points in a community.

Phyllida recommended using 'hot-seating' exercises to build up characters. In these exercises, an actor in character is seated in front of the rest of the company. The company are allowed to ask questions of this actor, who must answer in character. The actors' answers could be based on a combination of reading from the text, their interviews with real-life people and their own imagination. This process should be completed in rehearsal over a number of months. Even if an actor is playing a character similar to themselves, the character should definitely not be the same as them!

One approach to building a character is their 'obstacle'. The actor discovers a secret that their character is trying to hide, or something that they have to play against. For example, one of the boys could be afraid of violence, but he must hide this when he is caught in the group. The obstacles can be developed through 'hot-seating'. They should not change the play's story or be distracting for an audience, but they will give a fuller texture to a character.

The company could build a playlist for each character: what music do they listen to? The music that you choose in these playlists could become fundamental to the sound design of the production.

Writing a character list of everything that can be learnt about a character will prove an invaluable reference tool. What does the character say about herself or himself? What do others say about them?

The participants were split into groups, and charged with the task of identifying the key challenges of the characterisation of a specific character, and how these could be overcome. Below is what the groups came up with:

MISTER ELLODY

This role requires a performer with great maturity.

- Cush clarified that the protagonist's name Mister Ellody rhymes with 'melody'.
- Cush stated that he is second-generation Italian: his father was born in Italy, but he was born in the UK. She recommended that he does not have an accent, because it is important that there is not a big cultural gap between him and the children.

- She suggested that the play is in part about how Mister Ellody is frozen in inaction: he can't move forwards or backwards.

- She suggested that the hope that she'd like the audience to feel at the end of the play could be achieved by seeing Mr Ellody onstage after Mrs Greaves's death. The company could explore how the riot has changed his behaviour, and ask whether he could be positively influenced by something so awful.

- Thinking of (and perhaps wearing in rehearsals) clothes or shoes that Mr Ellody might wear could really aid in finding this character's physicality.

- His job requires great attention to detail, and a meticulous nature – keep this in mind when thinking of how he might move and reflect it in his body language.

- He is proud and precise – how can this be reflected physically?

- Think about his daily routine. What time does he get up? How does he brush his teeth? When and how does he open his shop?

- Research his Italian family heritage.

- Research the real Mr Allodi – whose accordion shop in Lewisham inspired the play.

MRS GREAVES (OLDER LADY)

- It is important that the actor playing Mrs Greaves rejects stereotypes and builds up their own idea of who this old lady is. It is more about understanding the inside of the character rather than imitating the outside.

- It was agreed that Mrs Greaves is a feisty old lady, and that her actions suggest she is a brave character. It was suggested that considering noises or mannerisms can help a character to come alive.

- Think about the position of the spine – it will not be straight like in a younger person, but will be more compressed and curved by time.

- Think about what part of the body leads when she is moving, but do not get trapped into generalised 'old' physicality. We know from her actions that she is 'passionate and strong-willed', so think about reflecting this in her desire to move.

- We know she is working class, and would have been twenty in the 1950s – does this affect or inform what she wears?

- What were the different rules of etiquette when she was brought up? Do they affect her body language and mannerisms now?

- How does her breathing inform her movement? Perhaps think of it like a stiff accordion.

BOY/GIRL

- Cush suggested that in their energies, the Boys and Girls are definitely not clear-cut: she does not intend them to be guilty or innocent. They do not go down to The Road with the intention of causing trouble.

- Cush stated that their behaviour in this riot is particularly fascinating because they are not mad or necessarily violent. Rather, it is a riot by a bunch of kids who just want to belong. She described how young people were obsessed with communicating through technology, creating an intense desire to belong and connect with other human beings.

- She said that it could be better to think of a riot as an 'energy cult', an uprising of repressed energy resulting from this desire to connect. There was every possibility that this gathering could have been positive, but in the play it turns out badly.

- It is crucial that the Boy and Girl characters are not all the same. Directors and actors are encouraged to ask who are the individual Boy and Girl characters within the group? One way of achieving this is by asking the actors to create an *obstacle* (see above) for the character, or by using status exercises to work out their status in and relationship with the group. Status is very important in groups of young people.

POLICE OFFICER

- It will be challenging for a young actor to play the Police Officer: someone who is both older than they are, and who is also losing their authority in the play. Explore what happens physically and vocally when this authority it lost.

- Status exercises might be invaluable for this character, who is in many ways defined by his/her authority.

- People with status do not necessarily act 'high status' but their status lies in the obedient way in which other people respond to them.

- Researching real police and riot footage will give great insight into how officers use their body to exert their authority. If projection is a possibility, maybe this footage could even be used during the performance?

NEWS REPORTER

- The News Reporter, although involved in some comic moments, is not on stage to be mocked or judged. The News Reporter represents the establishment, yet they are scared in a very human way. Cush suggested that you wouldn't achieve comedy from an audience if you're caricaturing or mocking the character.

- Consider the conflict between their public and private faces. This is open to interpretation and the actor should decide when and how they switch between these two modes.

- Think about their posture and physicality when they are presenting to the camera. How is this different to when they are not being filmed?

- Vocally do they sound different when they are off-camera?

- Does he/she have their own obstacle to overcome? (An interesting possibility was suggested that maybe they themselves came from The Road, or somewhere similar.)

- Avoid satirising this character; we should not judge or limit them with disdain.

TEACHER

- One challenge for the Teacher role will be avoiding the temptation for young people to judge the character. They should believe that they are playing this character, rather than playing the attitude or caricaturing their least favourite teacher.

- This role requires an emotionally mature actor who can understand the self-doubt in the character. The emotional truth of the character contrasted against the stylised choreography could make for a very strong production.

- The Teacher is trying to make a point to the audience throughout – was this riot the teachers' fault or was it the kids' fault? Your production should have them fighting their case with the audience until the very last minute.

Style and technique

A production's movement must serve the story. For example, Phyllida stated that an audience will stop listening to spoken text when a mob of people start moving in real time. Movement onstage should respect and accentuate the characters' thoughts and the text's punctuation. Experiment with different tempos and tension levels (see Exercises for Rehearsal, below) to marry movement and text.

It is important to understand that when you are staging chaotic scenes that *order* creates *chaos*. The performers should have rules or games that they are playing in riot scenes, rather than allow genuine chaos to occur. For example, performers can stay moving in the same patterns (the patterns can block or interfere with each other) or you can use the 'magnet' exercise, which is a useful device to keep fast-moving sequences safe. So if the character of the Older Woman is attempting to cross the road using tension level 3 or 4 (see exercise below), perhaps the crowd should be moving at a tension level 6, but should see the actor playing the Older Woman as being an oppositely charged magnet – they can get very close to her, but cannot make contact, as they will be repelled like a magnet.

It is important to have difference within the rioting mass and Cush suggested that it would be helpful for each character to develop their own individual physical work to distinguish them in the chaos of the riot. (The exercises below could help with this work.)

Moments of stillness before action could be extremely effective when staging this play. There can, for example, be a moment with a lot of people milling about, looking at their phones, in an image of seeming harmony and symmetry, before all the riotous action kicks off. The physicality of these moments is in the stillness, and in the audience's surprise at the company's outburst.

Exercises for use in rehearsal

Ann ran several physical exercises with the group that can be used with your company. She suggested that the body has an intelligence that doesn't depend on the head. These physical exercises can be helpful to get performers out of their heads and into their bodies.

Cush referred to these exercises when she was asked what her process would be if she were going to play one of the Girl or Boy characters. She would experiment with different levels of tension, different tempo levels and different levels of status.

These exercises can be used to build an ensemble at the beginning of rehearsal, and they can also be physical tools that can help you build choreography as you create the play. Cush agreed that her play allows room for a lot of physical work and sequences to be woven into its performance. She said that there was no limit to this type of work. She agreed that echoing or repeating lines within the play could work as a device, but that all the spoken text should originate from the play rather than group improvisations.

TEMPO LEVELS 1—10: WALKING WARM-UP

Ann asked everybody in the group to take a walk through the space. There should be no pattern to the movement –

everybody should move in a natural way and in a direction
that they want to at that moment. She expressed that this is a
great way to start any movement work, as it is not daunting –
it is real and it is human.

She then asked the group to just notice who else and what
else is around in the space. How many jumpers can you see?
What colour green was that? Where are the windows? Where
are the doors? How many lights are there in the room? The
group should make eye-contact with one another, holding it
for a short period of time as someone else moves on by. This
is level 5 – our neutral point in our space and in our world.

While continuing with this 'neutral' walk, imagine there are
ten levels (level 1 being the slowest and 10 being the fastest).
Ann then asked everybody to 'Take it to a 6'. This caused
everybody to move slightly faster in the space, increasing their
tempo. She worked up through level 7 and then to 8. These
instructions were posed to the group as questions – 'What's
my 8? What's my 7?' – which created an atmosphere of
exploration rather than a pressure to get it 'right'.

You can move below level 5 in this scale, moving slower than
your neutral walking pace. The group should be encouraged
to be as specific as possible in exploring their different tempo
levels. They should be reminded that level 7 is not the same
as 8, that 3 is not the same as 4, and so on and reminded that
the space does not become deactivated when returning to a
slower walking pace. Participants then walked at level 4,
then 3, then 2, then 1. At level 1 (which should be barely
moving), ask yourself: 'What's my heel doing? What are my
toes doing? How does my weight shift?' Then quickly return
to a level 5 walking pace. Then build to a level 7, then to a
level 8 (Ann gives an example that a level 8 is like rush hour
in Oxford Street). Then walk in a level 10 and suddenly back
to a level 1.

Sudden changes/juxtapositions of pace could be invaluable
when staging such moments as the riot and could help
develop other staging ideas. For example, everybody moving

at a level 10 apart from Mr Ellody who moves at level 1. By beginning with this kind of accessible and focus-inducing exercise, performers are encouraged to react rather than act, to listen and think outside themselves.

THE SEVEN LEVELS OF TENSION

Ann asked the group to take a walk around the space, both taking in all the details of the room and of the people around them. Once an energy and focus in the room had been established, the participants slowly brought themselves to lie on the floor. With closed eyes, Ann asked the group to feel the heat of their body, recognise its shape on the floor, and to feel the weight being evenly distributed.

The following instructions should be interpreted creatively by the actors, and you should feel free to improvise your own instructions within each level to encourage them.

Start with the first level of tension, allow the group to explore it, and then move on to the next level of tension.

1 THE JELLYFISH/POND-LIFE STATE
Participants start to move as if they had a jellyfish entirely taking over their body and breath. Their level of tension could be described as 'oozy'. Participants should allow sound to happen. They should allow themselves to roll over and to kneel.

2 STONED DUDE
Participants bring themselves on to their feet using slow, easy movements. Take a walk around the space – your senses are a bit muted, you're feeling happy – allow them to say hello to each other, maybe find a chair, sit down.

3 NEUTRAL/COMMUTER
Participants are like a businessman or a stage manager – they are efficient, there is more purpose to their movement than in the previous levels – they can find a chair, sit in it – make a decision that something needs to change, and make that change. The movement is not overly fast, actions are direct but don't hold emotional attachment.

Make clear eye-contact amongst the group and
purposefully greet one another. Efficiency is key in this
level of tension.

4   CURIOUS TODDLER/ALERT
The participants are discovering everything in the space:
everything is awesome, like when you were a toddler!
The movement around the space should be curious, led
by the head/eyes and encompassing different levels of
eye-line. Tension is driven by the desire to observe and
gather information. Begin to integrate sound and language
in this level of tension, but remember your eyes are
constantly pulling your focus to new things. Begin to
share and explore these observations and questions with
one another.

5   SUSPENSE/DISTURBANCE
In this level, there is a burst of energy from participants
and then a resolution – a constant starting and stopping
of energy, a very jerky, shocked movement. Ann used
the example of imagining trying to warn someone of
something, but just missing them; or thinking you see
someone you know, but suddenly realising you are
mistaken. Movement is alert and purposeful but also on
edge. Once this has been successfully established in a
walk, begin to integrate the movement of chairs and also
conversation with other participants into the state.

6   PANDEMONIUM/PANIC
This level is about the panic before some kind of
immediate threat, perhaps a bomb or a fire. It should
create a scene of complete disorder – running, shouting,
screaming – and be very difficult to sustain. It does not
have to consist solely of running, it is also about finding
places to take cover, but is also very active vocally. Again
introduce props, and interaction with others when the
state has been established.

7   PETRIFIED
A whistle was used to stop the action dead. All the energy
of 'pandemonium' is stuck in your body, but you are

frozen with fear. For example, witnessing someone
running in front of a car, when you are powerless to stop
it. The silence is almost deafening, and the tension is
palpable, without any movement.

The key to both these exercises is to just do them, and not to
spend too much time talking or explaining them. They are
designed to be accessible and to unlock performers. They are
also great tools when dealing with a large group of people and
you want everyone to have their moment, but there are only
so many lines of text. By using contrasting levels of tension
between performers, you can also create 'solo' moments for
individuals. For example if everyone save for one person is
moving in a tension level 6 or 7, our eye is immediately
drawn to the odd one out. This offers a great chance to
emphasise or highlight a character or a moment without the
use of text – an audience will attach meaning and story to
these juxtaposing levels of tension.

They can also help you to build characterisations. Cush noted
that Mr Ellody feels like he could constantly be at a level 5
state of tension. It could be interesting to explore characters'
differing relationships with the states of tension – for example,
Mrs Greaves may experience a level 6 of pandemonium/
panic, but her body is unable to express it.

Never in life do we know what will happen next, and these
levels of tension will help to maintain spontaneity both in an
actor's mind and body.

BIG DANCE, LITTLE DANCE

This exercise helps actors to work together effectively as a
physical unit. It forces them to listen to each other and to take
their focus away from themselves.

All participants should find a partner. The director should
play some upbeat music, at a low level to start with.

The first actor shares a move or gesture or smile, which is
then accepted and repeated by the partner. The second

partner then offers his or her own move, gesture or smile. At this first level, it doesn't even have to look like a dance move, it can just be a tiny action. The actors don't have to mirror each other, they just need to listen to what their partner is giving them and then respond.

Through this interaction based on sharing, reacting and connecting, individual movement moments or 'dances' between pairs start to emerge. Once the exercise has been established, partners do not have to be close to one another – 'dances' can be shared over wider and longer distances.

They can also be explored and punctuated using a sliding scale of movement (similar to the walking exercise) using levels 1 to 5 – level 1 being of small movements, level 5 being akin to a rave. Increase the volume of the music, and ask the actors to raise it to level 2. Their movements become a little accelerated at this level. Remind the group that they don't have to look cool, just listen to the movement and respond to it. Allow the exchange of movement to move you in a way that you wouldn't normally move.

Keep raising the volume of the music from level 2 to level 3 to level 4 and finally to level 5. Each time, ask the actors to increase the size and the speed of their movements, getting them to explore different levels and positions in the space.

This is an exercise in generosity and therefore quashes inhibitions and nerves. It is a quick and effective way of unifying the whole group. It also encourages the actors to accept offers that they are given by their partner: if someone does something fun, then you can copy it from them. It takes the focus off the individual actors, and it makes them more generous performers because they don't need to show off. In terms of staging, this exercise could easily incorporate props and furniture, and cross over short and large distances. Perhaps the use of accordion music could help tailor and connect this exercise to Cush's play?

Hacktivists

By Ben Ockrent

When Eloise is tasked with showing new girl Beth around the school she takes her to the 'hackerspace' where she and her gang of nerdy friends hang out – a disused Portakabin they've turned into a student-run IT lab. Although the gang call themselves hackers, their activities are entirely harmless . . . until their self-elected leader, Archie, is humiliated by the school bully and Beth inspires them to use their tech-savviness to avenge him. Revelling in their new-found power, the group allow Beth to lead them in an increasingly dangerous direction. With Archie usurped and everyone in Beth's thrall, just what kind of hackers will they become and what will it take to stop them?

Age suitability: 13+

Cast size: 13
Occasional strong language

Ben Ockrent's television work includes, for BBC1, *The Secrets*, *Waterloo Road* and *Material Girl*. Other TV includes *Youngers* (E4) and *Joe Mistry* (ITV2 pilot). His theatre work includes: *Breeders* (St James), *Provenance* (Manhattan Theatre Club, rehearsed reading), *Carrot* (Latitude Festival), *Bedrooms, Dens and Other Forms of Magic* (Theatre503), *The Pleasure Principle* (Tristan Bates Theatre) and *Honey*, which was nominated for an Olivier Award as part of Tricycle Theatre's season *Afghanistan: the Great Game* (which toured the US, including a one-off performance in the Pentagon). Radio includes: *Cordite for Breakfast* (BBC Radio 4), *Vital Statistics* (BBC Radio 4) and *Honey* (BBC Radio 3).

Ben recently co-directed and co-wrote his first short film, *Dust*, starring Alan Rickman, which was long-listed for a BAFTA. He's currently under commission to write two original comedy pilots, *This Ability* for TV LAND in the US and *Genius* for Tiger Aspect in the UK. He has been nominated as a *Broadcast* magazine 'Hotshot'.

Characters

Archie
Cath
Tania
Jenny
Hugs
Drew
Steve
Nisha
Mark
Pez
Eloise
Beth

All characters can be anywhere between thirteen and eighteen years old, with the exception of Archie, Beth, Steve and Eloise who should be at the upper end of that range.

Set

A 'hackerspace'. In our case, a large Portakabin within the grounds of a school. There's a spattering of tables and chairs. Further to this, there may or may not be an array of DIY worktops, power tools, computer monitors, projectors, whiteboards, computer servers and routers, fridges, televisions, radios (many at various stages of deconstruction).

Note

'Throwies' are small LED clusters. Each actor has one. During blackout scene-changes they are illuminated and used through choreographed movement to reflect the atmosphere of what's going on. They might represent atoms bouncing off each other, people being pushed and pulled apart, ideas exploding or digital information firing around the world. They might demonstrate a sense of energy or stillness, chaos or order, harmony or conflict. The more playful and inventive the better. The choreography suggested in the scene changes within the script are just that – suggestions, not instructions.

Scene One

House lights fade to blackout. As loud dance music suddenly starts thumping out, a single throwie appears glowing in the darkness. It starts to 'bounce' up and down, slowly at first but then with increasing speed. It pings off in one direction. As it bounces off a wall, another throwie appears, bouncing off in another direction . . . As the two throwies hit other walls, further throwies appear, also bouncing off walls, producing yet more throwies bouncing around in the darkness, until there are eleven. They bounce around each other energetically. Although chaotic at first, they eventually find a sort of harmony . . . only for the music to abruptly cut, while simultaneously the throwies are extinguished and lights come up on:

Lunch break in the Portakabin hackerspace. **Archie**, **Tania**, **Pez**, **Seb**, **Cath**, **Steve**, **Mark**, **Jenny**, **Hugs**, **Drew**, **Nisha** *are in a state of rising panic . . .*

Archie   What d'you mean, the door's locked?

Cath   The handle's jammed. It won't open.

Tania   You mean we're trapped in here?

Jenny   Told you this would happen.

Hugs (*loving it*)   Brilliant.

Archie (*to* **Drew**)   Spanner, I thought you said you knew how to install these card-reader things?

Drew   I do! Did. I mean, I thought I did.

Tania   Guys, no joke, I get proper antsy about confined spaces. I can't die in here.

Steve   No one's going to die.

Jenny   Not sure that's entirely true.

Steve   I mean today.

Tania (*to* **Steve**)   Touch wood. ProfessorV? Touch wood.

Steve   I haven't got any wood.

Tania (*furious*)   Oh, well, you've done it now!

Nisha   Maybe we should call the staff room? Get one of the teachers down?

Mark   I thought that was the whole point of installing the card-reader entry system? To keep them out.

Archie   We're not calling the teachers. (*To* **Drew**.) Spanner, what's your plan?

Drew   It was working when I installed it. It's probably just something wrong with the mini-reader.

Pez   Or the back-body.

Drew   Or the back-body. But I really hope it's the mini-reader.

Archie   Why?

Drew   Cos we had to set the back-body within the Portakabin wall and with the door shut that'll mean taking a sledgehammer to it to get it out.

Pez   And that wall's probably load-bearing. Take a sledgehammer to it and the whole roof could cave in.

Tania (*to* **Steve**)   Happy now?

Seb   Look, I dunno why you're all getting so stressed out. It's what we do, isn't it? We fix things.

Archie   Spanner, have a fiddle with the mini-reader. See what you can do.

Drew (*hesitates*)   Right . . .

Steve   What now?

Drew   No, nothing. It's just if I'm gonna pull out the mini-reader I'll need my toolbox.

Cath   So?

Drew   Well, when the door swung shut it was sort of on the other side.

Mark   So, climb out the window.

Jenny   He can't.

Tania   Why not?

Drew   Cos I sealed the windows shut last week.

Cath   You what?

Drew (*defensively*)   We took a vote! We all agreed security was a priority!

Pez   That's why we were installing the card-reader entry system.

Archie   Yes. To keep other people out, not us in!

Hugs *has to bring his hand up to his mouth to disguise his amusement.*

Tania   Don't laugh!

Hugs (*laughing*)   I'm sorry.

Nisha   Alright, now can we call the teachers?

Mark   No! They're not allowed in here. They agreed.

Cath   There's a letterbox in the door. Maybe one of the teachers can pass the tools through, then go? This doesn't have to give them access, does it?

Nisha   We've got to do something or we'll miss this afternoon's classes.

Hugs   Yeah, fat chance.

Archie   Alright, we'll vote on it. (*To* **Seb**.) IronHelmet?

Seb *doesn't respond.*

Archie   IronHelmet?

Cath *elbows* **Seb**.

Seb   What?

Cath   That's you.

Archie   Come on, Seb. We agreed whenever we're discussing official business we use our hacker names.

Jenny   Why is this suddenly official business?

Steve   Because we're taking a vote that could end up setting a principle for the collective.

Jenny   Which is what?

Hugs   Whether we involve the teachers or not when some idiot manages to lock us in the Portakabin.

Steve (*correcting* **Hugs**)   Whether or not we ever defer to outside help during a crisis.

Archie (*back on topic, to* **Seb**)   So. IronHelmet?

A beat.

Seb (*remembering that's him*)   Bollocks! Sorry, Archie.

Archie (*correcting him, annoyed*)   Skyclops! If we're discussing official business –

Seb   I address you with your hacker name. Got it. Sorry, Archie – (*Immediately correcting himself.*) Skyclops! I mean Skyclops. I just forget them sometimes.

Mark   You're supposed to be Secretary.

Seb   Cos I like stationery. Not cos I've a flair for memorising esoteric nicknames.

Cath   Why don't we just get on with it?

Archie   Fine. All those in favour of calling the teachers to come pass tools through the letterbox?

Nisha (*anxious*)   And we're just gonna raise our hands, are we?

Mark   That a problem?

Nisha   No, that's fine. It's just, aren't ballots supposed to be private?

Jenny   She's got a point there.

Archie (*exhausted*)   Fine!

Gestures for **Seb** *to see to it.*

Seb   What now?

Archie   Pass around some paper so we can vote in private.

Seb   I don't have any paper.

Archie   I don't believe this.

Seb   Oh right, cos you do?

Archie   No. But then I'm not the Secretary, Seb!

Seb (*correcting him, victorious*)   The name's IronHelmet!

Eloise *and* **Beth** *enter. Everyone turns to them, momentarily thrown by how they could have got in past the broken lock.*

Eloise   What's going on?

Mark   How did you open the door?

Eloise (*obviously*)   I turned the handle?

Archie *turns to* **Drew**.

Drew   Mini-reader.

He exits, followed by **Pez**. *Everyone turns to* **Beth**.

Archie (*concerned*)   Who's this?

Eloise   Her name's Beth.

Beth   Alright?

Eloise   She's new. Ms Gillan asked me to show her round. Help her settle in.

Cath   You've changed school mid-term?

Beth   My dad got relocated for work.

Mark (*to* **Eloise**)   And you thought it a good idea to bring her here?

Eloise   I thought that was supposed to be the whole point of this. Free access for all.

Steve   Then, you told her what this is?

Beth   She said it's a hackerspace.

Archie   Which is what?

Beth   A place hackers get together to hack from?

Hugs   Bingo!

Steve   And you're interested in that sort of thing?

Beth (*rhetorical*)   I'm here, aren't I?

Eloise (*to* **Archie**)   Satisfied?

Archie *decides to trust* **Beth** . . .

Archie   My name's Archie. Or as far as the web's concerned, Skyclops. (*Pointing at* **Steve**.) That's Steve.

Steve   Or ProfessorV.

Archie (*pointing at* **Tania**)   That's Tania. Hacker name, Oxlips.

Hugs (*teasing*)   Cos she's got a face like a beast.

Tania   'I know a bank where the wild thyme blows / Where oxlips and the nodding violet grows'? It's a line from *A Midsummer Night's Dream*? Which stars Titania? Titania . . . Tania?

Hugs   Urm . . . don't-care-nia?

Archie   That's Hugs.

Hugs   And my hacker name is MyHackername.

Tania   He thinks he's funny.

Hugs   I am funny.

Jenny   Nothing's funny. (*To* **Beth**.) My name's Jenny. Or Naysayer.

Hugs   No shit.

Archie (*pointing at* **Seb**)   That's Seb.

Seb (*pointedly, as much to* **Archie** *as* **Beth**)   Hacker name, IronHelmet.

Archie (*pointing at* **Cath**)   That's Cath.

Cath   Or Tolstory.

Mark   I'm Mark. Aka TheMogul.

Hugs   Cos he thinks he's gonna be the next dotcom billionaire.

Mark   I am.

Archie   Drew's fixing the door. He goes by Spanner. Pez is with him. Otherwise known as Paragon.

Nisha   I'm Nisha. Aka RainbowSpray.

Hugs *smirks.* **Nisha** *hits him.*

Archie   You already know Eloise.

Eloise   Hacker name, FleurD.

Beth   And what's the name of the collective?

Archie   We call this place Moe's Bar.

Beth   As in *The Simpsons*?

Steve   Moe stands for Means of Escape.

Jenny (*without irony*)   Because it's where we come to escape the repressive surveillance mechanisms of the autocratic governments and totalitarian corporations that mistake today's global interconnectivity for a means to enslave the common people.

Beth *smiles at* **Cath** – *but* **Cath**'s *not joking.*

Mark   It was the builders' Portakabin base when they were doing up the sports hall. After they finished we asked the school if we could keep it as a sort of student-run IT lab.

Beth   And they let you?

Steve   Not all the teachers were exactly sold on the idea. But the Head got behind it.

Cath   She even offered to pay for some of the kit.

Beth   Why?

Hugs   Cos if there's one thing that gets every school wet, it's the thought of creating the next Bill Gates.

Tania   Or Steve Jobs.

Mark   Or Mark Zuckerberg.

Eloise   So, they give us free rein. No one comes in here but us.

Beth   Leaving you free to use it as a hacking base?

Steve   Precisely.

Beth   Which involves what, exactly?

Archie   Alright, take Pez's throwies as an example.

Steve *lights a throwie and chucks it to* **Beth**. *She catches it.*

Archie   That's a cluster of magnetic LEDs. Throw it at any ferromagnetic building and it sticks.

Beth   Ferro-what?

Nisha   A building made with magnetic materials.

Archie   It's like digital graffiti.

Eloise   He made that.

Steve   At its most basic, that's what hacking is. It's breaking down barriers.

Archie   The intellectual barriers that might otherwise stop Pez from working out how to make a throwie.

Eloise   Or the social systems that would have us believe that public spaces can't be a place for creative expression.

Cath   Hacking is about freeing ourselves from limitations.

Archie   It's creative problem-solving.

Drew and **Pez** *return with the key-card system in tatters.*

Drew   Well, that's the key-card system bollocksed.

He chucks the lock heavily to one side. **Eloise** *glances at* **Beth** – *this isn't sounding quite as impressive as she'd hoped.*

Eloise (*persisting*)   See, Drew might have screwed up installing that key-card system –

Drew   That wasn't my fault!

Eloise   But he'll learn from that mistake. And should he choose to try again he'll do it better the next time.

Steve   And if he succeeds then that, too, will have been a hack.

Beth   And what about all the online stuff?

Archie   Oh, we do that, too.

Seb   We're even piggy-backing off a local wifi network so we can chat with other hackerspaces without anyone being able to trace it back to us.

Beth   You've nicked someone's wifi?

Nisha   We prefer the term piggy-backing. We've not taken it from them. We're just thumbing a ride.

Beth   So you can chat to people?

Archie (*proud*)   Exactly.

Beth (*disappointed*)   Is that it?

Everyone hesitates, suddenly embarrassed.

Eloise   What do you mean?

Beth   I mean, no offence. But I thought hackers, like . . . stole people's credit card details and . . . sent out viruses?

Cath   That would make us black-hat hackers.

Nisha   Or crackers.

Cath   We're white-hat hackers.

Nisha   We're the good guys.

Steve   Beth, we didn't build this place because we're a bunch of nerdy super-villains. We just wanted somewhere we could mess around with stuff.

Hugs (*needling* **Steve**)   Yeah, as far away from all the other kids as possible.

Archie   What's that supposed to mean?

Hugs   What?

Archie   As far away from all the other kids as possible? What's that got to do with anything?

Hugs   Nothing. I'm just saying. You're explaining why we come here. So let's be honest. A large part of this is also about having somewhere we can come to that's not, you know . . . out there.

Mark   What's wrong with out there?

Hugs   You know what I mean.

Mark   Not really.

Hugs   I mean we come here because it's safe.

Archie   You sort of make it sound like we're hiding from something there, mate.

Hugs   Cos we are.

Tania   Erm . . . speak for yourself.

Eloise   And what do you think we're hiding from?

Hugs   I'm not saying there's nothing wrong with it. I'm just saying, you can't deny Beth's got a point.

Steve   Which is what?

Hugs   That for a so-called hacker collective, we're not exactly pushing the envelope. We all know this. We're not exactly revolutionaries, are we? And I'm fine with that. I'm just saying there's no point denying it.

Cath   Doesn't mean we're hiding.

Hugs   Alright, so you're honestly telling me you'd still come here if you could be hanging out with, let's say, Daniel Cooper's lot instead?

Eloise   I could be hanging out with Daniel Cooper's lot if I wanted to, actually, Hugs.

Tania   So could I.

Mark   We all could. We just don't want to.

Nisha   Cos we prefer doing this.

Hugs   Fine. So, we're all okay about the fact that we didn't get an invite to his party, then, are we?

A beat. Nope, definitely not.

Nisha   What party?

Hugs   He's having a house party tonight. Parents are away. Apparently everyone's invited.

Tania   No one told me about any party.

Hugs (*sarcastic*)   Funny, that.

Steve (*conceding*)   Alright, so coming down here might make it harder to stay in the school's broader social loop.

Hugs   He didn't forget to invite us because we spend all our time in here, 'ProfessorV'. We spend all our time in here *because* people like Daniel Cooper don't like us.

Jenny   You can't deny coming here beats having things thrown at us in the common room.

Archie   No one throws things at us in the common room.

Seb   I took a Danish pastry to the back of the head yesterday.

Tania   It was probably meant for someone else.

Eloise   It's true. If anything, geeks are the cool kids now. Daniel Cooper probably wishes we'd bring him here!

Archie   Exactly. (*To* **Hugs**.) You said so yourself. Everyone's invited. He'd probably welcome us with open arms. (*To* **Beth**.) Beth, don't worry. You're gonna find this school a very friendly place.

Beth   Alright, then, prove it.

Archie *hesitates, suddenly nervous.*

Archie   How?

Beth   Take us all to the party. If he lets us in, you're right. Everyone loves you and the sort of stuff you get up to in here is perfectly adequate.

Archie   And if he doesn't?

Beth   You find the balls to turn this into a proper hackerspace.

The school bell rings – end of lunch break. The bell bleeds into a loud dance track. Lights black out simultaneous to each character's 'throwie' being illuminated, dancing around in what, at first, is an organised routine. But as the track develops, the formation starts to fracture, becoming increasingly chaotic, climaxing in . . .

Scene Two

Music cuts and throwies are extinguished simultaneous to lights up on **Archie** *and* **Beth** *facing each other adversarially*

Eloise *enters, followed by* **Mark**, **Steve** *and* **Cath**. *The atmosphere is tense . . .*

Beth (*understatement*)   Well, that was embarrassing.

Archie   It's his house. He was free to decide who he lets in.

Beth   But not to humiliate you.

Archie   He didn't humiliate me.

Eloise   He made you get down on your knees in front of the entire party and beg you to let us in.

Archie   He was just having a laugh. So what? That's fine.

Eloise   And did you find it funny?

Archie   Yeah, maybe I did, actually.

Eloise   You're lying.

Archie   Alright then, no. I didn't find it 'funny', exactly –

Cath   Then why did you do it?

Hugs *enters, followed by* **Jenny**, **Tania**, **Nisha**, **Seb**, **Pez** *and* **Drew**.

Hugs   It's all over YouTube.

Steve   What is?

Nisha   Archie on his knees in front of everyone at the party. Someone filmed it from a window.

Tania   They've made it into a song. Used a re-mix of that Madcon song, 'Beggin'.

Drew   Quite catchy, actually.

Nisha (*glancing at her phone*)   Uh-oh.

Mark   What?

Nisha   Someone's posted it on Twitter.

Pez   What's the hashtag?

Nisha (*reading her phone*)   HashtagMassiveBellEnd.

Hugs   Amazing.

Archie   But I can't have been down on my knees for more than ten seconds!

Jenny   They're fairly liberal with the slow-mo.

Cath   And the rewinds.

Tania   And the freeze-frames.

Archie   But why would they do that?

Hugs   Cos it's funny?

Nisha   It's not funny, Hugs. It's mean.

Pez   I could probably hack into the YouTube account and take down the video if you want?

Steve   Do it.

Archie   No. Leave it up. I don't care.

Steve   Mate, it's probably not even been seen by that many people yet.

Drew (*reading his phone*)   Twenty-three thousand, four hundred and nineteen . . . twenty . . . twenty-one . . .

Mark   We should stop it now before it starts trending.

Archie   Take it down and we make it look like Daniel Cooper's got to us. Don't give him the satisfaction. (*To* **Hugs** *and* **Beth**.) You were right. We weren't invited. I accept that. But you know what? I don't care. We're better than him. We're better than all of them.

Beth   Then maybe it's about time they found out.

Hugs   How?

Beth   By teaching this Daniel Cooper a lesson.

Archie   Now, hang on a minute –

Beth   We agreed. If he didn't let us in we'd start putting this place – all of your talents – to real use. You can't go back on that.

Hugs (*to* **Archie**)   Mate, a deal's a deal.

Archie   We said we'd turn this into a real hackerspace. We never said anything about teaching anyone a lesson.

Beth   I'm sorry, but can anyone remind me why the Headmaster let you have this place?

Pez   Because she wants us to become the next tech giants?

Beth   Sorry, tech what?

Eloise   *Giants.*

Beth   Oh, giants! Because that's what geeks can be these days. (*To* **Mark**.) Can't they, Mogul?

Mark   Potentially.

Beth   So long as what?

Mark   They know what they're doing.

Beth   Pez, you said you could take down that video.

Pez   So?

Beth   So, it sounds to me like you know what you're doing.

Drew (*dismissive*)   Cos he knows how to take down a YouTube video?

Seb (*to* **Beth**)   That's easy.

Beth   And do you think Daniel Cooper would find that easy?

Drew   Probably not.

Seb   Definitely not.

Beth   And yet he's the one telling you what you can and can not do? How does that make sense?

Steve   No one's saying it's fair.

Beth   Then it's our job to set things right.

Eloise   Can't deny she's got a point.

Hugs   I agree.

Archie (*with rising alarm*)   No, she doesn't. Okay, yes when the school gave us this place they hoped we'd use it to accomplish something. But not this. We're not going on some vendetta.

Hugs   Why not?

Steve   Because it's beneath us.

Beth (*correcting him*)   Pissing around with LEDs is beneath you. This is justice.

Archie   For what? I didn't even want to go to his party in the first place.

Eloise   That's not the point anymore.

Archie   Alright, then what is the point?

Hugs   Freedom.

Beth   You said so yourself. That's what hacking is. It's breaking down barriers. Overcoming limitations.

Eloise   We were denied access to that party because Daniel Cooper stopped us. He was a barrier to our access.

Steve   It was his house. That's private property. It was his choice to make.

Hugs   And when he made you get down on your knees?

Archie   He didn't make me. He asked and I agreed. I was just trying to get us in.

Beth   No, Archie. You did that because you were afraid. Now it's his turn to feel fear.

Jenny   You can't deny the lad could do with being taught a lesson.

Mark   Depends.

Beth   On?

Mark   What she's got in mind.

Steve   No one's attacking Daniel Cooper!

Mark   I'm not saying I'm in. I just want to know what we're talking about.

Beth   The course of action is yet to be determined.

Mark   I mean, in principle.

Hugs   Right now the bigger principle is whether, as a collective, we're prepared to keep getting bullied or not. I say not. And I don't seem to be the only one.

Archie   Very well. Then if it's a decision for the collective we have no choice but to take it to a vote. (*To* **Seb**.) IronHelmet?

*But **Seb**'s not with him again.*

Archie (*firmer*)   IronHelmet?

Seb (*remembering that's him*)   Bollocks! Sorry, Archie!

Archie (*correcting him*)   Skyclops.

Seb   Skyclops. It's these funny names.

Archie   Let's not get into all that again. Did you bring your bag today?

Seb   Negative.

Archie   Then I take it you've not got any paper with you, either?

Seb Positive.

Archie (*correcting him*) Affirmative.

Seb What?

Archie In linguistics the opposite of negative is affirmative.

Seb (*baffled*) You sure?

Archie I'm positive. (*Thinks, corrects himself, annoyed.*) I mean affirmative.

Pleased about having tripped-up **Archie**, **Seb** *raises his hand.* **Drew** *high-fives it.*

Archie This is ridiculous. (*Moving on.*) All those in favour of –

Jenny *clears her throat.*

Archie (*with some irritation*) What now?

Jenny You're going to chair the vote, are you?

Archie (*remembering himself, patience wearing thin*) I apologise, Chairman –

Cath (*correcting him*) Chairperson. We took a vote. We agreed all titles should be gender-neutral.

Archie (*trying again*) Chairperson Naysayer. As Chairperson it's of course your job to lead proceedings.

Jenny Thank you, Skyclops. All those in favour of taking action against Daniel Cooper please raise their hand. (*To* **Nisha**.) RainbowSpray, assuming you don't mind a public ballot?

Nisha In the absence of paper I'm prepared to make an exception.

Jenny (*back to the room*) Guys? All those in favour?

Beth, **Hugs**, **Eloise**, **Seb**, **Jenny** *and* **Tania** *all raise a hand.* **Jenny** *counts them.*

Jenny   That's a count of six to seven. The motion –

Beth (*interrupting, to* **Pez**)   Pez, given your talents, you can't tell me you're satisfied by just chatting to other hackerspaces?

Archie   He's free to make up his own mind.

Beth (*persisting, to* **Mark**)   What about you, Mogul? You want to be the next dotcom billionaire. You honestly think you're going to get anywhere chucking throwies at buildings?

Steve   The majority has spoken. Let it go.

But **Nisha***'s hand shoots up. Everyone turns to her, amazed.*

Archie   RainbowSpray, what are you doing?

Nisha   Admittedly this is somewhat out of character . . . But the truth is, I'm sick of it! (*With growing conviction.*) I'm super-clever and I work my fricken arse off. All I want is to be liked but I'm lucky if anyone else in the school will look twice at me. Even some of the teachers think I'm lame.

Archie   That's not true.

Tania   It is, Archie.

Nisha   I know it is. And why? Cos I'm not funny enough, outgoing enough? Cos I don't fit in like the other kids? (*To* **Archie**.) Skyclops, I think you did care that Daniel Cooper thought it was funny when you got down on your knees. And I do think you did it cos you were scared. But I think you also did it cos you just wanted to be a part of the gang. But you know what I think? I think we're the gang now. (*To* **Beth**.) So come on then, Beth . . . (*Then.*) No, hang on. You're gonna need a hacker name.

Steve (*sarcastically*)   The Pied Piper?

Eloise   Evey.

Beth   Why Evey?

Eloise   From V for Vendetta. The ultimate revenge heroine.

Nisha   So come on, then, Evey. What's it gonna be?

Archie   Guys, if you do this. If you use this place to attack people, you realise what that will make us?

Hugs   Superheroes?

Archie   Black-hat hackers. This isn't us. We don't attack people.

Seb   Democracy has spoken, Skylops. If you don't like the result I believe the door handle's been fixed.

Eloise   Same applies to the rest of you. If you want out, no one's making you stay. Pez?

Archie   She's barely been at the school a week! She can't just turn up here and change everything.

Eloise (*ignoring* **Archie**)   Pez?

Pez *turns from* **Archie** *to* **Eloise**.

Pez   Yeah. I'm in.

Drew   Me, too.

Archie   This isn't who we are.

Eloise   Cath?

Cath   Go on, then.

Mark   Well, I'm not just gonna leave the rest of you to have all the fun.

Beth   Steve?

Steve *turns to* **Archie**, *resigning himself to defeat.*

Steve   It's a democracy.

Archie *sucks up his pride. He's not getting behind it, but if everyone else is behind it, he's not going to block them.*

Archie   Then, I guess the majority has spoken.

Beth (*to the others*)   So, what are our options?

They all turn nervously to each other.

Pez   I was talking to a hacker at Ziyou.

Beth   What's that?

Cath   It's a hackerspace in Shanghai.

Pez   He was telling me about this security software called Metasploit. It was designed for people to test the vulnerability of their own computer. But in the right hands you can launch it on a network to isolate its weaknesses. We could use it to hack into the school's exam results database? Maybe fuck with Daniel Cooper's mock results? Give him 'D's.

Archie   Guys, you can't do that.

Jenny   He's right.

Archie   Thank you, Naysayer.

Jenny   Daniel's thick as pigshit. He's probably failed them all already. Changing his results to 'D's would probably be an improvement.

Archie   That's not what I meant.

Hugs (*ignoring* **Archie**, *to* **Pez**)   What about his bank account?

Pez   A bank's security would be a lot tighter. Though in theory Metasploit should work with any system running on Windows. I dunno about hitting his account itself. But at the very least, we could probably send him an email from the bank's network.

Eloise   Saying what?

Hugs   That we'd seized his assets?

Beth   Why?

Pez   Because he was the subject of an internal investigation?

Mark   Would he buy that?

Cath Does he have any assets?

Nisha Judging by his house, I reckon he could.

Beth (*unsure*) Even so.

Eloise What?

Beth I dunno. (*Thinking it through.*) If you got an email saying the bank had frozen your assets . . . Even assuming you believed it was authentic, if you knew you hadn't done anything wrong, wouldn't you just expect them to sort it out? It's got to be something more permanent.

Tania What about his medical record?

Archie No one's fucking with Daniel Cooper's medical record.

Hugs Wouldn't work anyway. Not unless he's waiting for some test results.

Tania No, but that's just it. He is.

Eloise How do you know?

Tania My brother's in the first eleven with him. They all had to go get these medicals done for the summer football tour to France. My brother said they took blood samples and everything.

Beth When?

Tania Week or two back? I don't think they've had the results yet. Maybe we could do something with that?

Beth Do you know where they went for them?

Tania I could find out.

Beth And what they got tested for?

Tania I don't think any of them really knew. My brother said it was for a bunch of stuff. Just left them to get on with it, sort of thing.

Eloise   That's even better, isn't it? If they don't even know what they got tested for we could make up anything?

Mark   Like what?

Beth   Depends. You guys know him better than me. What's the most important thing to Daniel?

Mark   His car?

Seb   His clothes.

Drew   His hair. You remember when we went to Centre Parks? Wouldn't even get it wet he's so obsessed with how it looks.

Hugs   Hair could be good.

Nisha   When my dad was a kid he had Lupus. It's an auto-immune disease. Apparently one of the symptoms was that it made his hair fall out.

Beth   What are the causes of Lupus?

Nisha   I don't think they know. It's one of those. Just happens.

Hugs   So, it could have just happened to Daniel?

They all glance at each other — this could be good.

Beth   Pez, if Tania could find out where they went for the medical could you hack into Daniel's file? Find out whether they've sent out the results or not?

Pez   With enough time, I reckon I probably could, yeah.

Beth   And hack some of their letter heading?

Pez   Wouldn't be hard to mock-up if not.

Archie   Obviously you're not gonna tell Daniel Cooper he's got Lupus?

Hugs (*excited*)   And make him think all his hair's gonna fall out? Too bloody right we are!

Steve   You realise that's completely illegal?

Beth   I thought you said you'd stolen someone else's wifi?

Nisha (*correcting her*)   Not stolen. Piggy-backed.

Beth   Then hacking into the clinic's network can't be traced back to us, can it?

Archie   It's not about whether we can get away with it or not.

Beth   Then what are you saying?

Archie   That it's wrong! You can't tell him he's got some disease. It'll screw him up!

Beth   Good. With a bit of luck he'll learn his lesson.

Steve   And how will it be a lesson if we can't tell him the truth – that he's being punished for what he did to Archie?

Beth *seems momentarily stumped.*

Mark   We could let him sweat for a bit then send him an anonymous message telling him he's okay. That it was just payback for generally being a massive twat to everyone all the time?

Hugs   There you go.

Archie (*rhetorically*)   And you don't think he'd realise it was us?

Mark   So what if he does? He can't prove it.

Eloise   And given we could mess with him like this, do you really think he's gonna want to push us to do worse?

Beth   Pez, how quickly could we get into his records?

Pez   Couple of hours.

Tania   I could text my brother and find out where they went.

Archie (*to* **Pez**)   And then what? You make it into the database and it turns out they've not sent out the results yet, you're telling me this is really something you'd be prepared to do?

Beth   Fuck yeah.

Archie   I'm asking Pez.

Pez (*hesitates*)   Yes.

Archie   Why?

Pez *glances at* **Beth**.

Beth (*encouraging*)   Go on.

Pez (*to* **Archie**)   Because Daniel Cooper needs to learn his lesson.

Archie   So say us?

Hugs   If no one else is going to.

Archie   And then what?

Eloise   How do you mean?

Archie   You claim a role like that – start playing the vigilante – what's next?

Beth   I dunno, Dad. But I'm gagging to find out.

The school bell rings – end of lunch break. Everyone apart from **Archie** *and* **Beth** *grab their coats and bags, etc.*

As before, the bell bleeds into a loud dance track. Again, lights black out and simultaneously each character's throwie is illuminated. Glowing in the darkness, they bounce about, more energised than before. There's greater harmony among the majority of them, too. A purposefulness – with the exception of two throwies, who can't break their way into the ranks. They become increasingly energetic in their attempts to break through, climaxing in . . .

Scene Three

Music cuts and throwies are extinguished. Simultaneously lights go up on **Steve** *and* **Archie** – *the two throwies who couldn't break through.*

Beth, **Eloise**, **Mark**, **Hugs**, **Jenny**, **Drew**, **Pez**, **Nisha** *and* **Seb** *sit about the room nearby. A nervous excitement is in the air. Some of them are laughing, perhaps playing an aggressive game of catch with a throwie. They seem empowered.*

Tania *and* **Cath** *enter, chucking chocolate bars at the others.*

Cath   Who wants? We've got Wispas, Crunchies, Snickers, M&Ms ... .

Tania   Dairy Milk, Yorkies, Kit-Kats . . .

The others scramble to catch the chocolate bars as they're thrown.

Drew   Don't tell me you hacked the vending machine?

Tania   Daniel Cooper's giving them out in the playground.

Seb *(amazed)*   For free?

Tania   Got a whole suitcase of them. Just dishing them out to whoever's passing.

Cath   Tania asked him what he was doing and he said 'making amends'.

Mark   Bollocks.

Cath   Seriously. He was well nice to us.

Tania   Well nice to everyone.

Cath *(amused)*   He looked terrified! Kept glancing around like he thought he was being watched.

Beth *turns triumphantly to* **Archie**.

Archie *(sarcastic)*   Congratulations. You've successfully terrorised Daniel Cooper?

Drew   We hardly terrorised him.

Steve You made him think his hair was about to fall out.

Tania And it worked. (*The chocolate.*) Look!

Archie He thinks he's being watched. He's paranoid.

Eloise Good. About time he knew what it felt like to be afraid.

Beth (*to* **Archie**) I'd have thought you'd have come round by now.

Archie To what? Team Beth?

Beth To what we're doing. Tell me this hasn't been a first rate example of 'creative problem-solving'?

Archie It's bullying.

Beth It's proving a point.

Steve Which is?

Beth That we're capable of making a difference.

Archie We already knew that.

Beth Then why weren't you? (*To the others.*) I don't know about you guys, but do you know what this feels like to me? It feels like an invitation.

Eloise To what?

Beth Well, that's the question.

Weary of being perceived as too much of a ringleader, **Beth** *turns to* **Hugs** *to take over . . .*

Beth Hugs?

Hugs Me and Beth came in earlier. Got online to Pez's mates over in Shanghai. Turns out there's all sorts of things they're getting up to out there.

Mark Such as?

Hugs   Like after the Bradley Manning stuff. When Anonymous attacked Paypal for withholding donations to Wikileaks. The guys at Ziyou were in on that.

Beth   Pez, they said you've been talking to them about this kind of thing for a while?

Pez   About the coding. We discussed some of their designs, but never their plans for them.

Beth   That's not how they see it.

Pez (*with rising panic*)   What do you mean?

Beth   They took your interest as a very clear indication.

Pez   Of what?

Beth   That they had friends in England.

Archie   They do have friends in England. So what?

Beth   So, friends like to do things together, don't they.

Steve   Such as?

Hugs   Who's heard about Operation Aurora?

Cath   That was the Google cyber attack. Back in 2009. Some other Chinese hackerspace –

Hugs   The Elderwood Group.

Cath   That's it. They attacked Google on behalf of the People's Liberation Army. It's why Google withdrew from China.

Tania   What did they do?

Cath   Hacked the Gmail accounts of a bunch of Chinese dissidents. People like that artist.

Nisha   Ai Weiwei.

Cath   That's the one.

Archie (*to* **Beth**, *accusatory*)   People who attack freedom of speech. These are the types of hackers you've been talking to?

Beth   That's the Elderwood Group. Ziyou means liberty in Chinese. That's the whole point. They want to combat that stuff. The Chinese state wanted to attack Google cos they reckoned it posed a threat to their power. But the guys at Ziyou are about dismantling state control.

Pez   From the conversations I've had with them they seem pretty solid about that sort of thing.

Steve (*accusatory*)   So much for only talking to them about coding.

Cath   So, what's any of this got to do with us?

Hugs   China's got one of the biggest populations on earth. Over the coming years the majority of them are gonna be getting online. And when that happens nowhere else on earth will there be a bigger trail of personal information.

Beth   And the way Ziyou see it, the more that happens, the greater the state's potential for control.

Steve   Still struggling to see what this has to do with us.

Hugs   If the Snowden leaks have taught us anything, it's how invested the British government already is in spying on us online. And not just British citizens. Everyone everywhere.

Beth   As far as Ziyou are concerned, this is a global problem. The more hackerspaces there are out there defending our privacy, the bigger the impact.

Jenny   So, what are you saying? Ziyou want our help?

Beth   This isn't about us helping them. It's about us helping each other. A shared objective.

Nisha (*concerned*)   Which is what?

Beth   Taking back the power.

A beat. As the seriousness of her suggestion sinks in . . .

Eloise (*helplessly excited*)   Holy shit!

Archie   Obviously this is a joke?

Beth   They're offering to help us with the coding and whatever extra kit we'd need.

Pez (*with rising excitement*)   Ziyou want to help us build a virus?

Steve (*deeply concerned*)   To attack who?

Beth   Whoever we think's most culpable.

Hugs   It's an amazing opportunity.

Archie   Yeah, to ruin our lives!

Beth   To make the world a better place! To actually do something! I dunno about the rest of you but I'm proud of what we did to Daniel. He was a bully who thought he could push the rest of us around and we've helped him think again. This is just the same.

Archie (*incredulous*)   How is this the same?

Hugs   Because it's about claiming back our freedom.

Beth   The freedom to walk down the school corridor without being tormented by some moron. The freedom to go online without having everything we do or say used against us.

Archie   Because that's really that big a problem?

Hugs   Do you know how many millions of emails the NSA steal every single day?

Archie   So, the government knows who I chatted to on Facebook last night. You know what? I don't actually care.

Beth   Then you're an idiot.

Archie   No, Beth. I'm just facing up to reality. This is the world we live in now. I've got nothing to hide.

Beth It's not a question of whether you've got anything to hide or not. It's a question of rights. Privacy is a right. It's in the Universal Declaration on Human Rights.

Hugs If we give this one up, who knows which ones will be next?

Steve I'm not saying it's a good thing. But you don't use Facebook because you like keeping yourself to yourself, do you? That's what social media is. It's sharing yourself. That's the culture.

Nisha 'I share, therefore I am.'

Seb What's that?

Nisha That's what they say about our generation, isn't it? That we feel like we don't exist if we're not telling everyone all about it.

Tania So, what's wrong with wanting to feel connected to people? I think that's nice.

Beth And I think you're right, Tania. That is nice. The only problem is that's precisely what they're preying on.

Tania Who?

Hugs These tech companies. Social media sites. Facebook, Twitter.

Cath How are they preying on it?

Hugs Through the way they design their websites, their apps. It's all carefully arranged to give you that feeling of connection. Like you're not alone. And why?

Eloise To make us keep on coming back?

Archie So what? These are businesses. They're allowed to chase customers.

Beth Yeah, it's just a matter what their business really is.

Hugs   It's us, Skyclops. Our lives. Our personal information. That's their stock.

Beth   The more we come back, the more information we feed them about ourselves.

Hugs ` Which agencies like the NSA and GCHQ take from them to spy on us.

Beth   Archie, I agree with you. We've all got to go online to live our lives now. And, Tania, I agree it's nice to feel connected to people. But we should be free to do that without the government keeping a record of everything we do and say. That's not a world we should resign ourselves to.

Drew   It's like what's-his-name – the one who wanted to fly –

Seb   Iron Man.

Drew   No, the Greek one.

Seb   The easyJet bloke.

Cath   Stelios what's-his-face.

Drew   Icarus. We're so in love with this new technology we can't see that it's gonna kill us.

Archie   Not sure it's gonna kill us exactly.

Eloise   Not our bodies, maybe. But our spirit? Our humanity?

Steve   And what's that?

Nisha   Our individuality.

Jenny   Exactly.

Nisha   The fact that we're all unique. Isn't that what makes us special? That we all think and speak and feel differently.

Beth   None of which means anything in a world where every form of self-expression is used to expand our government's control over us.

Pez   Acxiom.

Eloise   What's that?

Pez   They're one of the world's biggest digital data brokers. That's who we should target.

Steve (*sarcastic*)   Brilliant! Because sending a virus into some data broker's computer network will definitely fix everything.

Hugs   Maybe not. But it might get people to start thinking about the way their private information's being used when they go online.

Archie   You're deluded. You'll be lucky if it even makes the news.

Eloise   But it could still send a message.

Steve   Yes, that Acxiom need to beef up their security. It won't change anything.

Beth   Steve's right.

Steve   Thank you.

Beth   They're not high status enough. We've got to target something more public. Do something that will actually affect people.

Steve   That's not what I meant.

Nisha   What about Facebook? Or Instagram?

Tania   Or Twitter? They do it, don't they?

Mark   They all do it, Tania. Snapchat and Spotify and Amazon. They all harvest our information.

Hugs   But they only give it to the government because they're forced to. They're not the root of the problem.

Cath   Then who is?

Pez   The telecommunications companies. Verizon and Vodafone. And BT. They're the ones that own the actual hardware. The undersea cables that the internet actually runs through, that links it all up. That's how GCHQ accessed the networks. BT just handed it over to them.

A beat. **Beth** *begins to smile. A ripple of excitement passes through some of the others.*

Archie (*sheer disbelief*)   So, you want to launch a cyber attack at BT? Are you completely insane?

Beth   They had a moral responsibility to protect us.

Steve   You're talking about one of the biggest corporations on earth!

Hugs   And Google wasn't when the Chinese hacked them?

Archie   That's different.

Eloise   How?

Archie   You're not the Chinese!

Hugs   But we are, mate. With Ziyou behind us.

Steve   We all know what happened to Snowden. What are we gonna do, move to Russia?

Beth   No. Just cover our tracks better.

Hugs   Anyway, Snowden was a high-school dropout. We're already more qualified.

Archie   Okay, let's take this insane leap of imagination for a second and pretend this is even remotely possible. Even if you did manage to send the virus, they'd just absorb the blow. Bury it in some private investigation. No one would ever know. You'd accomplish nothing.

Pez   Not necessarily.

Beth   Go on.

Pez   In 2010, President Obama carried out a secret programme codenamed 'Olympic Games'.

Cath (*recognising where this is heading, excited*)   Fuck yes! That was insane.

Beth   Which was what? What happened?

Jenny   It was basically a wave of digital attacks on foreign targets.

Drew   The crown jewel of which was an Iranian nuclear plant.

Cath   What they did has kind of become legend among hackers.

Beth   Why?

Pez   The virus was genius. Firstly, it infiltrated the facility's monitoring systems and disabled the alarms.

Drew   Then it manipulated the centrifuges. Made them suddenly speed up or slow down until they packed it in.

Seb   Without the alarm system in place, no one even knew it was happening until the whole place was basically collapsing.

Pez   It was the first time a cyber attack had managed to cause actual physical destruction.

Cath (*to* **Archie**)   And a building caving in is something you definitely can't just hide.

Pez   Obviously BT's not running any nuclear refineries. They don't have the same sort of heavy machinery at play. Though with Ziyou's help – with enough time to plan – I'd be surprised if there wasn't something we could use.

Eloise   One of the world's biggest corporations going up in smoke? Can't deny that would make the papers.

Mark   It would make all of them. Around the world.

Archie   Alright, I'll hand it to you. What you did to Daniel Cooper was really something. He was a wanker and you made him realise that wasn't okay. It was a bit sick the way you did it. But whatever. Job done. That's one thing. But what you're talking about now would change everything.

Hugs   Yes. For the better.

Archie   No, Hugs. You could go to jail for this. Proper jail. This could ruin your lives.

Beth   And you think the French Resistance let those sorts of worries stop them?

Archie   You're not living under the Nazis!

Beth   Or whoever resisted the Stasi, then.

Archie   Nor the Stasi either! I'm serious. Once you do this there'll be no turning back.

Beth   If that's the price of freedom, then so be it. I am a human being, Archie.

Archie   Don't do it.

Beth   This is my life. And I don't want to spend the rest of it knowing that all the things I do and say – where I go, how I feel, the very things that make me the person that I am – are being stored in some government facility. That's not a world I'm prepared to live in. I refuse. Which I'm afraid means actually doing something about it.

Archie   It won't work. You'll fail. And you'll suffer the consequences.

Beth   But at least we're gonna try.

She crosses to one side of the room.

Right, guys? Who's with me?

A beat. **Hugs** *heads over to her.* **Pez** *follows. As do* **Eloise**, **Jenny**, **Seb**, **Nisha**, **Drew**, **Tania**, **Cath** *and, after a moment's hesitation,* **Mark**. *Only* **Steve** *and* **Archie** *remain on the other side. A beat.*

Steve   Ah, fuck it!

Steve *marches over towards them. Simultaneously the bell rings, we cut to blackout and a thundering dance tune kicks in. As before, the throwies are illuminated in the darkness, dancing in rigid formation. They're the most energetic we've seen them, bouncing purposefully around the stage – all but one, which stands motionless in the middle of it all. The other throwies dance away from him, reaching the periphery of the stage as . . .*

Scene Four

The music cuts and the throwies are extinguished. Simultaneously lights come up on **Archie** *pacing alone in the room. He looks distressed.*

Steve *enters with a toolbox. He seems surprised to find* **Archie** *waiting. They both hesitate for a beat.*

Steve   How did you get in here?

Archie   Every system has a weakness.

Steve   How?

Archie   Drew never sealed the back windows.

Steve   So you broke in? I thought only black-hat hackers did that?

Archie   It's not breaking in if it's my own property.

Steve   It's not yours.

Archie   No, it's all of ours. At least it was supposed to be.

Steve   It still is.

Archie   Not hers?

Steve   You shouldn't be here.

He collects a power drill from the toolbox and exits out the back. We hear drilling. **Archie** *waits.* **Steve** *returns and replaces the power drill in the toolbox.*

Archie   You've been avoiding me.

Steve   Evey thought it best if we keep to ourselves.

Archie   Evey? That really what you call her now?

Steve   It's her name.

Archie   Her hacker name.

Steve   Exactly.

Archie   Even though she doesn't understand the first thing about what hacking really is?

Steve   I'm not sure that's true.

Archie   Why, because of what happened with Daniel Cooper?

Steve   To begin with.

Archie   Steve, mate, she didn't do anything with Daniel Cooper. She instructed and everyone else obeyed. She didn't do that. Pez did.

Steve   What difference does it make?

Archie   What about my texts?

Steve   She thought it would be best if we swapped our old phones for burners.

Archie   And I've seen you're off Facebook now, too?

Steve   We're off all social media.

Archie   Why?

Steve   Keeping a low profile.

Archie   Because you're actually going ahead with it?

Steve   Why, what's it to you?

Archie   Have you even stopped to think about what you're doing? I mean, really think?

Beth *enters. She stops on seeing* **Archie**.

Beth (*to* **Steve**)   How did he get in here?

Archie   Back window.

Steve   I've fixed it.

Archie   See you got the key-card system working.

Beth   What d'you want?

Archie   To talk to the guys.

Beth   You'll have to come back. Now's not a very good time.

Archie   Because it's up to you, is it? (*To* **Steve**.) Well?

Pez, **Drew**, **Jenny** *and* **Seb** *enter, carrying new computer equipment. They stop on seeing* **Archie**.

Jenny   What's he doing here?

Beth   Nothing. He was just leaving.

Archie (*the equipment*)   Bloody hell, look at all this!

Seb   Just arrived for us at the porter's office.

Archie   Yeah? Chinese postage, was it?

Seb *turns to* **Beth**, *unsure what he's allowed to say.*

Beth (*to* **Seb**)   Well, don't just stand there.

Seb *and the others get on with connecting the new kit to the power supply and servers, etc.*

Beth (*to* **Steve**)   ProfessorV, why don't you see Archie out?

Archie   I know where the door is.

Beth   Then, why don't you use it?

Archie   I told you. I've something I need to say.

Beth   And I've told you we're not interested.

Mark, **Hugs** *and* **Eloise** *enter, carrying more computer equipment. They also stop on seeing* **Archie**.

Archie   Don't tell me there's more?

Hugs   What's he doing here?

Beth   Nothing. (*To* **Steve**.) If you wouldn't mind?

Steve (*trying to reason with him*)   Archie, you made your choice.

Archie   And I stand by it. I just never thought you'd be stupid enough to take it this far.

Eloise   Stupid? Don't take it out on us cos you were too scared to join in.

Archie   How close are you?

Mark   To what?

Archie   Launching it.

Nisha, **Tania** *and* **Cath** *enter with shopping bags full of beers, soft drinks and snacks.*

Archie (*amazed, panicking*)   Fuck, it's not today? Pez, I thought you said it would take time?

Throughout the following, everyone continues to unpack and set up the equipment and refreshments . . .

Pez   Turns out Ziyou were already quite far down the line. Whole bunch of other hackerspaces have got on board. Everyone's chipped in.

Drew   It's a co-ordinated attack.

Seb   We're like the Avengers of hacking. It's mental.

Nisha   Archie, I dunno why you're acting so surprised. This sort of thing happens all the time. Throughout history. It's just another cycle.

Archie   What cycle? What are you talking about?

Cath   Whenever new technologies come out the state gets frightened. Attacks human rights.

Nisha   Happened with the Gutenberg press.

Archie   Tell me you're joking?

Nisha   When Gutenberg developed a machine to mass produce literature the state clamped down on freedom of speech. And why?

Cath   Because so long as the technology's one step ahead of the legislation there's no laws to stop the state from attacking it.

Jenny   Which means it has to be left to the people themselves to stand up and fight.

Nisha   They did it then and we're doing it now.

Archie (*to* **Beth**)   This is you. You've fed them all this stuff to justify what you're doing.

Beth   I dunno what you're talking about.

Tania   'The revolution is not an apple that falls when it is ripe. You have to– ' (*Trails off, forgetting the rest.*)

Beth (*annoyed*)   'Make it fall.'

Tania   ' – make it fall.'

Archie   For God's sake, Tania, you're not a revolutionary! Look at you!

Drew   You don't have to look like a revolutionary to be a revolutionary any more, Archie. That's the beauty of the digital age.

Hugs   It's true. We don't have to build barricades in town squares. We've got everything we need right here in this room.

Seb (*sung, à la* Les Misérables)
   Do you hear the people type,
   Typing the code of angry geeks,
   It is the music of a people
   Who will out you with our leaks –

Drew (*simultaneously with* **Seb**)
   It is the music of a people
   Who will out you with your leaks.

Archie   But you're not leaking anything. You're not whistleblowers. You're not Snowden. This is completely different.

Eloise   But we're part of the same movement.

Archie   No. There is no movement. What you're talking about isn't a revolution. It's terrorism. Against one of the most powerful organisations on earth. They will stop you. Then they will find you. And they will punish you.

Hugs   You don't even know how we're gonna do it.

Archie   It's doesn't matter how, it's a foregone conclusion. (*Unable to resist.*) Why, how are you gonna do it?

Hugs   No, it's fine, mate. You just leave us to get busted.

Seb   Ziyou's got us routed through dozens of hacked proxy computers all over the world.

Mark   Seb, shut up!

Archie (*to* **Pez**)   And you think GCHQ won't be able to trace the traffic back to them?

Pez   To the first one, maybe. But they've all had Tor routers launched at them.

Cath   At each point the traffic multiplies a millionfold.

Pez   Twelve different computers with a million false leads each.

Eloise   It's a masterpiece.

Archie   Fine. Then, getting busted aside, you're copying the Olympic Games operation, right?

Hugs   So?

Archie   That means you're trying to wreak physical damage? What happens if someone gets hurt?

This seems to halt everyone momentarily – in the excitement of what they've been planning no one quite thought that prospect through.

Mark   Then they shouldn't have been working there.

Archie   Innocent people.

Nisha   We've all got to be responsible for our choices, Archie.

Jenny   Think of it as collateral damage.

Archie   Jenny, would you listen to yourself? You're not the American army. You're a bunch of schoolkids.

Cath   Actually, we're a technocratic junta.

Archie   This isn't a game. This is real life.

Eloise   Yeah, well, if you wanted to have a say maybe you shouldn't have walked out on us.

Archie   I didn't have any choice.

Nisha   You could have joined in.

Archie   You mean followed her, too?

Jenny   Who?

Archie   Beth.

Tania   We're not following her, Archie. We're not sheep.

Archie   Then, stop and think about what you're doing.

Eloise (*enough's enough*)   Right, I'm bored of this. I reckon it's time you left.

Beth   No.

Beth *suddenly piping up seems to trip everyone up.*

Eloise   What do you mean, no?

Beth   We can't let him go. Not now.

Tania   Why not?

Beth   Not before it's done. Not if there's a risk he might tell someone.

Archie   You can't exactly keep me here.

Beth   Course we can. (*To* **Steve**.) Steve, you got any duct tape in that toolbox?

They all turn to **Steve**. *He half smiles, unsure whether she's joking or not. Realising she's not,* **Steve** *turns from* **Beth** *to* **Archie** *. . . who makes a dash for the door . . . only to be grabbed by* **Drew**. **Archie** *tries to wriggle free but* **Hugs** *and* **Mark** *run to help* **Drew** *restrain him.*

Archie   Get off me!

Hugs (*to the others*)   Grab a chair.

Seb *pulls a chair forwards.* **Drew**, **Mark** *and* **Hugs** *back* **Archie** *onto it.*

Archie   Guys, for fuck's sake!

Mark (*calling to him*)   Steve?

Jolted into action, **Steve** *grabs his duct tape. While* **Drew**, **Mark** *and* **Hugs** *continue to restrain* **Archie**, **Steve** *tapes him to the chair with the duct tape.*

Beth (*prompting him*)   Pez, how we doing?

Pez *positions himself behind a computer and starts typing.*

Archie   Pez, listen to me. She's been lying to you.

Beth   Will somebody shut him up?

Archie (*simultaneously with the following*)   This is ridiculous. You don't just attack people because you're scared.

Hugs (*to* **Beth**)   How?

Drew   Hit him.

Beth   No, don't hit him. Gag him.

Seb   What with?

Beth   I dunno. Find something.

Everyone looks for something to gag **Archie** *with.*

Archie (*with rising panic*)   Nisha, you were wrong when you said I got down my knees that night cos I wanted to be a part of Daniel Cooper's gang. I did it cos that's what I was prepared to do to get us all in to his party. (*To* **Jenny**.) Because *that's* what makes us human, Jenny. Our capacity to adapt, to compromise. That's how you fix things. Not by lashing out.

Pez   Routers are good. Uploading the software now.

Seb *finds a canvas bag.*

Seb   What about this? We could sling it over his head?

Drew   Give it here –

He grabs the bag and approaches **Archie** *with it.*

Archie (*immediately, desperate*)   Beth didn't move here cos her dad got relocated! She made it all up!

Drew *stops.*

Beth   He's lying.

Archie   She was at St Anne's. That's where she moved here from.

Beth   That's not true.

Archie   You can look it up. It's in her records.

Beth   Drew, gimme the bag.

Archie   She moved here after they kicked her out for setting fire to the school petting zoo.

Tania (*furious*)   St Anne's has a petting zoo?

Beth   It's not a petting zoo! It's just two guinea pigs and a pigmy goat!

She grabs her own mouth. Everyone turns to her.

Archie   Only reason they survived was cos the goat pissed itself. The straw was too wet to catch.

A beat.

Eloise (*to* **Beth**)   Beth?

Beth   Well, so what? Doesn't change anything.

Archie   It changes everything. She doesn't care about any of this stuff. She's just stirring up trouble.

Beth   And why would I wanna do that?

Archie   Because it's what you do. (*To the others.*) She's completely insane!

Beth   Have you forgotten what you lot were before I showed up? Bunch of nobodies.

Archie   That's not true.

Beth   Shuffling around with your little LEDs? Now look at you. Fucking superheroes!

Archie   This won't make you superheroes.

Beth   Masked crusaders, fighting for justice?

Archie   It's not justice if you can't control the outcome. It's just chaos. (*To the group.*) Don't do it.

Pez's *computer automatically reboots. He turns to it.*

Pez   Software's uploaded. Just waiting for Ziyou to log on.

Archie   Hugs, you once said we were hiding in here. You know what? I couldn't agree more. And, Seb, I'm glad you struggle with those stupid hacker names. We already have our own names. They're Steve and Mark and Hugs and Eloise and Tania and Cath and Jenny and Drew and Pez and Nisha and Seb and Beth.

Pez   They're logged on. Just waiting to connect.

Archie (*with rising urgency*)   Okay, you were right. Everything we've been talking about. BT, GCHQ, all the privacy stuff, it's wrong. I absolutely believe that. But you don't make the world a better place by attacking things in secret. You challenge them. In public. Using argument and reason.

Pez   They're ready.

Archie   So, untie me and let's show them who we really are.

A beat.

Blackout.

Hacktivists

BY BEN OCKRENT

*Notes on rehearsal and staging drawn from a workshop
with the writer held at the National Theatre, October 2014.
Workshop led by Simon Godwin, with notes by Kate Budgen.*

How Ben came to write the play

The idea for the play came from thinking about how
technology is increasingly dominating our lives, and how
much the internet and being online play a part in young
people's everyday existence. So much so that the study of
computing, and specifically coding, is now mandatory across
all state primary and secondary schools, a huge shift from
when Ben was at school. He wanted to explore the kind of
questions young people might be engaging in as they learn.

He saw the Connections project as a fantastic opportunity to
create a piece of entertainment through which questions
could be asked about what the internet is/should/could be
and how we want to use it. He was excited by the potential
for the rehearsal process to open up discussion and for young
people to feel part of a larger discussion about how we
collectively move forward with the internet.

Talking to journalist Heather Brooke, reading her book *The
Revolution will be Digitised* and watching *In Real Life*, a
documentary film about how young people interact through
the web, inspired Ben. He also read Tim Berners-Lee's book
and the main thing he took from it was that the web was
created for connection and communication. And what started
as a beautiful and hopeful desire to allow people to connect
with each other is now moving towards something much
more complex and potentially more dangerous.

Ben was interested in the belief held by some that young
people are increasingly disfranchised and apathetic, when
there is so much evidence to the contrary. Young people care
deeply about their world and *do* want to move forward and
change things. He wanted to create a set of identifiable

characters that, over the course of the play realise their own power and the wider consequences their actions could have.

Ben also wanted to challenge the perception of hackers and make us think of them in a different way. Through his research, Ben found that hackers are often perceived as evil and dangerous, deliberately causing chaos and unrest, but hackers don't think of themselves in that way at all. They believe in freedom and access and Ben was fascinated by the idea that they are almost superhuman in their skills, and can do things 'normal' humans can't do. What would you do if you had those talents?

Approaching the play

All characters in the play are of equal importance. Simon Godwin, the director facilitating the workshop, suggested that for the first read, the company could sit in a circle and read a line each, including every stage direction/piece of information written in the script. Reading it as an ensemble allows the group to get to know the play collectively in rigorous detail, instead of focusing on the size of one part/trying to perform during the read-through.

After the first read-through in the workshop, the group returned to the first eight pages and then discussed what was important to address when staging the play. Below is a list of what was brought up.

- There is a lot of crucial storytelling information in the first eight pages. Characters are introduced and relationships are set up. How do you ensure that all the important information reaches your audience, considering the fast pace of the dialogue? How do you make the exposition seem natural? One suggestion was to give a character that is delivering exposition an activity to 'smuggle in' the storytelling.

- How do you make conversation dramatic? How do you create and maintain high stakes?

- Who is the most important character? Who *believes* they are the most important? Status-wise, who is collapsing and who is climbing?

- Consider the events within the play. An event is something that affects everyone in the room – for example, an entrance is an event.

- How do people speak in groups in life? People are not always polite and you don't know who is going to speak next. In a group dynamic, several people may want to speak, but the person who actually speaks is the one who gets in. Conversation is spontaneous and unpredictable. How do you reflect this dynamic convincingly in the scenes?

- There are many characters onstage at once. What actions/ activity will they be doing in a small room? Where are they in relation to each other? What were they doing before the beginning of the play? These questions could be brainstormed with the whole group, referring to the text for concrete facts and then adding details.

- It is likely that all characters will have mobile phones that they can actively use during the play.

- Where is the Portakabin in relation to the rest of the school? Draw a map to show the layout of the school grounds. This will have a bearing on the scenes.

- What does the Portakabin look like? What is it made out of? Is it messy? Tidy? What objects are in the room? Could some of the objects in the room support character choices: for example, does Archie have the posh chair to reflect his status within the group?

A useful exercise is to challenge the company to makeshift the environment of the Portakabin with what you have in the room, working together. Decide where the entrance is and how you will represent it. Once the Portakabin has been created, ask the cast to find themselves a place in the space and decide what they are doing before the play begins. Decide what time and what day of the week it is. The aim is to identify what normality is for this group of people. 'You can't have a crisis until you know what is normal.'

Ask the cast to improvise, non-verbally, their chosen activity. Pause the improvisation and go round each character asking who they are and what they are doing. Make sure they are specific (e.g. 'I am Tania, and I am tweeting about my latest discovery online/eating a prawn mayo sandwich/reading a tech magazine', etc.)

Ben commented that hacking is all about creative problem-solving and working together to break down barriers. Hackerspaces are often places of sophisticated discovery as everyone shares their skills and knowledge. The Portakabin is where these characters come together to share their enthusiasm and passion and work in unity. So the next stage of the improvisation would be to work out how to show this in their everyday activities. What natural groupings can be shown? Who is working with whom? What are they doing? What information can you give the audience about character relationships? Who is allied with whom? It is important initially to show harmony within the group, because this harmony is then turned on its head with the arrival of Beth.

You could choose to improvise these groupings or create a single image to represent the group dynamic at the start of the play. You could then ask the group to improvise the few moments before the start of the play, to discover how characters find themselves within the action of the play.

The group ran through the first few pages *in situ*, improvising their blocking from the context they created in the previous exercise. Simon stopped and restarted the action, asking questions about story and back story, suggesting alternative choices and going back to the beginning, each time adding more detail.

Below are some of the challenges and questions that the group hit as they worked through the opening scene:

- Does the play start with a bit of non-verbal action/activity? Or do you launch straight into the text? Which choice has more dramatic impact?

- Does everyone in the room hear the opening dialogue?

- How can the rising panic of being locked in build?

- Why is Cath trying to leave the Portakabin? Is there somewhere she has to get to urgently? The more she needs to leave, the higher the stakes and the more the audience's attention is caught.

- Be very concrete and specific in the choices you make about back story and the given circumstances. Always think about how these choices will help the story.

- As a general rule of thumb, in life we are always clear whom we are speaking to. Make sure that this is reflected onstage by ensuring that actors know to whom they are addressing each line. Keep the energy of the line right to the end and make sure the line has landed with the person it is directed to. The drama will be stronger and clearer as a result.

- When was the card-reader installed? How long has the door been locked?

- How serious is it that the door is locked? Is it more serious for some than others?

- Why is Tania so panicked at the thought of being locked in? Is she claustrophobic? Does anyone else suffer from a similar anxiety? Or does their panic stem from a different place? Explore what happens if there are more people in the room who are worried, about being trapped/being late, etc. Experiment with pushing things to the extreme and observing the dynamic.

- Perhaps the most dramatic decision is to have these events occur very close to beginning of the play, making the stakes that much higher.

- How do you show power/hierarchy/relationships of the group through blocking and intention?

- Does everyone always need to be speaking so that everyone else in the Portakabin can hear? Are any 'side' conversations taking place?

- How does everyone remain active onstage without pulling focus from the dialogue? When does action become distracting?

- The play needs to begin with high stakes. The higher the stakes, the better the energy. The aim is to grab the audience's attention straight away.

- Consider action and reaction. Be aware of what silence can do to the rhythm of dialogue. Experiment with non-verbal reactions to add texture. Be bold and expressive in reactions.

- At every stage, keep trying to discover the most alive choices. What tells the strongest story?

Ben was clear that he didn't want the play to provide answers, and it ends with a question. Archie's final speech is a passionate appeal to the rest of the group to find another way, but whether they choose to listen is left unknown. However, for this final moment and throughout the play, actors must know what each character wants to do and why they choose to act in the way they do. This allows an audience to see a rich array of conflicting opinions and multiple universes, which is exciting because they don't know how they are going to be resolved and which path the narrative will take.

Themes
- Justice.
- Choice.
- Power and status.
- Responsibility and doing the 'right' thing.
- Knowledge.
- Loyalty.

Approaches to characterisation

Ben wanted to create a piece in which characters go through
a process of gaining access to power, and by doing so, realise
that their physical actions have consequences beyond the four
walls of the PortaCabin. These characters have a responsibility
to one another, to themselves and to society. Simon said it
could be helpful to think about circles of awareness: the inner
circle (how characters are feeling); the second circle (their
relationship to their immediate peers in the Portakabin); and
the third circle (how the Portakabin relates to the rest of the
world).

Everyone has opinions and makes choices according to what
they think is right, but Simon was careful to point out that
particularly in relation to the theme of justice, everyone is
right, and everyone is wrong. Every character's argument has
validity and the more each character has a view they can hold
on to, the more interesting and rich the play will be.

In the stage directions, Archie, Beth, Steve and Eloise are
older than the others. It might be interesting to discuss why
this might be. Is it to do with status in school being very much
age-specific? How old is each character? Is there a wide range
of ages or are they all close in age? Consider what the benefit
is theatrically of each choice. Is there a greater contrast in
energies and opinions if there is a greater difference of ages?
There is potentially greater fun to be had in contrast.

Ben suggested it could be useful to think about the group as a
disparate bunch of characters who outside of the hackerspace
feel lonely and isolated, but through the hackerspace they have
found each other. They all come together in this Portakabin
to connect and make change. This might allow for a more
unconventional mix of ages, and might also throw up some
interesting choices in terms of status and hierarchy. What are
characters like in a school/home environment? How are they
different in the hackerspace? In this particular group, power
might come from unexpected places and the hierarchy within
the hackerspace might not necessarily be the same as within

the school. Characters with power and status in the hackerspace might be determined less by how old they are and more by their skills and knowledge of technology.

Simon did a useful exercise to begin character discussions, accruing knowledge in a simple way. He asked for a volunteer to represent each character and stand in a line. He then went along the line, asking for initial impressions of each character based on what they knew from the text, involving the whole group in discussion. The volunteers changed position in the line according to how they fitted in relation to each other.

For example, Steve and Archie stood next to each other because of their close relationship in the play, then Eloise and Beth stood next to each other because Eloise was chosen to show Beth around. Suggestions of ages were proposed, and volunteers stood in age order. This was then discussed. Did the group agree with the age choices? If not, why not? The idea of the exercise was not to come up with final decisions, but to get to know the characters and their relationships and to try out some choices. Anything can be changed as discussions continue and knowledge about the play deepens.

The group was asked to come up with an active tag line for each character, as an initial provocation. The play presents a complex set of characters that are neither 'good' or 'evil', and Simon referenced Peter Brook in saying that whatever character you are playing, the character has to be 'more than you'. By looking up at your character, instead of looking down on him/her, the performance will grow. If you label them as 'good' or 'bad', you limit the playing choices available and performance will be narrow. Therefore, when encouraging your company to describe characters, try to find terminology that is open, playful and active.

Simon then asked the volunteers to reorganise the line in order of status at the beginning of the play, in terms of how the character feels about themselves. What does the line look like? Does this feel right? If not, why not? Again, this is a useful starting point just to see where characters are in relation to one another.

Looking at the characters

Below are some of the character details that the group discussed during this exercise. These serve as a starting point for discussion and are by no means fixed. Make choices according to what information you can uncover in the script and what is most interesting for your company to explore.

ARCHIE   'The Governor'. Perhaps in the sixth form. Perhaps not quite as good a leader as Beth. Ben suggested it might be interesting if there was a bit of sexual tension between Beth and Archie, but only if this dynamic is useful to explore.

ELOISE   'The Rock'. Perhaps she is quite reliable and trusted within the school, hence being given the responsibility of showing Beth around. There is something quite motherly about her. She is keen to be Beth's friend. What was Eloise's role in the group before Beth came along?

BETH   'The Rebel'. Subversive, the instigator, she is the catalyst for the play, the wild card. Does she come in with the intention that she is going to stir things up? Are her actions premeditated or are they opportunistic? She is confident and outspoken and keen to involve herself in this world. She gains power and status by antagonising. Perhaps she causes chaos because she likes attention. She plants seeds. She has great leadership skills.

STEVE   'The Reluctant Deputy'. He is best mates with Archie. They have possibly been at school together for years.

MARK   'The Entrepreneur'. Has high aspirations of success. Is it an interesting choice if he is one of the youngest in the group?

TANIA   'The Romantic'. Prone to overreaction and being overly dramatic, a bit of a drama queen. She is quite emotional and interested in both classical literature and modern technology.

HUGS   'The Provocateur'. The joker of the pack. Influential. Technically capable. A bit of a shit-stirrer. He throws things into the mix just to see what happens.

CATH   *'The Critic'*. Very smart, quite critical and pragmatic. She needs a bit of convincing to go over to Beth's side. Perhaps she is not quite as confident as some of the others?

JENNY   *'The Naysayer'*. Her hacker name is a clue to her character. She is quite serious and to the point. She has a level of responsibility in the group as chairperson. She has a tendency to put a downer on things. Perhaps a bit of a cynic.

DREW   *'The Flawed Mechanic'*. Thinks he is good at DIY but perhaps not as good as he would like to be. Is he one of the younger ones?

PEZ   *'The Young Genius'*. The genuine 'geek'. He designed the throwies. Hoovers up knowledge. Loves the internet and has a natural brilliance when it comes to computers. The group relies on him a lot.

NISHA   *'The Seed'*. Individual and independent, perhaps feels she doesn't fit in. Perhaps lacking in confidence, but during the play she finds her voice and emerges.

SEB   *'The Opportunist'*. There is tension between him and Archie. Perhaps he likes to undermine in shifting allegiance to follow Beth. He seizes the moment according to where is best for him to be. A bit of a politician and a bit of a chancer, but funny with it. Perhaps he is close in age to Archie?

Casting

Ben made it clear that characters are not gender-specific and casting can be flexible according to the needs of your group. Female parts could be made male and vice versa, or it could be interesting to keep the gender of a character male and have a female playing him. Such choices will not affect the thematic heart of the play. Heather Brooke said that, in reality, most hackers were male, but Ben thought it would be more fun theatrically to offer more of a gender balance and so decided to sacrifice authenticity to engage young people across the board. The group thought that an interesting discussion to have during rehearsals might be to talk about if/how young males and females engage differently with the internet.

Production, staging and design

The play is set throughout in the single location of the Portakabin. It is a small, claustrophobic space. Emotions can become magnified and arguments intensified while news spreads like wildfire. In such a small space, the stakes are high. It is up to your company to determine how best to represent this microcosm onstage. Do you make the setting in the round? With audience on three sides? How will you create the locked door? Do you fill your playing space with 'stuff' that the hackers use in their various projects? If you are creating a naturalistic environment, how will the more expressionistic scene changes work within that?

Style, technique and language

The text could be described as 'heightened naturalism': it reflects the energy and adrenaline of teenagers. It is big and bold, 'like a fast car that likes being driven quickly'. The dialogue is rhythmic and fluid, and it is vital that the play begins with pace, energy and attack. These characters know each other well and the snappy dialogue reflects this familiarity. They have a natural rhythm together and Beth breaks this rhythm when she appears.

The more expressionistic, physical scene changes offer an exciting counterpoint to the heightened naturalism of the language. They are a visual from of theatricality that helps shift the action from scene to scene. It is important for the company to experiment with the physical language of the scene changes and how they can support the narrative.

What are throwies? How will you represent them? Why are they there? What do they represent? Apparently throwies were made in hackerspaces in the USA, and Ben thought this little bundle of LED lights was a lovely encapsulation of themes and a sweet and innocent manifestation of the hacker's dream. He talked about them being a physical manifestation of hacking and of characters that can be used in a theatrical way to explore relationships beyond the scenes themselves.

Ben encouraged the group to experiment with this physical language and to use his stage directions as a starting point. Consider how a build up of energy could be created before the play begins.

The choice of music is essential to generating the energy and tone needed to launch an audience into the play. What can the choice of music reveal about the characters and the world of the play? Ben recommended music that has a strong beat: something energetic, uplifting, repetitive.

Exercises for use in rehearsals

Simon Godwin introduced a number of exercises that could be done with the company during the rehearsal process.

INTRODUCTIONS

- Go round the circle and ask everyone to say their name and what kind of animal they feel like in that moment. This is a helpful way of allowing individuals to acknowledge and share how they are feeling which can be liberating.

WARM-UP EXERCISE 1

- Ask the group to stand in a long line. Give them a category that has lots of elements (e.g. things people have for breakfast; different types of footwear; ice-cream flavours; famous Americans). Go along the line with everyone giving examples as quickly as possible. If someone hesitates or repeats something that has already been said, they go and stand behind you in the 'sea of shame'!

WARM-UP EXERCISE 2

- Stand in a circle. Pass a single clap around the circle. Do it a couple of times until there is a steady rhythm.

- Still in the circle, send a clap to someone across the circle. That person receives the clap, then sends another one to someone else. Encourage the group to be really specific as to whom they are passing.

- When people have got to grips with this, ask them to move around the room keeping the clap alive and keeping the energy and clarity of where the clap is going.

- Clap volleyball. Split the group into two equal teams. Ask them to stand facing each other on opposite sides of the room. Ask each team to come up with a team name. Choose one person to serve. They send a single clap across to the other team, who sends it back to someone opposite with focus and direction. This continues. If there is a double clap, hesitation, or if it is not clear whom the clap is being sent to, the other team gets a point. Teams can also send a clap along their own team until someone makes the choice to send it back to the other team.

This clapping exercise is really useful to keep in mind when approaching the text. Just like the clap, the words need to be kept alive and delivered with precision, attack and focus.

CHORUS EXERCISE TO HELP WITH SCENE CHANGES

Simon asked the question, 'How do you work on the physical life with a group?'

Just inviting your company to walk in the space is a very important foundation. There you establish the seed of presence. If you can do this exercise simply but well, the world is your oyster!

- Ask the company to begin rooted, neutral and open. Ask them to find their neutral focus, a slightly lifted horizon point. Centralise the whole body and *breathe*. Bring the shoulders up and down and breathe in and out. Then shake it out.

- Very simply instruct the company to see a space and walk into it. Encourage them not to huddle in the centre, to keep heads up, jaws relaxed, and to find a neutral rhythm. Then gradually increase the speed without bumping into anyone. Be alive and precise and walk with purpose. Keep energy high. Move to a light run. Then bring the tempo down again gradually until standing. Resist the temptation to fiddle. Stand and have power. This is the foundation of everything.

• Do a stretch and raise both arms in a circle twice, then flop down, bring arms over head, knuckles on the floor. Wriggle shoulders and take deep breaths. Come up slowly to a standing point. Do a windmill motion with one arm, then the other, then both together in the same direction, then in a different direction.

• Split the group into two. Ask one half to go and sit down and observe. Ask the other half to form a huddle in the corner.

• Choose a leader who will travel forward. Everyone else is to follow in the same rhythm, copying exactly what he/she does. There will be a moment where the group will turn and find a new leader.

• Swap groups. Then feedback. What was it like to be in it? What was it like to observe?

Working with the 'throwies'

It could be useful to experiment with how the throwies might work and invest in some 'research time', where the group can play and explore to see if there are any moments that can be taken forward into rehearsal. In the workshop, the group went back to the stage directions at the beginning and then brainstormed some ideas, some of which were tried physically by volunteers in the space. The group then split into smaller groups of two or three and were asked to create a movement sequence that explored starting as individuals and coming together. They were then shown one by one. After each experiment and each showing, the group was encouraged to feedback on what was successful.

What can be learnt from each experiment? What did you appreciate? What were the challenges? Opportunities? What story is being told? Does it fit in with the narrative of the play?

For the purpose of the workshop, small balls were used to represent the throwies.

Some questions and suggestions which resulted from the brainstorm follow:

- Google 'throwies' and see exactly what they look like and what they do. There are lots of examples on YouTube. This could be a good starting point to decide what your throwies are going to look like and their function.

- Do throwies stick to surfaces? Could they be magnetic? Is this theatrically a good choice, or is it better to create something fluid and constantly moving with no end point? It might not be useful to have them sticking somewhere, because then the narrative of the throwies stops.

- Can the throwies be switched off or hidden from view?

- Are the throwies operated as if actors were puppeteers? For example, the actor's focus is on the throwie, so if they are visible, they do not pull focus from the object.

- Try the chorus exercise detailed above, but this time let the object lead. How can you fill the space with the throwies? Explore different speeds, shapes, planes and rhythms. When are they at their most dynamic?

- Could the throwies be put on sticks so there is a distance from the throwie and the operator?

- How can you show harmony and unity and chaos through the movement of the throwies?

- How can you represent the story of how the characters came together to use these lights? They were potentially loners and individuals before finding the group. Through the hackerspace, the different individuals came together and found a form. They find a sense of security and belonging that they haven't been able to find elsewhere.

- How can the throwies take on the energy/personality of the characters?

- It doesn't necessarily need a lot of movement from the operator to produce a lot of movement for the throwie.

- What effect do different movements have? Can throwies be thrown and caught? Can you create a sense of magic in terms of how throwies 'appear', 'disappear' and multiply in the space? There is potential for comedy and playfulness in terms of how the throwies interact with each other – for example, having one out of sync, or a bit late!

- What is the effect of repeated movement? What is the effect of soft/hard/jagged movements?

- There is a duality to the meaning of the throwie. There is the physical image of the object in space, but it is also reflective of a kind of code/wavelength. It is abstract but representative of something.

- The aim is to develop a physical language than can communicate meaning. The narrative you are telling needs to be simple, clear, timely and allow for accumulation and growth. It is important to remember the throwies are a vehicle for transition. They should not be isolated and disconnected from the play, but a way into and out of each scene. How can you use the throwies to get from A to B? For example, what would happen if the throwies 'gathered around' the character/object that is of focus at the beginning of the next scene?

Suggested references

Who Owns the Future? by Jaron Lanier.

In Real Life, a documentary film.

The Revolution will be Digitised by Heather Brooke.

Weaving the Web: The Original Design and Ultimate Destiny of the World Wide Web by Tim Berners-Lee.

Big Data: A Revolution that will Transform how We Live, Work and Think by Viktor Mayer-Schonberger.

www.instructables.com/id/LED-Throwies (making throwies).

www.ted.com/talks/keren_elazari_hackers_the_internet_s_immune_system (TED talk about hackers).

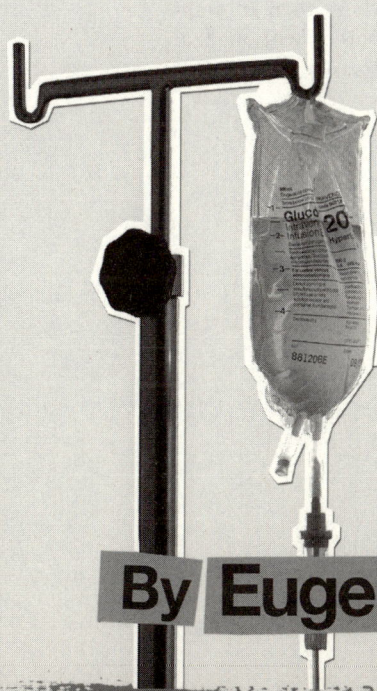

Hospital Food

By Eugene O'Hare

Set in the present day, ten teenagers from the ages of fourteen to seventeen are the residents of a teenage cancer unit in a city hospital. All of them (a mix of boys and girls) are undergoing various conventional treatments for different cancers at different stages of progression. Their shared illness bonds them and they support each other as they reveal their fears and hopes for the future while confronting, head on, the very real prospects of untimely death. The teenagers have a special room called The Retreat where they can have peer meetings without adult intrusion – a place to go where it is calm and where their thoughts can be intimated to each other without fear. What is discussed in The Retreat stays in The Retreat.

Age suitability: 15+

Cast size: 10
Occasional strong language

Eugene O'Hare was born in Ireland in 1980. He was chosen by Channel 4 from over 3,500 applicants for the 4Screenwriters placement for which he wrote the psychological thriller *Shopping for Boys*. Previous play commissions include *Refuge* for the Abbey Theatre, Dublin. He is currently adapting the 1979 cult film *Scum* for the stage alongside its original writer Roy Minton. His full-length play *Sydney and the Old Girl* goes into production in 2015 with Phillip Breen directing.

Eugene is a member of Field Day Theatre Company, founded by Brian Friel and Stephen Rea in 1980. As an actor he has performed both on and off Broadway, at the National Theatre, Royal Court, Old Vic, Tricycle, Hampstead, Abbey Theatre, Arcola, Glasgow Citzens and extensively across Ireland. He has worked on several film and television productions and created the role of Aaron Monroe in the hit BBC2 series *The Fall*. He lives in London.

Author's notes

Hospital Food is set in a modern residential teenage cancer ward. The patients are at various stages of treatment. All will have been treated by either chemotherapy, radiotherapy, surgery or combinations of all three. On the ward the patients have a special room called The Retreat. This is an association room where they can escape the 24/7 of doctors, nurses, parents, and be with and confide in one another, safe in the knowledge that everything discussed in The Retreat stays in The Retreat. That's the rule of the room.

Costume and set

T-shirts, pyjama bottoms, leggings, sweaters, slippers, socks, one or two dressing gowns, trainers, colourful headgear.

It is suggested that some of the male characters are visibly bald. For the sake of authenticity and the visual impact this will have, shaved heads, where indicated, are very much encouraged for the good of the production. But nothing is mandatory.

The Retreat is a relaxed space with colourful furniture: beanbags to sit on, a sofa on wheels, cushions, magazines, a plastic table with games, books, etc. A few colourful plastic chairs. Two hospital beds (preferably) or single beds on wheels are required for the room in which Josh and Gus share. All props and set must be taken on- and offstage by characters as part of the play. This should be choreographed fluidly and should inform the energy of the succeeding scene.

Sound

Between scenes, the steady bleep of a heart monitor is underscored with a low monotone hum like that of electrical mains. It should have a somewhat unsettling effect.

Characters

Gus, *a popular boy of fifteen. Shaved head. Receiving combination therapy for relapsed neuroblastoma and secondary brain tumour. He wears a back-to-front Yankees baseball cap to cover the bandage dressing at the top of his head and the fact that he is bald. An IV drip on a portable trolley is attached to his hand.*

Josh, *a boy of fifteen. Shaved head. Best friend and room-mate to Gus. Receiving chemotherapy, but currently on a chemo break. He has a bandage round the middle of his arm where his vascuport is fixed.*

Cain, *a boy of fourteen. He wears a bandanna. Never without his iPad. He also has a bandage round the middle of his arm.*

Sol, *a boy of fifteen. He wears a beanie over his bandaged head and a dressing gown. An advanced student of chemistry. He carries a heavy textbook and pencil.*

Joe, *a boy of fourteen. Shaved head. Always has a hankie for his constantly running nose – a side effect of his chemotherapy.*

Reece, *a boy of thirteen to fourteen. Wears a vest. Short hair/shaved head. A red rash from aggressive radiotherapy. His neck is bandaged with some plaster and gauze.*

Layna, *a girl of fifteen. Leukaemia. She wears a bright headscarf to cover her baldness and a dressing gown. She has an IV drip on a portable trolley attached to her hand.*

Elsie, *a girl of fifteen. On a crutch to help her get around. She has a tumour in her right leg. She wears a bandanna.*

Karis, *a girl of fourteen. Her head is bandaged from above her eyes which also hides her hair loss.*

Sadie, *a small girl of thirteen. She wears a tight red headscarf to cover her baldness. She wears a bunch of beaded necklaces which she designs with Karis.*

Scene One

The Retreat.

Darkness. Bare stage. After the first three 'pings' of The Killers' 'All these Things that I've Done', a soft spotlight down centre stage slowly fades up.

From the back of the stage **Gus** *very slowly walks into the light, looks up at it and then stares out front. The light slowly continues to fade up.*

He has his portable IV-drip trolley by his left side and the long tube is attached to a bandage on his left hand. The fluid bag is about three-quarters full. He is breathing slowly and deeply – we can see it in his shoulders.

After the third 'Hold on' when the bass drum starts to thud, **Gus** *looks at the fluid bag, then at his hand, then back at the fluid bag, then at the audience – it isn't an easy decision, his heart is pounding, he takes a deep breath and just when the guitar kicks in he pulls the tube out of his hand and lets it fall. He stumbles back slightly, registers the brief pain and realises the enormity of what he has done. He looks at his left hand – now free. He looks back at the audience and then, just around the 48th second of the song, quickly disappears stage right.*

On his tail the other characters are arriving from stage left. Lights fade up during this sequence but not to full strength. Lights could flash, colour could be used to accompany the characters' arrival.

They are aware of the music, its punchy rhythm – there is a vibrancy to their interaction, a playful familiar energy among them as they bring on all the furniture and props that will create The Retreat. Swiftly, in the colourful tumble of characters and props bounding on to the stage, **Josh** *whips* **Gus***'s IV drip offstage right and joins the others setting everything up. They own this space – they fill it.*

A sofa is wheeled on, cushions are dropped on it. On the 69th second of the song **Reece** *throws a bunch of flimsy magazines up in the air – he gets a kick out of them falling down around him.* **Sadie** *and* **Karis** *bring the small plastic table down centre stage left with books and beads on them. Plastic chairs arrive for them courtesy of* **Cain**. **Sadie** *puts* *beads around* **Karis***'s neck – they briefly dance together and then busy themselves with the beads at the table.*

Beanbags are dotted about, plastic chairs, cushions – perhaps even a large exercise ball to be used as a seat. A couple of beakers and a plastic jug of water are placed on the table. **Joe** *and* **Elsie** *fire a throw over the back of the sofa. They are laughing as he helps her sit down on it.* **Layna** *tidies the magazines.* **Sol** *fans the massive chemistry book, takes his pencil from his ear and sits on a beanbag making notes – still in touch with the music, as they all are.* **Cain** *ends up on the sofa next to* **Joe** *and* **Elsie***. He begins mucking about on his iPad.* **Reece** *plonks down, gets his phone out.* **Layna** *ties up the long bits of her headscarf.* **Josh** *has made his way downstage left, unzipping his hoodie and throwing it on the arm of the sofa along the way.*

With his IV drip reattached, **Gus** *enters and moves downstage right opposite* **Josh***.*

Then:

Real time. Music stops, lights full strength, bodies alert, more urgent, everybody is unsettled – trying to make sense of the news **Gus** *has just told them. The dialogue is quick-fire snappy.*

Reece   Homie what?

Gus   Opathy. It's not important it's only one of the –

Cain   Opathy?

Gus   Homeopathy. I shouldn't have even mentioned –

Reece   *What* is it?

Karis   Sol will know.

Reece (*to* **Sol**)   What's homeopathy?

Sol   It's when you stay at home all day and drink your own piss.

Karis   *What?*

Gus   Sol.

Layna   It's not.

Sol   No, drinking your own piss is probably more medicinal.

Sadie   That's dirty though, isn't it? Isn't that dirty?

Karis   Just a bit.

Reece   Is it like that thing Polly does for us?

Elsie   No, Reece, that's reflexology.

Gus   Wait, I haven't even explained –

Layna   You don't need to, cos it's a wind-up, right? This *is* one of your wind-ups? Josh, is he winding us up?

Josh shrugs. *He hopes it's a wind-up. He shuffles. Hands in pockets.*

Layna   Did you know about this?

Josh   No.

Cain   He's joking. He's not going anywhere. Are you?

Gus   It isn't a wind-up. I haven't told Josh. I haven't told anyone I'm leaving.

Sadie   But it's not for good, right? Not for ever?

A beat. A look from **Gus**.

Gus   The only people who know are me and my mum. And now you lot. And that's all. No doctors, no nurses, not my dad. Not anyone else. Just you. And that's how it's staying. Right?

Layna   Just like that, Gus? 'Nice knowin' ya, I'm just gonna sneak out of hospital now in the dead of night, hop on a plane and disappear,' and we say, what? Like – nothing?

Joe   What if you don't come back?

Gus   I'd come back if I got better.

Layna   But you . . . you can't if you went! . . . You *wouldn't* get –

Sol   Shushh, Layna!

Elsie   They'll hear you.

Josh   Stop it!

He looks his best mate straight in the eye.

Let him speak.

A few beats. **Gus** *is on the spot now.*

Gus   What is this room called?

Layna   What?

Gus   What's it called?

A beat. No one answers.

What is it called?

Elsie   The Retreat.

Gus   Right. And what's it for? This room. What's it for?

Cain   For retreating to.

Gus   Yeah.

Reece   To hang out in.

Gus   With who?

Elsie   Each other.

Gus   And do what?

Cain   Play *Angry Birds*.

Sadie   Not just that.

Joe   To talk.

Cain   Oh yeah, to talk to ourselves.

Joe   You talk to *your*self mate – I don't.

Cain   I didn't mean that.

Sol   He meant to each other. To confide.

Gus   Right. Without who?

Sadie   Old people.

Reece   Tests.

Joe   Student doctors.

Karis   Needles.

Elsie   And those annoying Z-list celebrities doing their bit for all the baldy kids.

Joe (*sarcastic*)   Gratitude.

Sol   It's The Retreat. It's our room. Patients only. What's the point of the question?

Gus   What's the point of the room?

Layna   What do you mean?

Gus   The point of having this room. What's the rule – the rule of the room?

Karis   'What we say in The Retreat –

Sadie   – will stay in The Retreat.'

Sadie and **Karis** *acknowledge their teamwork with a look.*

Gus   Golden. Golden rule. What we say in The Retreat will stay in The Retreat. I've probably been here longer than most of you; if you add up all the months I've been in and put them all together – take away my two remissions and what's left has been stuck in here – relapses, shrinkages, growths, old diagnosis, new prognosis, three Christmases, four birthdays – in and out, in and fucking out – I feel it's all I've ever known.

Since though – since I came here that's always been the rule of this room so I know I can tell you anything in here? Can't I, right? – anything. You've all sworn it, so it doesn't leave these four walls. And that's how it should always be. Otherwise nothing's ever . . . (*Searching for the word.*)

Sol   Sacred?

Gus   Right.

Elsie   It's our bond, we know that but –

Joe   If we break it, I mean if we break it, it's a –

Sadie   – betrayal.

Elsie   Alright – a betrayal. But this isn't some little secret, Gus. It's hardly easy on us to –

Gus   Easy on *you*?

Elsie   I don't mean that, I mean –

Layna   Yes – on *us*. It's up to us, just because it happens to be the rule of the room, to keep our mouths shut and sit by and watch your mom, in a . . . in a . . . fit of desperation –

Joe   Layna –

Layna   I'm sorry, but to stop your treatment, to . . . to smuggle you off to the other side of the world to live on some – what is it – alternative healing centre for crackpots?

Gus   My mum's a crackpot then, is she?

Layna   No! Look, you're on combination therapy, Gus. Who could even count how many chemo cycles you've had? I know myself when it feels like they've all just run into one. I *know*. I do. But it's medical. Its science. Proven science – tell him, Sol.

Sol (*not helping* **Layna**)   About what? He's been through more than I have.

Layna   Look, you've said it yourself already – *remission* – you've been in remission before. That's because of your treatment here. It's why you're still with us. Why we're all still making it. You think spirituality, homeopathy, and . . . and what else do they offer? Let me guess, crystals – crystal healing and shark-fin frigging soup – you reckon this is a step up? The rest of us just kidding ourselves staying here, are we?

Maybe we should all pack our toothbrush and jump on the plane with you.

Josh   Leave him.

Layna   No, Josh! You're his best friend – this is ridiculous. He's said nothing to you about this?

Josh   I've told you already, no.

Layna   Then talk him out of it!

A beat.

Well, go on.

A few beats. **Josh** *looks at* **Gus**.

Gus   He can't.

Layna *sits down, exasperated.* **Josh** *drifts upstage,* **Gus** *watching him.*

Reece   My mouth is burning.

Gus*, as he continues to speak, pours water for* **Reece** *and gives it to him.* **Reece** *drinks.*

Gus   You're my mates in here. Think of the worst things we've gone through – who we've lost. But we look after each other, you know? Some of you've told me stuff in this room and I'd never breathe a word of it. You know who you are. I wouldn't breathe it. Even if my life depended on it. Only reason I was worried about telling you I was leaving is cos I thought you'd get upset.

Karis   We will be if you go.

Layna   Of course we will be! We *are*!

Gus   I know. But I weren't worried that by telling you –

Sol   We'd end up telling them?

Gus   Yeah.

Sol   Well, we won't.

Some of them look at him.

Nothing leaves this room. No matter how big. Like you say, we've sworn it. So we won't.

Layna *now looks at* **Sol**.

Sol   Will we?

Elsie *(reluctantly)*   No.

Cain   Nobody will.

Sadie   Nobody.

Gus   They'd tell my dad – he'd stop it. Lawyers. Judges even. They'd all stop it. Mum says they would.

Layna   But not even being able to tell your dad – do you get how totally messed up all this sounds?

Gus   He'd only stop us to get one over on Mum. He's a prick, you know that. Anyway, he's got his own family now, he doesn't need to know.

Joe   He's your dad but . . .

Gus   Yeah, Joe. And when was the last time you saw him up here? Before they had to cut my head open or after it?

A beat.

Reece   My grandma says she can't visit me any more because she can't cope.

A beat.

But our Tom reckons it's because she has to wear big nappies now and she's too embarrassed to leave the house.

Cain *tries to stifle a snigger and* **Reece** *laughs – although he knows he shouldn't. It breaks the tension.*

Gus   This place, guys. This place I'm going to . . . it's . . . My mum's not gonna bring me somewhere that's gonna make me more sick. She's not gonna do that to me. She'd die instead of seeing . . . you know? She's not gonna . . .

Joe   Are they like faith-healers, then, these people?

Gus   Kind of. Probably. Some of them probably, yeah – I think.

Elsie   Kind of? Probably? Probably definitely maybe.

Sadie   My Irish auntie on my dad's side – she said the Holy Ghost lowered her cholesterol.

Joe   Yeah, I hear he's good at that.

Sol (*to* **Gus**)   They ban all conventional medicine?

Gus   They're getting results by using like a hundred other things that just don't happen to be chemotherapy.

Layna   If it was true we'd know about it.

Karis   We'd be there.

Sol   Governments don't get into bed with faith-healers and sugar-pill peddlers.

Cain (*to* **Reece**)   What's he mean?

Reece *shrugs.*

Gus   People worse than me have been there and they've gone into remission.

Josh (*almost out of nowhere*)   People crash and burn and then they rise up again.

A beat as some of them look back at him.

It happens all the time.

He puts his hoodie on and pulls the hood up as he wanders back up stage.

Sadie   You remember that healer Danny B's parents brought in that day?

Elsie   Oh don't, Sadie.

Cain   He wasn't a healer he was a fuckin' mentalist.

Sol   Or evangelist. Same thing.

Karis   I wasn't here when Danny B was. What happened?

Reece   You don't wanna know. We shared a room. They asked me to leave.

Karis   Who?

Reece   His mum and dad, when they came into our room – this mad-looking bastard with them. He was proper scary looking – weren't he, Cain?

Cain   Proper. Eyes like a frog. Sweaty like a frog too.

Joe   It was an exorcism.

Karis   What, like in the film?

Elsie   They thought cancer was a demon inside him.

Karis   A demon?

Cain   Or a witch or something.

Sadie   It was horrible.

Reece   I looked through the crack in the door. His mum and dad just stood there holding hands and watched it.

Joe   Arseholes.

Reece   The mad fella was covering him in oil. Pressing down on him. Hurting him. Rubbing his hands all over his face. When Danny started screaming that's when everyone ran in.

Joe   Security guys had to kick the bloke out.

Elsie   I hope they kicked his bollocks down every street on the Monopoly board.

Joe   Nice.

Karis   *Was* he nice – Danny B?

Sadie   Lovely. Kind of smiley – like all the time. Apart from that time.

Reece   When he first came in his mum bought all these Spiderman pyjamas for him like he was six or something.
I gave him my Raiders hoodie and he kept it zipped up. I let him keep it. He was still wearing it when he had his last sleep.

Sadie   For our remembering night we had popcorn and ice cream in here. Didn't we?

Joe   Yeah.

Cain   We watched *Jurassic Park III*.

Reece   It was pants.

Sadie   Didn't really watch it though. We just sort of talked about Danny B till way late.

A few beats.

If your mum doesn't change her mind, when will you have to go?

Gus   Any day now.

Reece   What, like tomorrow?

Gus   Could be – might be.

A general stir.

I don't know. She'll tell me when. I have to keep my phone on. It could be any time.

Layna *stands up. Fiddles with the tube.*

Reece   If we have a remembering night for you like we had for Danny B, what movie do you want us to watch?

Sol   Reece.

Reece   What?

Sol   Really.

Josh *has had enough. He leaves the room stage left.* **Gus** *stands.*

Gus (*gently*)   You choose.

He peruses **Josh**. *A few beats.*

Reece   I probably shouldn't have said that, should I?

Layna *leaves stage right. A silence.*

Reece   I'm such a dick.

Lights down as sound comes up – the electrical hum with the heart monitor beeping over the top. Everyone leaves. Some of the props and set are removed so that all that remains is the sofa, a couple of beanbags, a few books on the plastic table and one plastic chair. The Retreat is in darkness.

Scene Two

A corridor.

Immediately after the last scene. A sharp strip of light across the front of the stage. **Josh** *enters from stage left, his hood still up. He gets just a little over halfway when* **Gus** *enters stage left.*

Gus   Josh!

Josh   I've got physio, I'll be late.

Gus   You haven't, so you won't.

Josh *stops. Turns. Pulls his hood back.*

Gus   I know how often you take a piss, mate. You think I don't know when you got physio?

A beat.

Josh   Why didn't you tell me on my own? I'm supposed to be the brother you never had. You tell family something like this first.

Gus   Yeah, I know.

Josh   Well, why did you have to tell me in front of everyone else? I felt like shit in there.

Gus   I know you did.

Josh   Like we were all just sort of kettled in together for the big news.

Gus   I didn't want to go through it twice. I didn't know how to explain it the first time.

Josh   Still don't make no sense. Not to me anyway.

Gus   Yeah.

A beat.

Josh   It's a fucking hospital, you know?

Gus   Yeah.

Josh   The place you go when you're –

Gus   Yeah, right.

Josh   It's a fucking . . .

A few beats.

Gus   I'm sorry –

Josh   I mean if you want ice cream you go to a freezer, you see what I'm saying? It might sound simple but –

Gus *gives an outward breath of a laugh.*

Josh   Don't laugh. Not now.

Gus   I wasn't. Sorry. Just the way you say things.

Josh   Can't say things other than how they are.

Gus   Um.

A beat.

Josh   Has your mum lost her fucking deck?

Gus *half shrugs. A few beats as* **Josh** *calms.*

Josh   You know my dad only learnt how to use the internet because I was diagnosed. He was prehistoric before that. But once he typed in Google, well – he was gone, tearing through cyberspace like a thing possessed. He musta typed in the word cancer a million times. That and big tits. He's definitely typed in big tits. When he does his two daily visits to me I wonder if one visit's for me and the other one's for him to get a perve at Nurse Barbara's double Gs.

But mainly he went all Google crazy because he refused – refused to believe – that a hospital was the only place I could be cured, ye know? That there was something out there – some miracle – somewhere – out there. Maybe it was hiding in a Brazilian monastery or the Chinese had it. Yeah, what was it? – Chinese pearl barley – he was buying that up in bulk. Selenium tablets, powdered grass. I think he even mentioned a coffee enema at one point – I nearly decked him. And apricots. Christ. I were shitting apricots for days before he finally gave it a rest. Then came the conspiracy theories – how all the big pharmas were suppressing a cure. Well, that went on for a coupla months. Eventually he calmed down a bit though. Learned to . . . breathe a bit, ye know? And let them get on with it. Let me get on with it.

I'm saying it cos . . . ye know . . . ?

They do go a bit mental too . . . dads, mums. Sometimes at the start they're calm. Doesn't faze 'em almost. Cos he's not gonna die from it – my Josh? Fuck that, Doctor Jones, out of the question – my Josh? *Mine*?

Some go mental at the start and then calm towards the end. Others, well, it's the other way round – or they go up and down or who knows what way – different people – different ways.

But they all go a bit mental at some point. Hardly blame 'em. They feel it inside as well. Just not near as much as we do . . . but they *want* to – they *want* to feel it – what we feel. All of it.

They want to feel the same and share it. All the pain, the shitting, the vomiting – the *fear*. And carry some of it, like, *with* you. Together. *With* you. Ye know?

A few beats.

Gus   Your hair's growing back.

A beat.

Josh   Bits of it. Yeah.

Gus   And you're moving quicker.

Josh   Well, I'm on chemo break. You know what it's like – feeling almost alive for a while till they plug you back in again.

Gus   Hospital food.

Josh   Wha?

Gus *touches his IV bag.*

Gus   Hospital food. Chemo in a bag. Poisoning us just to keep us alive. Looks clean though, doesn't it? That's the thing, it looks so, so *clean*. Like water from a spring.

Josh   Do you actually *wanna* live, Gus?

Gus   I wanna be *alive*.

Josh   Same thing.

Gus   Different.

Josh   Same thing.

Gus   Different.

A beat.

Different.

A very short beat.

Mum's gone off her head? Maybe she has, who knows?

Josh   It wasn't meant to be an insult –

Gus   I know. But maybe she has. Maybe I'm all swept up in her . . . *mania* . . . her enthusiasm. I don't care if I am.

She can't stop touching me lately – Mum. Keeps stroking my face, kissing my hands. She says she never thought she could love me any more than *total* love but that she does now. 'As madly as the sun burns,' she says.

A few beats.

She's not sleeping. Just planning, planning. Planning.

Our big escape.

Writing every chapter of it before it even happens. I think if I had a brother or a sister she'd be less . . . you know? She could divide it up maybe . . . the love. Be a little less . . . in*tense* – I don't know. Do ye know what I . . . what I mean?

Josh   Yeah.

Gus   Like it would be . . . yeah. Less intense.

A beat.

I don't wanna just *live*, Josh – not like I'm living now – not like I'm gonna keep living – I wanna be *alive*. Just for a bit. Just be alive for a bit. All these things Mum has planned – this clinic in the States, this new life, these . . . therapies, prayers – whatever they are – if they don't work I'll do them for her anyway. Anything she wants. But I'll be free for *me*. You get me? Do you see what I mean?

A beat.

I keep dreaming of those few seconds – you know it, those seconds? – when the plane finally gets out of the clouds and you look down and you're above them all? Right up above them? I can hear the motor of the engine in my dream and I'm looking out the window just looking down at them – a mad white floor of clouds and it looks so solid – like there's no danger – like I could go take a walk on it – but it's not that kind of dream – it's a *real dream*. And I fall asleep on the plane but when I waken – the floor of clouds – it's still there – and we're still moving above it and we're still escaping everything below it. We're still moving . . . still fucking moving!

Josh *moves closer.*

Josh   Yeah. I know.

Gus   Do you see?

Josh   Yes.

Gus   I'm sick of being sick, mate. I'm sick of feeling trapped, attached to this fucking thing – I'm sick of feeling *sore*. I'm spending so much time with my head in the toilet – getting dizzy with it – and everything, *everything* is sore. My skin, my fingertips, my lips, the skin on my back, the heels of my feet are hot. I waken some days feeling like I'm up to my neck in warm cement – but not poured over my body – poured *into* it – poured into it – into my body – from the inside of my big toe right up through to the inside of my mouth. You hear me some mornings when they're all round me – about seven of them all just trying to get me to breathe, to breathe, to keep on fucking breathing like it's the easiest thing in the world –

Josh   It's not –

Gus   Cos I understand – I understand, see? – I'm like maybe three of us, no four of us, on this ward who really *understands* their diagnosis: understands it, *accepts* it. Relapsed neuroblastoma – secondary brain tumour to boot – brain tumour they can't shift, *they* can't shrink, and *I* can't scream out. I tried. One night, in bed, screaming inside of my head to scream the fuckin' tumour out – I actually thought I could do it – I could go inside my own head and scream it out. You were asleep right across the room from me – I were screaming inside of my head and I was looking at you – but then I thought – what if it works? – what if it works and I can scream this tumour out of my head? I'd still have here to do . . .

He points to his abdomen.

Gus And here –

He quickly takes **Josh**'s *hand puts it all along his left side.*

Gus And here –

He puts **Josh**'s *hand all along his right side.*

Gus And here –

He puts **Josh**'s *hand all along his chest.*

Gus And I can't scream that loud, so I started laughing. Laughing! Looked at you fast asleep there, across from me – across the room – and I just started laughing – out loud – and you turned in your sleep when you heard me – and I put my hand over my mouth to stop it but I don't think I did – I don't think I could – I think I just fell asleep that night laughing. That night – that fucking night – laughing, laughing my fucking arse off and *screaming* from the inside of my head!

Josh *forcefully takes* **Gus** *in a firm embrace. Calms him. A long silence. Slowly they come out of the embrace.* **Gus** *recovers.*

Gus I'm the one who usually hugs you.

Josh Yeah, well.

He takes a king-size Snickers bar from his pocket. Opens it and takes a bite. A beat.

Gus Don't I have a mouth?

Josh *checks that* **Gus** *has a mouth.*

Josh Oh yeah.

Gus Greedy tit.

Josh *breaks off half and gives it to* **Gus**. *They eat.* **Gus** *in small bits, finding difficulty swallowing. A long silence.*

Josh You'll be happier, will you . . . ? If you go?

Gus I'm not exactly Coco the Clown at the minute, am I?

Josh Everyone loves you in here. Life and soul and all that.

Gus   It's just a mask I wear. When you're too long in a place you forget to take the mask off. Playing the fun guy, the prankster – whatever – it becomes easier. Leave the mask on too long and you forget what you look like underneath.

Josh   What do you look like underneath?

Gus   Just normal, I think. I don't know. You forget. Forget what you were like before all of this. You sort of just become *who* you are because of *where* you are and how *sick* you are. You forget.

A few beats.

Are you eating all the chocolate off first?

Josh   Yeah. Makes it last longer. And since you took my other half, ye bastard.

Gus   Can't barely eat it. Throat's on fire.

Josh   You want water?

Gus   I'm alright for a minute.

A beat.

Josh   Who am I gonna talk to?

Gus   When?

Josh   When you go?

Gus   Me.

Josh   How?

Gus   Do you *know* what year we're in, brick brain? We got FaceTime, we got Skype . . .

Josh   Yeah, I know. Not the same though, is it?

A beat.

When you're going – when your mum gives you the signal . . . I don't want you to tell me.

Gus   Why not?

Josh   I just don't want to see you. I don't want to see you go. I don't know why.

Gus   Okay.

Josh   Okay?

Gus   Yeah.

A beat.

Josh   Is that weird?

Gus   No.

Josh   You sure? Doesn't sound like . . .

Gus   I'm sure –

Josh   But call me after. When you've gone.

Gus   I will.

Josh   Give it a few days first and then call me.

Gus   Okay.

Josh   Okay.

Gus   Okay.

A few beats.

Josh   I, erm . . .

Gus   What?

A very short beat.

Josh   You gonna go through the goods lift?

Gus   Yeah.

Josh   And then the basement floor on to Severton Road?

Gus   Yeah.

A beat.

Josh   By the John Peel pub?

Gus   Yeah. Mum'll be waiting there.

A beat.

Josh   You know when?

Gus   This week. End of, probably. Few days yet though, Josh.

Josh   Okay.

A beat.

Gus   Few days.

Josh   Yeah.

A beat.

How you gonna do the goods lift without passing the nurses' station?

Gus   You know that door at the back of the schoolroom?

Josh   Yeah?

Gus   Leads right through. So you pass the double doors and you're at the lift out back. Right in front of it . . . Sol stole the key for me.

Josh   Did he already know you were going?

Gus   No. I just begged a favour a few days ago and he stole it for me. Didn't even ask me why I wanted it. He's always in that schoolroom – swotting away. He's gonna be a science professor.

Josh   You reckon?

Gus   Yeah. He lugs those big books around – you've seen him. Doesn't bother with an iPad much. Likes *the weight of information in his hands*, he says. He says he likes *thumbing* them.

Josh   Thumbing? Thumbing what?

Gus   Books.

Josh   Bit weird.

Gus   Yeah.

A beat.

He's sound though, Sol.

Josh   Yeah.

Gus   So you can talk to him too. If you ever need to.

Josh   Um.

Gus   You know? . . . If I'm not –

Josh   Yeah.

Gus   And Layna – you can talk to her.

Josh   God.

Gus   What?

Josh   She'll probably slit her wrists when you go.

Gus   Piss off.

Josh   Yeah she will. She's mental about you.

Gus   She's mental alright. But she's good to me. Just a bit highly strung, that's all.

Josh   Yeah. Just a bit. Hates me.

Gus   No, she doesn't.

Josh   She does.

Gus   Why?

Josh   Cos I'm always with you, aren't I? Joined at the hip's what she says.

Gus   Jealous.

Josh   You reckon?

Gus   Yeah. She's just jealous of us, mate. Take no notice.

Josh   I don't.

A beat.

I was thinking, earlier, when we were in there – in The Retreat – and everyone was talking and everything was all a bit, like, fucking, mad, you know?

Gus   Yeah?

Josh   Well, I was thinking, the way you do . . .

Gus   About what?

Josh   I dunno, I was thinking, what to say to you, I mean what I'd say to ye if, you know – if you really went – if you'd really gone – and I couldn't persuade you to stay . . .

Gus   Yeah?

Josh   I was thinking about what I'd want to say to you and how I wouldn't want it to be something I wished I'd have said if I'd gone back in time. Ye know what I mean?

A beat.

Gus   What did you wanna say?

Opens his mouth. Trying to find the words.

Josh   Um . . .

Gus   Go on.

Josh   Um . . .

Frustrated.

Fucking *chemo-brain*, not now.

Gus   Take your time.

Josh   I can't . . .

Gus   Don't worry about it –

Josh Find the, uh, think of the . . . uhhh . . . words. I can't
. . . fuck sake! . . . Uhhhhh . . .

The sound of the electrical hum begins, but without the bleeping. **Gus**
watches **Josh** *trying to put his thoughts together, failing further with
each second, his mind fogging over.*

Josh To be something I'd have wished I'd said . . .
Uhhhh . . To be something I'd have uhhhh . . . to say – yes –
uhhhh . . . nothing's . . . not . . . I, um . . . fuck . . . I can't
find . . . I'll start again . . . ehhhh . . . Let me just get my
uhmmm . . .

Lights begin to fade.

To say . . . to to to to to to say . . . Uhhhhh, could . . .
ummmm . . . to say . . . to to you . . . to say to you that . . .
that that I . . . I couldn't? Can't – no couldn't – couldn't?
Yeah . . . ummmm . . . find the ehhhh . . . fuck . . .

The bleeping now begins over the hum, growing in volume. Lights fading.

That that that . . . if you, if you, *go* that if you . . . that that if
you . . . that if you, go . . . if if you, go . . . that if you go . . . if
you go . . .

Darkness. Sound continues.

Scene Three

The Retreat.

Lights up as sound fades. Later that day. **Layna**, **Sol** *and* **Elsie** *are
centre stage left.* **Sol** *is sitting on the left arm of the sofa,* **Elsie** *in a
plastic chair, her crutch by her side.* **Sadie** *is on a beanbag centre stage
right. She is preoccupied with her hand. She has lost her jewellery. She
threads a new necklace with her plastic beads which she dips into from a
box beside her. She half listens to the conversation.*

Layna You gave him a *key* to it?!

Sol   Yes. He asked for the key so I –

Layna   So you just gave it to him, did you?

Sol   He asked for the key.

Elsie   What key?

Sol   He *asked* for the key, so –

Layna   So he just gave it to him. He just gave him the bloody key.

Elsie   What key?

Layna   Just like that. No questions. He just gave him the key.

Sol   Well, why wouldn't I? It's Gus. What's he gonna use it for? I didn't think about it.

Elsie   He gave a key to Gus?

Layna   Yes – keep up, Elsie.

Sol (*to* **Elsie**)   Back door of the schoolroom.

Elsie   Oh. Goods lift?

Layna   Yes.

Elsie   What did you do that for?

Sol   Cos he asked me.

Layna   After he asked you to put your hand in the fire?

Sol   What?

Elsie   Well, he needs a safe way out – if he has to go – he's not gonna deliberately get caught, is he?

Layna   Don't side with him, Elsie.

Elsie   With who?

Layna   With Gus. Don't start bloody siding with him now.

Sol   Who's on the other side then? You?

Layna   It's not like that.

Elsie   What's it like then?

Layna   'What's it like then?' she says.

Elsie   Yeah, what's it like?

A beat.

We're not *all* not upset he's made this decision, Layna? Just you who's upset, is it? Just you upset he's going?

Layna   No one's going anywhere.

A beat. **Sol** *stands.* **Sadie** *hears.*

Sol   What are you saying?

Layna   What?

She looks around. **Sadie** *is busying herself with her beads again.*

Sol   What are you saying?

Layna   Nothing.

A beat. **Layna** *fiddles with her IV tube.*

Elsie   That you're gonna tell?

Layna (*feigned innocence*)   Who? That I'm gonna tell who?

Sol   You. You're gonna tell on him? You're gonna betray him? You're gonna stop him? You're gonna betray him? (*To* **Elsie**.) Do you hear this?

Elsie *manages to get up off the chair.*

Elsie   She's just angry. She's tired. Come on, I'll take you for a lie down.

Layna   Lie down?! Lie *down*? You think I can *sleep*?! You're all sending him off to his death and I'm just supposed to lie down?

As they continue to speak, **Sadie** *gets up, looks under the beanbag, then under the sofa and scans the floor around her before she sits back down again. She constantly fiddles with the third finger of the right hand.*

Sol   To his death?

Layna   What else is it, Sol? He doesn't stand a chance if he leaves here.

Sol   He doesn't stand a chance either way!

He drops his book. A beat. Picks it up. Silence.

Layna   What?

Sol   Don't play dumb.

A beat.

Elsie   Have a nap, come on.

Layna   Nap? What do I want a nap for?

Elsie   Fair enough.

Layna (*to* **Sol**)   What do you mean, Sol?

Sol   I mean use your fucking intelligence, Layna.

Elsie   He's just said fuck for the first time probably in his whole life so listen to him. Please.

A beat.

Sol   He's not well. He's really not well.

Layna *sits on the sofa, pretending not to hear.*

Sol   He's not well in the same way that we . . . (*Checking* **Sadie** *can't hear.*) that *we* might have a chance at being well. He has *no* chance. I'm not stupid. And you're not stupid. Let him go.

Layna *rests her head on her knees. A silence.* **Sadie** *spreads her hand out in front of her face. Touches the bare fingers.*

Elsie   We're all too focused on each other's chances. It's an ugly fixation. It's not right. Every time there are ten people in the room I'm looking around to see which two are screwed — and I'm never looking at myself.

Layna   I can't let him go.

Sol   Why, because you love him?

Layna   No!

Sol   It's okay to say you do.

Layna   I don't . . . *know*! I don't know! I just want to keep him here so he can be saved.

Sol   He can't. He's terminal.

Layna   He's not.

Elsie   He might be.

Sol   He's terminal. I'm telling you. He's terminal.

Layna   That's not true.

Sol   It's got to be. There's nothing else to explain —

Overlapping:

Elsie   Him taking off —

Sol   Last minute —

Layna   He can't be —

Sol   He has to —

Elsie   You can't betray him, Layna, either way —

Layna   One more cycle —

Elsie   No, it's the rule of the room —

Layna   That's all he needs —

Sol   He needs to get out —

Layna   He'll be fine after just *one* more —

Elsie   No more nothing – Listen to Sol –

Sol   You're gonna betray him cos you love him?

Layna   What?

Elsie   You can't, Layna. What we say in The Retreat –

Layna   Betray? Betray what? –

Sol   – will stay in The Retreat –

Elsie   Friendship – you can betray friendship –

Sol   As an act of love – it doesn't make sense. Tell her –

Layna   What doesn't?

Elsie   Friendship – betraying it – as an act of love –

Layna   I feel sick –

Sadie   Can someone help me find my silver ring? –

Sol   Betraying a friendship as an act of love –

Elsie   That doesn't work. It doesn't work like that. It doesn't add up –

Layna   That's not what I'm trying to –

Elsie   You are –

Sol   You're gonna smother him with love he doesn't even know about?

Layna   What?

Elsie   He wants to be with his mother –

Sol   You gonna smother him and stop him from being with his mother?

Elsie   Think about it, Layna!

Sol   Who are you gonna tell?

Layna   Doctor Ling.

Elsie Ling?

Layna Yes – Doctor Ling.

Sol Doctor Ling – she's gonna tell Doctor Ling.

Sadie It's white gold, not silver, a tiny stone on the top of it –

Elsie He'd hate you.

Sadie Can you help me find it?

Sol Gus wouldn't hate you – he'd more than hate you – he'd never forgive you –

Elsie You'd betray everyone in this room –

Sadie It's small but if we looked for it –

Layna My stomach's churning –

Sol Tell him you love him and say goodbye –

Layna What?

Sadie We could find it if we looked –

Elsie Tell him you love him and say goodbye –

Sadie Together –

Sol Tell him, just tell him you love him and say goodbye!

Elsie Tell him, Layna, just tell him, just tell him, just tell him!

Layna GET OUT!

Sadie *hides behind the beanbag. A few beats.*

Layna Get out! Get out. Get out. Please, Elsie, please. Just leave me . . . Sol, please . . . Just leave me for a while.

Sol *and* **Elsie** *leave.* **Layna***, exhausted, rests her head on her knees. After a pause,* **Sadie** *takes off one of her beaded necklaces and goes to* **Layna***. She sits down beside* **Layna** *and rubs her back.* **Layna** *looks up.*

Layna   Sadie.

Sadie   Here. It's for good luck.

She gives **Layna** *the plastic beaded necklace.*

Layna   Thank you.

Sadie   Have you still got the letter?

A beat.

Layna   Yes.

Sadie   You didn't rip it up?

Layna   No.

Sadie   You didn't show it to anyone?

Layna   No.

Sadie   Are you still going to give it to Doctor Ling? You still gonna tell Doctor Ling about Gus leaving?

A beat.

Layna   No.

A beat.

Sadie   So, Gus can go? Nobody's gonna tell?

A beat. **Layna** *stares at the beads.* **Sadie** *stands up and moves stage left.*

Layna   Would you forgive me?

Sadie   If what?

Layna   If I told something you made me promise not to?

Sadie   In this room? (*Considers.*) Depends what happens after. Probably, though, forgive you, after a while.

Layna   Would Gus?

Sadie   Are you going to then?

Layna   I have to, Sadie. I have to save him. I have to break the rule.

Sadie   But you swore. We all did. What we say in the room will stay –

Layna   In the room – Yes, I know – that stupid fucking phrase – but I have to! I have to. Nobody will ever speak to me again and I don't care but I have to.

She puts her head down, upset.

Sadie   He might already be gone before you do.

Layna   I'll tell tonight.

Sadie   *Tonight?*

Layna   I will. I'll tell Nurse Barbara when she comes on the late shift. She won't say it was me.

Sadie *puts the beads around* **Layna**'*s neck.* **Layna** *holds* **Sadie**'*s hand briefly.* **Sadie** *makes to go stage left. She stops. Turns.*

Sadie   We had a German Shepherd the whole time I was growing up. His name was Ruben. My dad got him as a baby a bit before I was born so he was kind of the same age as me when we were kids. He never strayed from us. He was always there. We had to move his kennel just outside my bedroom window because that was where he slept at night. Even when it was pouring down – he would just lie there in the rain just underneath my windowsill, so we had to move his kennel there. So he could sleep. And be dry.

Before I got my diagnosis, and I had to move in here, just a couple of months before, Ruben kept disappearing in the morning times. He'd started digging a hole behind the hawthorn bushes at the back of our house. Dad got a metal detector to see if there was something buried in it but we couldn't find anything. We kept covering the hole up but every morning Ruben would be there – at it again – digging and digging behind the bushes where nobody could see him.

A few days after I came in here Ruben went missing. At first my dad couldn't find him but then when he checked properly behind the hawthorn bushes . . . well. Dad said maybe Ruben knew for a while that he'd be dead soon because that's why he'd been digging that hole all those months – out of sight from everyone else – so as he could lie in it and the rain'd wash the soil in on top of him and nobody would have to bother with him that way.

He wanted to do it on his own. He didn't . . . he didn't want to die in front of us. He didn't want us to see. See?

A few beats. **Layna** *looks at her, hard.* **Sadie** *starts to leave, looking at the floor around her.*

Sadie   I keep losing the ring my gran bought me for my twelfth birthday. It used to fit on my third finger just so snug but now it keeps slipping off. I keep losing it. It's ever so tiny.

If you find it will you save it for me?

Layna *gives a slight nod.*

Sadie   Thanks. I'm tired again. I'm always tired now.

She makes to go again then stops.

Good thing I like sleeping though, isn't it?

Layna   What?

Sadie   Sleeping. I asked Nurse Barbara on Tuesday that when I die will it just be like having a sleep except I don't have any dreams any more. And she said yeah – but it'll be an even deeper sleep than the deepest sleep I can ever even remember having. Even deeper than the one I had just before I was born. So that's alright, I suppose. It'll be so deep that I won't even know if I want to waken up from it or not. So that's alright then. I suppose.

She exits. **Layna** *stares after her, turning a single bead between her fingers. Lights fade on her as the sound comes up to accompany the scene change.*

Scene Four

Joe's bed.

*The Retreat is cleared. A beanbag and **Joe**'s hospital bed stage left. The right side of the stage is dark. **Joe**, **Reece** and **Karis** are sitting on the bed. **Cain** is on the beanbag. Behind the bed, out of sight, is a large backpack, jogging bottoms, a hoodie, a scarf and trainers.*

Reece   I went into the schoolroom after lunch to borrow a pen.

Joe   What for?

Reece   To write something.

Joe   Write what?

Reece   A letter.

Karis   Which one?

Reece   You what?

Karis   Which one? A – B – C . . . F?

Reece   Not one of those letters, you tosser – a *proper* letter.

Karis   Oh yeah?

Cain   Who to?

Reece   Doesn't matter, nosey arse. I went into –

Joe   To borrow a pen, yes – go on, Reece.

Reece   And Sadie was there on her own, crying.

Karis *makes to get up.*

Karis   I'll find her.

Reece   No, don't.

Karis *hesitates.*

Reece   She said not to tell anyone.

Karis   What do you mean, not tell anyone? What was wrong with her?

Cain   She's had news, hasn't she?

Reece   No – can't have. Her mum and dad would come if she had news. Wouldn't they?

Joe   Course they would. What was wrong with her?

Reece   I don't know. She wouldn't tell me. I just got the pen and left.

Karis   Its cos she's getting thin.

Cain   Thin?

Karis   Yeah – she's been beating herself up about it. She says when she were ten she would look at magazines and wish she were thinner but now she wished she'd never wished it at all because she's losing weight so fast and she can't control it. She thinks her clothes are hanging on her. She's so sweet – I do love her. She made me these beads.

Cain   What did you write?

Reece   Eh?

Cain   With your pen –

Reece   Oh that. Postcard with Margate beach on the front.

Joe   Margate?

Reece   Yeah. I found it under my pillow and there was nothing written on it so Nurse Barbara gave me a stamp and told me to send it off somewhere – so I posted it this afternoon.

Karis   Where did you post it to?

Reece   Here. Posted it here. Stupid, innit?

A beat.

Joe   You posted it *here*?

Reece   Yeah.

Joe   To this hospital?

Reece   Yeah.

Joe   To who?

Reece   What?

Joe   To who?

Reece   To who?

Joe   Yes, to who?

Karis   Yourself?

Reece   No. To Gus. Wishing him a safe flight.

A beat.

Cain   You utter knob!

Karis   I don't be*lieve* you!

Reece   What?!

Karis   Are you totally stupid?!

Reece   What do you mean?

Joe   Christ Almighty –

Cain   *I'm* stupid – I know I'm stupid – but that's brilliant stupid –

Joe   What if they read that bloody card before he leaves?

Reece   Who?

Cain   *Who?*

Karis   The people who get at it in the postroom, you dick.

Cain   And then Nurse Barbara – she checks all the post before she hands it out.

Reece   She's not gonna *read* it!

Joe   It's got no fucking envelope round it you pillock – it's human nature to read it.

Karis   Everyone reads postcards! Postmen, the lot – they all read 'em.

Cain   You're a fucking joke you are, Reece.

Joe   Gus is going nowhere if they see that.

Reece   They won't see it.

Cain   How do you know?

Reece   I'll stop it. I'll call the sorting office.

Karis   This gets better.

Reece   Can't I do that?

Joe   No, mate. You can't. Your best bet is it gets lost in the post.

Reece   Fuck sake.

Cain   Knob.

Reece   I wrote stuff on it though. Will they read *all* of it?

Joe   What stuff?

Reece   Stuff about being a mate and all that –

Karis   All what?

Reece   Just *stuff*. I don't know – I told him that cancer – that it *destroys* things, ye know?

Joe   Bet that was news to him –

Reece   I meant it though. I said that it destroys things – like bodies and people and stuff but that it can't destroy things like friends – friendship – that only friends can destroy friendship.

A beat.

Cain   That must be the grimmest, most depressing postcard anyone would ever want to get through their letterbox – that's all I'm saying.

Reece   No, it's not!

Cain   Come on! The worst postcard ever: Monday morning, cock crows, check your post – oh, I've got a postcard from Margate. Let's read it: 'Cancer can't destroy friendships – only *friends* destroy friendships'? What a cheerful start to the week.

Karis   Ease off him.

Reece   Yeah – don't take the piss. I meant all of that. Meant every word of it.

Joe   Who posted it for you?

Reece   Nurse Gemma when she was coming off shift. She said she passes a red box on her way home. Fuck sake.

Joe   Bloody hell, Reece.

A beat.

Reece   I hope it gets lost in the post now, I do.

Joe   Don't worry – postman'll read it and go, 'Nah, nobody needs to read this shit today,' and he'll chuck it in a bin when he's doing his rounds.

Reece   You reckon?

Joe   Yeah. Course he will.

Cain   Course he will. Course. Fuckin' hell, Reece.

A beat.

Karis   What stamp did she give you?

Reece   What do you mean?

Karis   Nurse Barbara. What stamp? First or second class?

Reece   Second.

Karis   Right.

Joe   He's got two days then.

Karis   Royal Mail second class, Joe? – He's got at least three days. At the least.

Joe   Probably, yeah.

A beat.

Reece   Was it wrong when I asked him about what movie we should watch when we remember him – when I asked Gus that? Was it wrong to ask him?

Karis   A bit. Yeah. We only have Remember Nights when someone's actually died.

Cain   Layna stormed out after you asked that.

Joe   She was only doing it cos Josh stormed out before her.

Karis   Josh. Bloody Josh. Can anyone actually speak to Josh?

Cain   Nobody can. Not really. Apart from Gus.

· **Joe**   If Gus goes we'll have to look after him.

Cain   Who?

Joe   Josh, you ninny. Josh. That's who we're talking about isn't it?

Cain   Yeah – sorry. I'm feeling sick.

Karis   Are you?

Cain   Yeah. Down here.

Joe   Vomit sick or normal sick?

Cain   Normal. I'm alright. Calm down. I'm not gonna boke all over your sheets, Joe.

Joe   You'd better not, sicko.

Cain   I won't.

Reece   Cos if I had to choose, choose a film for all of you to remember me by, I'd just tell it to you. I'd just tell you – I'd just tell it. It's not a big deal that I won't be here when you watch it. I only asked Gus in case he'd thought of a film – you know? If he'd had one in mind – what film he wanted? And we could watch it, all of us, and remember him. Cos if it was me I'd choose *Tomb Raider*.

Joe   What?

Reece   *Tomb Raider*. I'd choose *Tomb Raider*. That'd be my film.

Cain   *Tomb Raider*? 2003?

Reece   Yeah.

Karis   Why?

Reece   Cos I like it.

A beat.

Joe   *Tomb Raider*?

Reece   Yeah.

Cain   *Tomb Raider*'s shit.

Reece   Well, that's what you're watching when I'm gone and you don't have any say in the matter so deal with it.

Cain   Fair enough.

Joe   *Tomb Raider*?

Reece   Yeah – *Tomb Raider*.

Joe   For a boy with cancer that's a very morbid title.

Reece   What is?

Karis   That title. *Tomb Raider*. It's morbid.

Reece   What does morbid mean?

Joe *puts his hand on the top of* **Reece**'*s head.*

Joe   Happy go lucky.

Lights down. Sound up.

Scene Five

Gus and Josh's room.

Very late that same night. Bare stage but for two beds. The sound fades and the half light of **Gus** *and* **Josh**'s *room gently up.* **Joe**'s *empty bed becomes* **Gus**'s *bed stage left.* **Josh**'s *bed at the opposite side. The noise of vomiting off, stage left. It's* **Gus**. **Josh** *sits up in bed. The vomiting stops. A beat.* **Josh** *lies down. More vomiting.* **Josh** *sits up. He hangs his head back, looking up. The sound of* **Gus** *vomiting might never end.*

Sadie *runs on from stage right into the centre of the room. She enters hassled. She's been crying. She holds her beads so as not to make noise when she moves.* **Josh** *sees her. She puts her finger to her lips.*

She looks in the direction of **Gus**. *She listens to the noise of him vomiting. She looks to* **Josh**. *Hesitates. The vomiting stops. She doesn't know what to do. She decides and moves to* **Josh**. *She whispers in his ear. He closes his eyes for a few seconds – digesting the news. She tells him again. She exits the way she came, stopping only for a final brief look in the direction of* **Gus** *before she disappears.*

Josh *takes his phone from under the pillow, touches the keypad – the screen illuminates. He shifts his eyes in* **Gus**'s *direction then back to the phone. He lies down, pulling the covers over himself just as* **Gus** *enters, weak and tired. His IV bag is almost empty. He steadies himself by the bed. Exhausted. He attempts to lie down but his phone bleeps. He picks it up, looks at it – a message. He reads, quickly stands, alarmed.*

Gus   Josh?

There is no response.

'Cornerstone' by Benjamin Clementine begins to play.

Combating the fatigue and the nausea, **Gus** *looks stage left to see if the coast is clear. He removes the IV drip from his hand, shrieking slightly*

*with the pain. He puts his hoodie on over his T-shirt and pulls some
tracksuit bottoms over his pyjamas.*

*He sticks his feet in a pair of trainers. He grabs a backpack from under
the bed and hurriedly stuffs some other clothes in it. He keeps looking in
Josh's direction, who remains under the covers.*

He puts a coat on over the hoodie and a scarf around his neck.

He puts his phone in his pocket.

*He makes to go, stage left, wrapping the scarf around his face. Stops.
Moves quickly to the bottom of **Josh**'s bed. Touches the outline of
Josh's leg. Rubs it. **Josh** pulls his leg away. **Gus** smiles.*

*He makes to go again but stops centre stage, facing out. He bends
forward a little, carefully removes his Yankee hat, revealing a shaved
head and a bandage at the top of it.*

*He goes back and places his cap at the bottom of **Josh**'s bed. He returns
centre, puts his hood over his head and wraps the scarf around his mouth
again. He takes his left trainer off and removes the schoolroom key from it.
He slips the trainer on again, looks back to **Josh** just once more, and
then disappears stage left.*

Josh *pulls the covers down. He gets out of bed, lifts the Yankee cap and
moves centre to **Gus**'s last position. He looks towards **Gus**'s exit then
out front, trying his best to keep it all together – but he's fighting tears.
He puts **Gus**'s hat on. He turns it back to front just as **Gus** always
wore it. The lights begin to fade on **Josh**'s bed.*

Josh *moves to **Gus**'s bed and climbs into it.*

*He lies back on **Gus**'s pillow and pulls the covers over his face.*

*Light intensifies and then a slow fade. Music fades just before the last of
the light goes.*

*As the actors take their curtain call, 'All these Things that I've Done' by
The Killers returns – fading up from 3 minutes 57 seconds in.*

Hospital Food

BY EUGENCE O'HARE

*Notes on rehearsal and staging, drawn from a workshop
with the writer held at the National Theatre, October 2014.
Workshop led by Phillip Breen, with notes by Kirsty Housley.*

How Eugene came to write the play

'I was asked to write a play for NT Connections, but at that
stage I didn't know what I was going to write – I have to wait
until something, an idea, really hits me before I can start to
write. Soon after the meeting I started reading Christopher
Hitchens's book *Mortality*, which is unfinished – he died before
completing it. I got to the end of it, and couldn't sleep.
Instead I started to write, and I wrote half the play that night.

At first, eleven characters appeared to me: the eleventh was a
girl who didn't speak. Eventually that character disappeared,
as I couldn't see how she fitted into a room that was active
and open.

Once I'd started writing, I went to visit the Teenage Cancer
Trust, which was overwhelming. I was offered the opportunity
to return, but it was very important to me to listen to my own
characters, and not be too influenced by real people.

Although I did read *Bad Science* by Ben Goldacre, the play
doesn't have a message about traditional or alternative
treatment for cancer – that's not something I want to do with
my writing, I'll leave that for journalists. I try to step back and
not put words into my characters' mouths.

When I wrote the opening scene, the image came first and
then the music ('All these Things that I've Done' by The
Killers) just seemed to fit. My timings are suggestions, and at
this stage I relinquish my authorship and hand the piece over
to you: the directors and actors. The suggested timings feel
right to me, but you can create the same feeling in other,
different ways. It's up to you now: you can either use my
suggestions or find your own way.

I've been asked what happens after the play ends, but I honestly don't know if Gus lives or not. I only know about what I've written, and so that knowledge ends with the last page of the play.

If it helps at all, I think of this as a play about survival.'

Approaching the play

These approaches are an overview of how Phillip Breen would approach the play: his preparation and rehearsal process in miniature.

What is in the play?

In Russian, the words 'to write' are closer to 'receive' in English. So how can we, as writers, but also actors and directors, receive this play? How do we ensure that we're really listening to it and engaging with what's on the page?

Initially, there might be one image or moment that jumped out at you following your first and second readings of the play, and this is something you can hold in your mind and work with – it can act as a starting point.

The group identified the following images they were particularly struck by:

- Sadie's ring.
- An empty hospital bed.
- Crashing and burning and rising up again (Josh).
- The IV drip.
- Gus 'screaming inside his own head'.
- Josh taking Gus's place in bed.
- Gus leaving.
- When a plane finally gets out above the clouds.
- The general absence of play.
- Primary colours of The Retreat.
- Sadie's dog dying.

- The postcard.
- Gus getting Reece a glass of water.
- The film to be remembered by.
- The slow fade of lights as Josh tries to find the words for Gus.

They were also struck by the following moments of dialogue:

- Elsie's line about Z-list celebrities doing their bit for baldy kids.
- Gus and Josh arguing over the difference between being alive and living: Gus says 'different' three times.

And the following themes:

- The lack of control for young people – everything about their illness and treatment is out of their hands
- Friendship and emotion in a sterile place.

These things are a first step into the world of the play. There might be other images that jump into your mind from other art forms – things that speak to the play and its themes. Phillip thinks of *Pharmacy* by Damien Hirst, for example.

The setting of the play may be a cancer ward, but try to find what's underneath that. For example, *One Flew Over the Cuckoo's Nest* is set in an asylum, but it's not about asylums. So *Hospital Food* isn't just about a teenage cancer ward, and it's not just about a room called The Retreat. It's about being a teenager, having others control your life, growing up, trust, keeping secrets, leaving things behind, and a part of you dying and moving on.

Phillip asks three questions in order to try to 'listen' to and 'hear' the play.

WHAT WAS GOING ON . . .
IN THE HEAD OF THE WRITER?

We know that Eugene has read *Bad Science* and *Mortality*. We know that he loves David Bowie. We know that he loves Pinter, Beckett and Sam Shepard. Phillip recommends 'reading around' the play in order to better understand where the writer is coming from. If other plays are available, Phillip also recommends reading the writers' other work, as well as plays that have influenced him. From his influences we might understand, in this instance, that we're not in a completely naturalistic world, and the books that inspired the play can act as useful research tools for both director and performers.

WHAT WAS GOING ON . . .
IN THE WORLD WHEN THE PLAY WAS WRITTEN?

- Stephen Sutton's fundraising for the Teenage Cancer Trust, and his subsequent death made headlines.

- Ashya King's parents took him from Southampton General Hospital, as they wanted him to have proton beam therapy. A manhunt across Spain then ensued until Ashya was found and offered treatment by a company in Prague.

- The Health and Social Care Act was passed despite nobody voting for it, allowing the NHS to be put out to tender, opening up £60 billion worth of NHS contracts to private and voluntary sectors.

- It was the NHS's sixty-sixth birthday.

As well as having direct implications for the characters in the play, it also raises issues of democracy and control.

- The European Parliament elections were held.

- The US pharmaceutical company Pfizer tried to buy out AstraZeneca for £55 a share, with their bid totalling £69 billion. This raises the issue of illnesses and their treatment being profitable.

- Kickstarter campaigns, no-make-up selfies and ice-bucket challenges were everywhere, encouraging us to see medicine as about money and profit.

WHAT WILL BE GOING ON . . .
IN THE WORLD WHEN THE PLAY IS PERFORMED?

Obviously this is something we can't answer yet, but by looking at where these three elements intersect, you may begin to see what the play could mean to an audience now.

This is about really listening to the play and not getting blinded by your own ideas or concepts. This doesn't mean that you have to be literal – you're looking for the essential feeling of the play, and beginning to think about how that might be realised. You can use your imagination, but make sure that what you're doing is enabling the play, rather than smothering it.

Scene by scene

A really useful thing for a director to do prior to rehearsals beginning is to break the play down and look at each scene separately. For this, Phillip divided the group and allocated each small group a scene to look through. Each group then noted down every question the scene raised for them.

SCENE ONE

- Where are we and where have we been?
- What stage of treatment is each character at? Are they all having the same treatment? What are their levels of fitness?
- How well do they know each other?
- What does Sol know?
- Where is Gus going?
- Where are the doctors?
- What is the room for?
- How is everyone sworn into the room?
- What is combination therapy?
- What is alternative therapy?
- What is remission?

- What does it feel like to pull a drip out?
- What's in the bag?

SCENE TWO

- Where is the corridor, and does it lead to the physio room?
- Why does Gus enter from stage left? Where has he been? Is that where the retreat is?
- How long before Gus enters after Josh?
- How often does Josh piss?
- Where are they? They talk about the mother losing her deck – what's their dialect?
- Has Gus's mum 'lost her deck'?
- Does Gus want to go, or is he just pleasing his mum?
- When did his parents split up?
- How long has his dad had a new family for?
- How much is kept from his father?
- Where is Josh going?
- Why didn't Gus tell Josh on his own?

SCENE THREE

- Why doesn't Sol question why Gus wants the key – does he know about and support his escape mission?
- How does Layna feel about Gus and why is she going to betray him?
- Why is Sadie so distant from the rest of the group? Nobody answers her questions. And why do they hide Gus's terminal illness from her?
- How do they look at each other?

SCENE FOUR

- Whose room are they in?
- Why did Reece need to borrow a pen to write the card? How did it just appear? Where did it come from?

- Why does he choose to send a card, rather than speaking to Gus directly?
- Why does everyone take the piss out of Reece?
- Is Reece just naive because he's younger than the others?
- Why are they worried about Barbara seeing the card when Reece asked Nurse Gemma to post the card, so she might have read it already?
- How much do they talk about dying?
- Why is Gus the only one who can talk to Josh?
- Is Cain feeling sick through nerves, or just ill, or sick from chemotherapy?
- What does 'boke' mean?
- Do the group approve of Gus's escape and what are the implications of his action for them?
- What time of day is it?
- What stage of treatment are they at?
- Why do they not talk about the future or the past? Does their illness make them live more in the present?

SCENE FIVE

- Where is Gus?
- Why is he vomiting offstage and not in the room?
- Why is he being so sick? Is it the illness, the treatment, or nerves about his trip?
- Is there anyone else in the room?
- Why does Josh sit up, then lie down, then sit up again?
- Why is Sadie hassled? And why has she been crying?
- Why does she whisper to Josh not to speak out loud? What is she saying and why does she say it twice? Why was she unsure about telling him?
- Who does Josh text? Is it Gus? If so, why? What does the text say?
- Why is Gus alarmed?

- Why is his IV drip nearly empty? And how long will it take before it is completely empty?

- Where are the nurses? Are they present in the corridor outside the room?

- What is Gus's escape plan? It might be useful to map this out for the group.

Generally, the answers to most questions can be found in the text, or in the case of a question like 'What is combination therapy?' by researching the topic. Very rarely, there's not a definitive answer to be found (for example 'Why didn't Gus tell Josh on his own?') and this is where the creative team intervene. The play still offers clues, but in order to find an answer you all have to make your own imaginative leap.

Phillip really recommends finding everything you can from the play and your research and getting creative only with the gaps in between the hard facts. It's best to avoid making things up if the information is already there on the page. You risk undermining the play or simply missing out on some key elements.

The questions listed above can be used as helpful markers throughout the process, particularly if you find you're getting too close to the play and can't see the wood for the trees. They are a reminder of your first instincts, and also a way to structure rehearsals. For example you could spend one rehearsal exploring a particular question. This way of working isn't intended to be prescriptive, but more a structured way of opening up the play.

Characters

Either before or during rehearsals your actors will need to find some ways into their character. In pairs, the group took on a character each and looked through the script to find out what the other characters say about them. This exercise is a good preparation for your acting company, and again looks to the play to provide the answers.

GUS

- Cain initially thinks that Gus is winding them up about leaving – he thinks it's a joke.
- Sol says Gus has been through more than he has.
- Sol says Gus doesn't stand a chance of surviving either way – he's really not very well. He has no chance of surviving, unlike the rest of them. He's terminal.
- Layna says Gus will be fine after just one more cycle of chemotherapy.
- Elsie says that Gus wants to be with his mother.
- Elsie says that Gus would hate Layna and never forgive her if she told Dr Ling about his escape plan.

SOL

- Karis says that Sol will know what homeopathy is.
- Gus says he's always in the schoolroom, swotting away. He's going to be a science professor. He lugs big books around with him, as he likes the weight of information in his hands.
- Elsie says Sol just said 'fuck' for the first time in his life.

JOE

- Cain says that nobody can talk to Josh apart from Gus.
- Joe says if Gus goes, they'll have to look after Josh.

REECE

- Karis asks Reece if he is totally stupid.
- Cain says Reece is a 'fucking joke'.
- Cain calls Reece a knob.

LAYNA

- Gus says Josh can talk to Layna.
- Josh says Layna will probably slit her wrists when Gus goes. She's mental about Gus.

- Gus says she's mental, but she's good to him. A bit highly strung though.
- Josh thinks she hates him.
- Gus says she's jealous.
- Elsie says she's just angry and tired when she threatens to betray Gus.
- Sol says Layna's not stupid – she must know how ill Gus is. She should let him go.
- Sol says Layna's going to smother Gus with a love he doesn't even know about, and stop him being with his mother.
- Elsie says Layna would betray everyone in the room if she told on Gus.
- Joe says than Layna only stormed out of The Retreat (in Scene One) because Josh did.

SADIE

- Karis says that Sadie is beating herself up because she used to wish she was thin, and now she's losing weight so fast she can't control it.

You can learn a lot from what is said about your character, but you can also learn from what is left unsaid. When you look at all of these lists together you start to get a sense of how the relationships might work between the group. For example, Josh is only spoken of in relation to Gus, and Elsie isn't spoken of at all, although her best friend Layna is spoken of constantly. Karis, Josh and Cain aren't spoken of at all, so the next step would be to look at why they're not spoken about. Layna is spoken about a huge amount because she is in love with Gus and she's considering telling a nurse about his planned escape – if she does act as she threatens, the whole plot of the play would be turned upside down. Therefore Layna holds the balance of the story in her hands. Elsie, on the other hand, seems to follow others and not stick her neck out. Josh, Cain and Karis seem similarly not to rock the boat – their position seems to quietly support Gus and in the course of the play they don't consider taking any actions that could turn Gus's life, or their whole world, upside down.

Design

Phillip recommends working on design ideas from pre-production throughout the process. Inspiration can be found in images, works of art, photos from news stories and other sources. This will create a mood board from which you can start to see what your palette might be. Again, looking to the play, try to find images that resonate with particular characters and give yourself some options to play with.

For the purpose of the workshop, the group was divided into set, lighting and hair and costume design.

SET

The group looked at images from a teenage cancer ward and used these as a starting point. The colours in one image were purple and green, which apparently represent spirituality and nature. The group were struck by the colours as they made the ward look so different to other, adult wards. They found the feel was similar to that of an Ikea showroom, with all the chairs, walls and tables brightly coloured. They also noticed motivational, spiritual images on the walls – pictures of lakes and forests and waterfalls and skies, which contrasted starkly with the clinical, unnatural surroundings. Their overall impression was of an adult's version of a teenager's bedroom – very asexual, with things like Bart Simpson posters on the walls – 'cool' in the eyes of adults, but definitely not cool in teenage eyes.

LIGHTING

The first image to strike the group was of a flickering fluorescent tube light, perhaps as something that can be used to light the transitions between scenes, with the light coming on full for the scenes themselves. The music and movement of the opening could have a softer, warmer light, so that when you slam into the first scene, the harsh light comes as a shock. The light could either be used literally like this, to create a sense of real place, or it could be used more expressionistically, to underline the moods of each scene, choosing from a pallet that ranges from very harsh to very warm. There are moments when the imaginative world of the teenagers stands in direct contrast to their surroundings – for example with the image of being in a plane soaring high above the clouds – and this is something lighting might be employed for. The group were struck with the image of a child's nightlight with rotating shade, throwing images of clouds on to the walls. There might be the chance to get creative with lighting in moments like this.

In the corridor scene, Eugene has deliberately specified a shaft of light shining through the space. He imagined the light as something that isolates the boys in that moment – it traps them in it and forces them into confrontation.

HAIR AND COSTUME

The first thing the group noted is that all the characters use accessories in some way to cover their lack of hair. And in doing this their personality is conveyed. The hair, or lack of it, can clearly indicate the stage of treatment that they're at. The issue of hair is an important thing to discuss with the group in terms of how realistic they want to be. If a group or individual decides that being without hair is too difficult, then they can use this for their character development: how might it feel to have no choice about losing your hair?

Eugene has clearly used costume as a way of making each character distinct. We hear about Danny B's childlike Spiderman pyjamas and how Reece lent him his Raiders hoodie. So we can glean from this that Reece might have some branded clothing, and enough to give items away. Similarly we are told that Gus wears a back-to-front Yankees cap, but we are told nothing of Josh's labels. So one approach might be to go for a more branded look with Gus and keep Josh label-free. Their clothes can also tell the audience a lot about how well they are: Who is really feeling the cold? Who needs layers and layers and still feels chilled? And who is more comfortable in short sleeves? There is something crucial about the fact that they wear nightwear, or 'loungewear' all day – they're not going anywhere so they have no need for outdoor clothes. This is very important. There are still decisions to be made within this, though – who stays in their night clothes all day, and who gets changed into different pyjamas or dressing gown or joggers every day?

On a final hair note, it is suggested that if any cast members do want to shave, they could raise some money for an appropriate charity by doing so, and therefore make the performing of this play a political act that's part of a broader picture.

Remote

By Stef Smith

A girl called Antler steps out of her front door and throws her phone on to the ground. She stamps on it. She then climbs the tallest tree in the park. She doesn't want to be found, not by anyone. The lives of seven teenagers all intertwine over the course of a single evening as they make their way through the park on a seemingly normal autumn's night.

Remote is a play about protest, power and protecting yourself.

Age suitability: 13+

Cast size:
7 main characters, plus chorus
which can be 2 or as large as you like

Stef Smith studied Drama and Theatre Arts at Queen Margaret University in Edinburgh. She is currently best known for supplying the text for the critically acclaimed, sell-out show *RoadKill* at the Edinburgh Festival in 2010, and 2011, which won an Olivier Award in 2012. Other plays include: *Cured* (Glasgay!), *Grey Matter* (Aberdeen Performing Arts), *Falling/Flying* (Tron, Glasgow), *The Silence of Bees* (The Arches) and the radio drama *Tea and Symmetry* (BBC Scotland). Stef has also been on an invited residency at the Banff Centre in Alberta, Canada, writer on attachment with the National Theatre of Scotland and was part of the National Writers Group at the Royal Court Theatre in London.

Author's note

The smallest number of performers this play could be
performed with is nine; there is, however, no maximum
number due to the use of a chorus.

The lines denoted with a dash (—) can be said by any
performer.

Lines may also be altered, where appropriate, to suit the
dialect of the performers. References to high school can also
be changed to college, if needed.

This play can be set in any park. The staging can be simple or
complex and is open to the interpretation of the group. There
are no scenes, but rather this play is one long moment,
flicking back and forward between other moments.

Ultimately the writer wishes for the group to imagine their
own world within *Remote*.

Characters

Antler, *female*
Oil, *male*
Crystal, *female*
Blister, *male*
Skin, *female*
Finn, *female*
Desk, *either gender*

Desk has currently been written as a male but if this character is played by a female the gendered pronouns in [square brackets] simply need changing to female.

Blister's crew have no lines but should be represented on stage when Blister is in a scene, until they disband halfway through the play

Lines prefixed by a dash (—) can be spoken by any number of performers (minimum of two) of any gender. Characters can be any age. The only suggestion the writer makes is that Blister appears to be the oldest and Desk the youngest.

— Lock

— Open

— Handle

— Door

— Push

— Step. One foot

— Then the other

— On to the front step

— She closes the door behind her

— Fresh air hits her face

— Smell of clouds and cold. All that autumn stuff

— She pulls out her phone

— Places it on the second step

— Lifts up her foot and slams it down

— Again

— And again

— And again

— Screen. Buttons. Circuit board. Everywhere.

— That little piece of plastic

— Broken into smaller pieces of plastic

— And her chest is suddenly free and full

— And she stands for a moment

Antler   Good riddance.

— Good riddance she says.

— And it's one foot in front of the other

— It sounds like an easy task

— And most of the time it is

— And it's steps

— No, not steps, strong strides

— Strong strides forward, always facing forward

— She pulls her hood up over her head

— But it isn't that cold

— It's more for like, an atmosphere

— A mood

— Determined.

— Yeah, a mood best described as determined.

Antler   I've got somewhere I need to be. Simple as.

— The park, mostly it's the park she needs to be at

— It's only a few minutes walk from her home

— Her parents' home.

— She used to come here often

— When she was kid

— Swings and roundabouts. All that kid stuff

— Tarmac and iron

— Faded painted

— Mums with prams

— Eight-year-olds with adventure in their blood

— The rest of the world ahead of them

— Tarmac and iron

Antler   Huh. It looks the same as it ever did.

— She steps into the park

— Walking with purpose

— Like she is listening to loud headphones

— But she isn't

— Nothing is blocking those ears

— Just those heavy thoughts sitting in between them

— Swirling around her mind like a magic eight-ball

— And in the middle of this park is a tree.

— A big old rustic looking one

— Been there since always

— Always been there

— Got names carved into it

— Chewing gum stuck to it

— Holds the snow in the winter

— Back when it used to snow

— And she stops at the bottom. Looking up.

— It's been a long time since she looked at it

— And for a moment she recognises

Antler   Nature is pretty cool.

— And with that thought she takes one last look behind her

— The park at eye level

— And then she reaches for the nearest branch

— Grabs it and begins her climb

— Upwards, onwards.

— Branch after branch

—   Heaving herself up it.

—   One foot then the other

Antler   Those gymnastic classes when I was six are really paying off

—   She climbs amongst the autumn leaves

—   Flakes of orange and brown

—   Falling like snowflakes

—   Like back when it used to snow

—   She finds a branch, solid and strong

—   She has never been good with heights

—   But then she has never been bad with them either.

—   Breathe hard

—   Breathe deep

—   Taller now.

—   The height of a second-floor window maybe

—   Maybe even third

—   No other trees about here, not any more.

—   This tree stands alone.

—   Surrounded by a world of cars and street lamps

—   Of tall buildings and people talking

—   Of coasts and cliffs

—   Surrounded by this country

—   A piece of land

—   And after all a piece of land is only a piece of land

—   And she shouts

Antler   My name is Antler. And I will not be part of the world. Not this world. Not any more.

—   And so we cut to the other side of the park

—   A boy called Oil takes his phone out of his pocket

—   Three bars of reception

—   No new calls

—   He shuffles from foot to foot

—   Got new trainers for his birthday

—   They look pretty good but don't fit quite right

—   Clicks contacts

—   Clicks call

Oil   Pick up.

—   His phone does a double ring

—   Goes to voicemail.

Oil   Hey Antler, it's Oil. Where you at? I got your weird text. What's up with you? Where in the park are you? Why the park? Anyway. I'm out. Call me back.

—   Somewhere not far from here a girl knocks on her sister's door

Crystal   Antler – you in? I'm coming in.

—   But there is no one there. Not a note. Not a sign. Not a nothing.

—   Just a well-made bed and a weirdly tidy room

—   She pulls out her phone.

—   Compose new message

Crystal   Yo Sis, exclamation mark. Mum says you're to get washing-up liquid from the shop. You out, question mark. Crystal, kiss. Face with its tongue sticking out.

— Checks her phone again. Nothing.

— She grabs her jacket

— Opens the front door

— Crunch

Crystal   What was that?

— Broken pieces of plastic

— Smashed screen

— Tiny pieces of circuit board

Crystal   Antler's phone.

— Back in the park a group of shrugs and sighs collect

— Checking pockets

— Look in their bags

Skin   Nobody got any cigarettes?

Blister   What about cash?

The whole group shake their heads and pat their pockets.

Skin   Nothing.

Blister   You lot are worse than useless. Well. We better go find some then.

— Antler sits. In silence.

— Looking out for change

— Listening out for change

Desk   What you doing up there?

Antler   What?

Desk   I said what you doing up there?

Antler   I'm thinking.

Desk   Can't you just think down here?

Antler   Can you leave me alone please?

Desk   It's dangerous being up there so high. At least without ropes. I mean if you had ropes it would definitely be more safe. But you don't have ropes, so it really isn't safe. I'm Desk. Who are you?

Antler   Your name is Desk?

Desk   Sure.

Antler   Weird name.

Desk   What's your name?

Antler   Antler.

Desk   Antler? Why you called Antler?

Antler   It's a long story.

Desk   Have you got somewhere else to be?

Antler   Can you just go? I'm having a private moment here.

Desk   I'll go once you tell me.

Antler   Why are you called Desk?

Desk   Because it's my name.

Antler   Not much of a name, is it?

Desk   Works for me.

—   [He] looks up at her

—   She looks down at [him]

—   They pause in that moment

Antler   What? Stop watching me. Just move along.

Desk   You just seem a little old for climbing trees.

Antler   No age limit on climbing trees – is there? No age limit at all.

Desk   How long are you staying up there?

—   Antler doesn't know how to answer that question

—   Not yet

—   Images of screeching cars

—   And flags in the air

—   And police throwing gas canisters

—   And homeless people

—   And exam results

—   All flick through her head

Antler   It's a protest. You're not meant to know how long a protest is.

Desk   A protest?

Antler   Yeah.

Desk   Have you just decided that?

Antler   No.

Desk   What's it about then?

Antler   It's private.

Desk   I don't think protests are mean't to be private.

Antler   Well, this one is.

Desk   Shouldn't people know why you are protesting so they know what it is you want done?

Antler   It's not that kind of protest.

Desk   Don't you want something done? Like something changed or fixed?

Antler   Yes.

Desk   Well. What is it then?

Antler   How many times do I need to say it's private.

Desk   I don't think you're very good at protesting.

Antler   And I don't think you're very good at listening. This has nothing to do with you.

Desk   Can I come up then?

Antler   Look. I am sorry but go find something else to climb.

Desk   Well. You don't own the tree. No one can own trees. They're just, there.

Antler   Yeah? So?

Desk   So I'm coming up.

—   [He] tries to put one hand on the branch.

—   Lifts [himself] up

—   The branch snaps

Desk   Merde!

Antler   What?

Desk   Means 'shit' in French.

Antler   Well, get you.

Desk   Can you help me up?

Antler   I'm doing this solo, kid.

Desk   Is there a nice view? I'd like to see

Antler   You can see the whole park from up here. I mean sure. It's pretty.

Desk   Can you help me up?

Antler   Sorry, but there is only room for one up here. Only room for me.

—   The wind whips around them both

—   It's suddenly very cold where Antler stands on the branch.

Desk   It's a giant tree. There must be room for me.

Antler   You should go home now. Your mum or legal guardian or whatever will be worried.

Desk   What about your mum?

Antler *sits down on the branch.*

—   Antler cuts Desk in half just by looking at [him]

Desk   I best be going. (*Joking.*) Same time, same place tomorrow?

Antler   Bye.

—   The [boy] zips up [his] jacket

—   Takes one last look at the girl in the tree

Desk   You're bonkers you are.

Antler   See you later, Chair.

Desk   It's Desk. My name is Desk.

—   Just north-west from here a boy called Oil also zips up his coat.

Oil   Freaking freezing.

Checks his phone again. Nothing.

—   His mum says he is addicted to checking his phone

—   But he isn't

—   He can stop any time he wants

—   And he is starting to feel a fizz in his throat

Oil *bites his nails.*

—   Oil can taste blood in his mouth

—   He chews his fingers till they bleed

—   He never used to

—   He just started doing it this year

—   And now he can't seem to stop

Oil   Just call me back.

—   Just as he says that

Oil   Aw crap.

—   A herd of chants and chewing gum arrive

Blister   Oh! Oil-spill. Where is your girlfriend at? Not like your mum to let you out alone.

Oil   Hi, Blister.

Blister   What you got for me then?

Oil   Excuse me?

Blister   Can I borrow a fiver?

Skin   Better give him a fiver.

—   This girl called Skin chips in.

—   She might be Blister's cousin but no one is sure and no one dare ask

Oil   I'm still waiting on that fiver you borrowed last week

Blister   I spent it. Need another lend.

Skin   He needs another fiver.

Blister   Anyway the price of smokes has gone up. Inflation, or something.

—   Blister didn't know what inflation meant but it didn't matter

—   He looked much older than his age

—   This was due to a mixture of smoking

—   And wearing jackets that were three sizes too big

Blister   Me and my friends here, are desperate for a smoke. We get in a real bad mood if we don't have a smoke after a hard day

Skin   And it's been a real hard day.

Blister   Really hard.

Skin   Really really hard.

—   Blister has a gaggle of groupies who follow him around.

—   None of them say much

—   Minus the occasional shout of something about someone's mother

Oil   I haven't got any money, Blister. I only got my phone on me.

Blister   Well then give us that. I'm in need of a new phone, about time I got an upgrade.

Skin   You heard the big guy.

Oil   You're joking?

Blister   Do I look like a comedian?

Oil   I mean you're funny looking –

Skin   What did you say?

Blister   Phone.

Oil   I got it for my birthday. My mum forked out a fortune.

Skin   'My mum forked out a fortune'. Whatever.

Blister   Now it's your present to me.

Oil   No. I'm not giving you my phone

Blister   What did you say?

Oil   What I'm saying is I'm not giving you my phone.

Blister   You want to rethink that?

Skin   You're probably gonna want to rethink it.

Oil   Why? What are you going to do?

Blister   Why don't you imagine what we'll do and then times that by a hundred.

Oil   Why can't you times it by a hundred yourself?

Blister   I'm dyslexic

Oil   No, you're just dumb and there *is* a difference.

Blister   What did you say?

Oil   I mean, what I meant is . . .

Skin   Do you want to repeat that for us? Oil-slick.

—   At this point the group is silent.

—   Blister clenches his fists

—   Skin doesn't blink

—   And Oil just felt his stomach do a high kick into his throat

—   He instantly regretted everything he just said.

—   Oil had a problem with opening his mouth and just letting the words fall out

Oil   Look. Blister. I'm sorry. I'm just messing. I didn't mean to say those things . . . I'm waiting on Antler calling and I've got all uptight is all.

Blister   Your girlfriend? You guys going on a date are you?

—   The good thing about Blister is that due to his over-use of Facebook and Twitter, he was distracted easily

—   No thought or person held his attention too tightly

—   And being the oldest of five siblings, Oil knows how to play a distraction to an advantage

Oil   Yeah, something like that. But I mean we're not actually going out.

Blister   She'll be angry you're late. For your date.

Skin   Tut. Tut. Girls don't like lateness.

Blister   And she should know. She's a girl.

Oil   You know. You guys are right. I better go . . . thanks for the advice.

—   And just like that

—   Oil slips around the group

Blister   See you around.

Skin   See you around.

Oil   Yeah see you around.

—   Disaster narrowly averted

—   Oil gnaws at his nails again

—   He dare not look back as the group walks away

—   And Blister shouts

Blister   Enjoy your date!

—   And Skin follows up in the distance with

Skin   Oil and Antler up a tree, K-I-S-S-I-N-G.

—   Just as they disappear

—   Oil bumps into this [boy]

—   Walking at the pace of a snail

—   Which is incorrect because snails don't actually walk

—   But still.

—   But still.

—   All the while Antler had been watching Desk

— Like a bird perched following a mouse

Desk   Sorry.

Oil   Watch where you're going

Desk   I said sorry.

Oil   Oi. You might want to turn around.

Desk   Why?

Oil   Bunch of idiots around the corner.

Desk   That's okay. I can look after myself.

— From high up in that tree in the middle of the park

— A voice yells

Antler   Oil!

— She shouts it loudly but she is too far up

— And he is too far away

— From down here she just sounds like birds

— Or the wind

— Or a car in the distance

Oil   It's your life.

Desk   Thanks anyway.

Oil   Whatever

— The two of them collide only for a moment

— And pace off in different directions

— Meanwhile Crystal paces the street near her home

— She doesn't want to tell her mum, doesn't want to get Antler in trouble

— Even she knows something has happened

— Meanwhile Oil paces the paths of the park

—   I mean, it isn't that big but if someone wants to get lost

—   There is always some way to get lost

—   Meanwhile Antler sits in the tree. Colder now.

—   Staring across the skyline.

—   She whispers to herself

Antler   My name is Antler and I won't be part of this world. Not any more.

—   But there is a slight crack in her voice

—   As if from seeing her friend

—   She isn't so sure any more

—   Her strength loosens

Antler   It's fine. I'm fine. You're doing this for a reason. You're doing this for a reason.

—   And she is fine

—   As she thinks about earthquakes

—   And flooding

—   And fires tearing down forests

—   And she looks back up at the sky

Blister   Oi! You.

Crystal   What do you want?

Blister   We saw your sister's boyfriend kicking about the park. (*Sarcastic.*) Bet you're jealous of her getting a stud like him.

Crystal   You saw Oil?

Blister   You jealous?

Crystal   No. I'm looking for Antler

Blister   Well, we haven't seen her

Skin   Seen nothing of her

Blister   She probably sucking the face off that numb nut Oil. I mean they really suit each other. Both total losers.

Crystal   Which way did he go?

Blister   Round that way, in past the swings.

Skin   Off on his date.

Crystal   Right. Thanks

With that she goes to walk past **Blister**, *but he grabs her by her arm.*

Blister   Now. Now. We need payment for that information. That information wasn't free of charge.

Skin   No free passes here

Crystal   I haven't got any money.

Skin   She says she hasn't got any money, Blister.

Blister   Tut. Tut.

— He twists her arm

— Everything closes in

— Blister can be real brutal when he wants to be

— Everyone knew that

— Crystal's arm burned

— And Blister's eyes lit up

Crystal   That hurts!

Blister   You've gotta have something.

Skin   Someone always has something.

Crystal   I don't have nothing. You're hurting my arm.

Finn   Careful. That's a girl you're hurting

Blister *lets go of* **Crystal**'*s arm.*

—   What was that?

—   Who said that?

—   No one, especially not those in this group, question what Blister is doing

—   Not on Blister's watch

Blister   What did you say?

Finn   It's just not . . .

Skin   Tiger got your tongue?

Finn   It's just manners!

Blister   Since when have you cared about manners?

Finn   You always said manners are important

Blister   Right. But it isn't manner-ful to question what I am doing

Skin   The man has a point.

Finn   She's younger than you and a girl. She didn't do anything. No disrespect –

Blister   No disrespect?

Skin   You got an eye for her?

Finn   What?

Blister   Do you fancy her?

Finn   No. No! It's just . . . I've got a little sister about her age. It's like you're doing it to my sister

Blister   But I'm not.

Skin   But he isn't.

Finn   But it's like you are. I'm sorry, Blister, but you just gotta be . . . you know . . . when it's a girl . . . I think . . .

Skin   Not so mouthy now – are you?

Blister   Did I open this up for discussion? For a big chit-chat about manners? Or was I just after some money so I could buy you some fags? Shut up, Finn. Or you can see what happens when someone really has no manners.

For a moment there is silence.

— This girl called Finn never said anything to anybody

— But when she imagined her sister being there

— Blister with his big hand around her little arm

— Finn didn't like imagining that

— She didn't think it was manners at all.

— And all the while, Antler was watching

Antler   Don't you dare hurt her!

— It was too far to hear them

— Too far to see the details.

— And she had no idea what to do

Antler   I said don't you dare hurt her!

— But she was shouting into the air

— And she couldn't help but feel totally powerless.

Finn   I'm outta here. See you guys later.

Blister *grabs* **Finn**'*s jacket.*

Blister   Where do you think you're going?

Skin   Have you suddenly got somewhere else to be?

— And just like that all the sides change

— Friendships, allies, enemies, unknowns, the powerful, the voiceless

— Everything changes

Skin   Go on then.

Finn   Go on what?

—   Suddenly Finn sees a part of Skin that she has never seen before.

—   Eyes close in on her

—   Like a predator

—   Tigers

—   Lions

—   Panthers

Blister   Run.

Finn   What?

Skin   He said run.

Finn   Blister. Don't be a –

Blister   You turned on us.

Skin   Now we're turning on you.

—   So quickly, everything switches

—   But no one said any of this would be fair

—   No one said anything about fairness

—   Finn's nerves make her taste sick

—   And her guts make her heart race

And with that she grabs **Crystal***'s hand.*

Finn   Come on!

—   One foot in front of the other

—   One foot in front of the other

—   Blister and his sidestepping crew just stand there

—   Watching

—   Cruelly giving them time to run into the park

— And up that tree Antler is suddenly starting to feel very stupid

— She is suddenly starting to feel very pointless

— I mean if she got down

— No one would have to know she was ever there

Blister What do you think, fellas? Time to set off after them?

Skin I say we give the little puppies a head start. You know. I never . . . really . . . well . . . trusted her.

Blister Oh yeah? What did she do to you?

Skin I just never had a good feeling about her. You know that way? When your gut twists?

Blister No. But, yeah.

Skin Right. That's enough time, let's head after them.

Blister You calling the shots now?

Skin No. Of course not. I'm not calling the shots . . . I'm just doing as you would do. Aren't I?

Blister Yeah. Yeah. We better go after them.

— The heavy footsteps of Blister trail off into the park

— I don't think I like him much

— I think that's the point

Antler Keep running!

— Panicked, Antler is stuck

— She thought it would be easy

— Easy to stay up in the clouds

— But she forgot stuff would keep on happening on the ground

—   She hadn't really thought this all through

—   If you ask me, it's a stupid thing to do

—   But she's done it, hasn't she.

—   I mean no one would have to know she was up there at all

—   She just has to step down off the tree

Desk   You coming down then?

Antler   What? No. No . . . I'm just . . . Why are you back?

Desk   I've lost a glove. It was in my pocket and now it's not. My mum is gonna be as mad as a bag of cats if she knows I lost a glove. She says I go through gloves like dogs go through bones. Which, if you ask me, is a weird thing to compare it with. Because I don't eat the gloves . . . I just lose them. So you given up on your protest? It didn't last very long, did it?

Antler   No, I haven't . . . I wasn't . . . I'm just getting comfortable.

Desk   It's more comfortable down here. I can promise you.

—   Antler feels a wash of embarrassment over her

—   She didn't want to seem so weak

—   Because this wasn't a phase

—   All of this – it wasn't just a phase

—   It was delayed buses

—   And milk prices

—   And the age of consent

—   It wasn't just a phase

Antler   Did you see a group of guys messing with a girl?

Desk   What?

Antler A guy called Blister. Face like a bag of smashed crabs.

Desk Blister? Why is he called Blister?

Antler Back in primary he gave this boy a Chinese burn so bad it blistered his arm. Name stuck like chewing gum on new Converse. You should stay away from him. He'd eat you alive.

Desk Well, I haven't seen them. How come?

Antler You see it's just my little sister is . . . never mind.

Desk Your little sister what?

Antler It doesn't matter.

Desk Don't suppose you can see it from up there?

Antler What?

Desk My glove.

Antler Your glove?! No. I've got more important things to see than your glove

Desk Well. It's important to me and that means it is important.

Antler Why care so much? It's only a glove. Go to corner shop, get sixteen of them for a quid.

Desk I don't have that kind of money.

Antler You don't have a pound to buy some gloves?

Desk No.

Antler Just ask your mum then. It's only a quid. You shouldn't stress the small stuff. Plenty of big stuff to be stressing about.

Desk My mum doesn't have that type of money.

Antler Yeah, right. She doesn't have a pound? Whatever.

Desk   She doesn't work.

Antler   Then you should get a job.

Desk   How am I supposed to get a job?

Antler   Do I look like a careers advisor?

Desk   I don't have time for a job. I look after her.

Antler   Oh.

—   With that Antler delves into her pocket.

Antler   Here. Catch.

—   She throws down a pound coin

—   Which was nice of her

—   I think we'd all agree that was a nice thing to do

Antler   You can buy a new glove with that.

Desk   Really?

Antler   Don't look at me like that. I'll give you another pound if it makes you go away.

Desk   No. You don't have to . . . Thanks. For the loan.

Antler   You don't have to pay me back. I don't need your life story either. Just move along.

Desk   If you ever need . . . a pal.

Antler   I don't need another friend. I don't need anything from *you*. Best be moving, yeah? Why don't you go and see if you can find that other glove . . . Keep the pound for something else.

Desk   Yeah. Yeah. Good idea. See you. I'll give the pound back if I find it.

Antler   Whatever. See you.

—   Desk wonders off with [his] eyes to the ground

— Looking for [his] lost glove

— And Antler looks back but she can't see her sister

— Can't see Blister

— Just the sky slowly turning dark

— And her stomach grumbles

— And her teeth grind

— Listening out for her sister

— Listening out for change

Crystal   What was that?

Finn   Hey, I helped you

Crystal   He wasn't going to hurt me. Not like, really hurt me.

Finn   You don't know him. I've seen him pin kids up to walls and turn them upside down

Crystal   Then why hang out with such a −

Finn   Protection. You know how in the ocean little fish hang out with big fish so they don't get eaten.

Crystal   No.

Finn   Well they do. That's what I'm doing. I know I'm a little fish. Just trying not to get eaten.

Crystal   Sounds like you're being a coward.

Finn   Would a coward do that?

Crystal   It's not like you saved me.

Finn   You looked like you needed saving.

Crystal   I was fine. I would have been fine.

Finn   I was just . . . I've seen enough folk get ploughed through. Between Blister and then there's my brothers . . .

well . . . you get bored of watching people get hurt. It gets boring after a while.

— Unexpected

— That's the word you'd use for right now

— Unexpected

Crystal   What's your name?

Finn   Finn.

Crystal   I'm Crystal. You don't go to my school, do you?

Finn   I don't go to any school.

Crystal   Oh yeah?

Finn   Nah. Don't see the point.

Crystal   Oh, you're right. Hanging out with Blister is a much better plan.

Finn   Better than nothing. In fact, in my life it's better than anything else.

— Both of them stood there

— Knowing nothing and everything about each other

Crystal   What's your plan then? They just gonna chase us around the park for ever?

Finn   They'll get bored soon. We just gotta stay one step ahead. That's all. You coming?

— Just like that Crystal takes Finn's hand

— Crystal realises in that moment she hasn't held anyone's hand since she was a kid

— Like, really a kid, younger than now

— She takes it and they walk further into the park.

— Crystal likes the small fish, so it seems.

—   And small hands. She realises Finn has remarkably small hands.

Antler   What am I doing . . .

—   Now Antler was starting to think about this choice she had made

—   It seemed like a simple choice

—   A choice of strength

—   A choice of courage

—   But now she wasn't so sure

—   To be honest I'm not entirely sure either

—   Maybe she was too old for this

—   Because she wasn't a little kid any more

—   She wasn't a child any more

—   The world had made it very clear there was nothing childish about her

—   Exams

—   Pounds

—   Euros

—   Holidays with just friends

—   Saving up for a flat

—   Saving up for a car

—   When you turn old enough

—   But just maybe, this was a rash thing to do

—   I mean what teenager sits up a tree?

—   All of a sudden it felt like a childish thing to do

—   A grown woman wouldn't do this

— Would they?

Oil   Pick up your phone.

— Oil's walked half the park

— Can't see his friend

— Can't call his friend

Oil   Look, Antler, it's Oil. Has your phone run out of charge? I mean, I know there is no point in leaving this voicemail if your phone's died but I mean . . . if it hasn't and you get this. Can you call me back? I'm waiting for you. It's not cool to leave me just waiting . . . hope everything is alright. Call me.

— Somewhere else in the park, feet are shuffling the leaves

— Eyes focused on the pavement

— Sunken into thought

Desk   Excuse me? I was wondering if any of you guys had seen a glove.

Blister   A glove?

Desk   Yeah, it looks like this one, because it's a pair. You know?

Skin   Do we look like we've seen a glove?

Desk   I don't know . . . What does someone look like when they've seen a glove?

— Silence falls on the group

— All of them a bit confused by Desk's distinct lack of fear

— I mean, let's face it, they aren't the sharpest pencils in the pencil case

Blister   Where you going?

Skin   Did you hear him? Where you going?

Desk   I'm just looking for my glove.

Blister   Where you been?

Skin   Where you been?

Desk   Just in the park . . .

Blister   Bit old for parks.

Skin   Yeah, bit old.

Desk   Do you have to repeat everything he says?

Skin   No. I can say what I want.

Desk   Then you should.

Skin   What?

Desk   Say what you want.

Skin   I do.

Desk   Good.

Blister   Hold on, what is happening here?

Desk   Nothing. Excuse me . . .

Skin   Hey, wait. We are looking for these two girls, they were running that way

Desk   I've seen a girl up a tree but not two girls running.

Blister   Girl up the tree?

Desk   Sure. The tree up the top of the park.

—   Like a mouse who walks through an alley way filled with stray cats

—   Desk disappears

Desk   Thanks anyway.

Blister   What do you say we go and help that girl down?

Skin   What is that supposed to mean?

Blister   Well . . . From up by the tree we can see the whole park. Might be able to spot your friend.

Skin   She isn't my friend.

—   Doesn't sound good, does it?

—   I'm with you on that.

Antler   It's fine. I'm fine. Buck. Up. Get yourself together.

—   Antler knew it wasn't madness

—   She knew it came from deep inside her

—   But she also knew somewhere in that park her sister was looking for her

—   And she missed Oil.

—   Missed his jokes

—   It was that familiar balancing act of what your skull wants

—   And what your ribcage wants

—   Caught in between what came before

—   And what comes next

Antler   Another sixty years?

—   If she doesn't smoke or take up an extreme sport

—   She's got another sixty years of this

—   And that was the problem

Crystal   Is it true what they say about Blister?

Finn   About what?

Crystal   About those pills. At that house party.

Finn   Dunno. Depends what people are saying. It's more his big brother's thing.

Crystal   Is it your thing?

Finn   I mean . . . not really. Why?

Crystal   Just wondering.

Finn   Is it your thing?

Crystal   Are you kidding? My big sister would kill me if I went anywhere near anything like that. She's all protective of me.

Finn   There is no way I'd let my family run my life.

Crystal   You don't know my big sister. And I'd rather take her advice than your best friend Blister.

Finn   Can you just drop all that Blister stuff . . . He isn't really a friend. Like, not any more.

Crystal   Then why bother? You'd be better off just locking yourself indoors than hanging out with him.

—   What Finn wanted to say is that she had been stuck with them

—   For two years she had stood at the back of that crew

—   But they had been there when her mum kicked her out for a night

—   Or that time that her brothers took her wallet

—   But she had grown up quicker than them

—   More than them

—   But it was better to have them than no one, she thought

Finn   You know they're not that bad, just immature.

—   Even Crystal knew that wasn't the truth

Skin   This is taking too long. They'll be out of here before we get halfway to them.

Blister   Just go home. The rest of you. Just split.

—   The group pause and look at Blister

Skin   Yeah. He's right. We can do this alone. We don't
need your dead weight.

Blister   Alright, Skin. Cool it. No need to get nasty on the
ones who do stick around . . . but yeah. The rest of you can
split. We'll see you tomorrow. And bring cash. No empty
pockets tomorrow. Unless you want another day without fags.

—   Just like that, the group starts to fade away

—   Nobody else wanted to chase two girls around the park

—   Nobody else really cared

Blister   Just us then.

Skin   Looks like it.

—   Antler can see this.

—   She sees the group break up

—   She could feel sweat in her palms

—   Could feel her eyes twitch

—   Everything had switched

—   And she had no idea what to do

Antler   Screw this.

—   It's so much harder than she thought it would be

—   Because no one had warned her how hard it would be to
change

Skin   You should be worried, Blister. Finn leaving us. Don't
want anyone else getting ideas, you know. Ideas like that can
be contagious. Can be poison. When people get busy making
their own ideas of how things should be, well, that's when it
gets dangerous for big fish like us.

Blister   Big fish? I'm allergic to fish.

Skin   Big tigers. Lions. Whatever. You know, back in the day there would have been wolves here. And that's us. We're the wolves now. And it's important people know that.

Blister   I thought there used to be a Tesco here?

Skin   Before that. Before all the humans. Wolves have real sharp teeth. And they aren't afraid to use them.

Blister   I've never been afraid, Skin. Even with everything that's happened, I've never been afraid.

Skin   Thats why you're my friend, Blister. That's why all that lot respect you.

Blister   Yeah. Yeah, you're right. Better go then.

Skin   You lead the way.

—   And with that Skin could hear her brother's voice ring in her head

—   Protect yourself

—   The world is filled with wolves

—   Protect yourself

Oil   You have got to be kidding me. Antler? Is that really you?

—   The two of them just look at each other

—   Connected in silence and confusion

Oil   What are you doing up there? You hate climbing trees.

Antler   Oil, you gotta go after Crystal. Blister is after her

Oil   What?

Antler   You gotta go.

Oil   What's wrong with your legs?

Antler   I can't come down, Oil.

Oil   Are you stuck?

Antler   No . . . I just –

Oil   I tried calling you.

Antler   I smashed my phone up.

Oil   What?!

Antler   Don't need it.

Oil   You don't need it?

Antler   I don't need it.

Oil   You're not going to –

Antler   Not any more.

Oil   Not any more?

Antler   Is there an echo? Look, can you just go and check and see if Crystal's okay?

Oil   Why don't you come down and we can go and look together?

—   No words found Antler

—   She felt this strange double feeling of shame and strength

—   And her mind flicked to news broadcasters

—   And trashy magazines

—   And size zero

—   And kissing boys

—   And not kissing boys

—   And definitely not getting pregnant before you're twenty

—   And turning off lights when your leave the room

—   And recycling

—   And all she could mutter out was –

Antler   I can't.

Oil   Look. Come on. Enough of this. Let's go see what happening.

Antler *shakes her head.*

Oil   Look, I'm not going after Crystal without you. This is stupid. Just get down. Blister is rolling around the park looking for trouble. You want to be up there when he comes?

Antler   I don't care if Blister wants me

Oil   Are you being a hero all of a sudden?

—   The truth is Antler had never felt less like a hero

—   She takes a deep breath

—   Like the kind you take before you dunk your head under water

Antler   I'm not being a 'hero' . . . but I don't want part of any of it any more.

Oil   Part of what?

Antler   Anything. Everything.

Oil   School?

Antler   No.

Oil   Something at home?

Antler   No. And yes. All of that. All of everything. I mean take a look around. This . . . well . . . It's a protest.

Oil   A protest? Can you have a protest with just one person?

Antler   It's a protest against all of that

—   Both Antler and Oil take their eyes off each other

—   And they look at the ground

—   Look at the sky

—   Look at everything they know

Antler   It's all turning to shit.

Oil   I don't . . . Since when . . . Can you just come down?

Antler   No. Not any more.

Oil   It sounds like you're being a bit . . . Look. It doesn't matter. Come on. Protest on the ground or something.

—   Her hands were shaking

—   Her eyes were welling up

Antler   Can't you see? Everything matters.

Crystal   Look. Thanks for . . . well . . . I dunno . . . but I'm gonna split. I gotta find my sister.

Finn   Just like that? Gone?

Crystal   What do you want?

Finn   I can't leave you to wander off by yourself . . . You don't know where Blister is.

Crystal   It's fine. I don't think he is half as tough as you think he is. You've got some idea of him in your head. He's just a guy . . . whatever.

Finn   You kidding? A couple of weeks ago he found this little dog. This little three-legged thing. It was old, more scabs than fur. Skin pinned the dog down to the ground – it was yelping and crying and then Blister picked up this big rock and dropped it on its head. And it stopped yelping but he didn't stop. He just picked up the rock again and smashed it into the dog and he smashed and smashed and smashed. Until . . . well until the dog was nothing.

Skin said it was kinder to put it out of its misery but the dog had seemed fine to me. And they just left it there. It's just the other side of the park. And they've still got blood on their shoes. All dried in their laces. I haven't ever seen something like that before . . . and I don't want to see it again.

Crystal   Why didn't you stop them?

Finn   What was I suppose to do? When they get their mind on something . . . I mean, look at us. I'm not gonna just let you go wandering off into the park.

Crystal   I can look after myself.

Finn   I got you into this mess.

Crystal   But I'm not a three-legged dog. I'll be alright.

Honest.

Silence.

Finn   That boy you were looking for

Crystal   Oil?

Finn   Yeah. He was walking up to the top of the park. Towards the tree.

Crystal   Thanks.

—   And with that she leans forward and kisses her

—   Right on the lips

—   It was a short kiss

—   No tongues

—   Crystal knew she didn't have to be saved but she didn't mind the gesture

—   And both were a little surprised by the kiss

—   But neither were particularly scared

Crystal   See you.

Finn   See you.

—   One foot in front of the other

—   One foot

—   Then the other

—   Different directions

522   Stef Smith

Oil   Look. Come down. We'll find Crystal and sort this out.

Antler   How many times do I need to say it?

Oil   Come on. It's getting dark. And I don't have a torch. My phone has ran out of battery, yours is smashed. Your sister could be lost in the park for all we know. It's not just you here! Stop being so stupid. I'm gonna walk away, Antler . . .

—   The sky dims

—   Clouds move in

—   Right enough, it was getting dark

Oil   Your mum will be worried

—   It was a cheap shot but it was enough to make Antler's heart jump up to her tongue

Antler   I told her I was staying at yours

Oil   I'm not sure she'll buy that excuse when you don't come home for a week.

Antler   I just can't do it. Not any more. It's too hard. My mum cries. A lot. My room is next to the bathroom and I hear her cry. I don't know why, Oil. She just cries. And you know it isn't good when your mum cries.

Oil   How long has she been crying?

Antler   Long enough. And my dad has taken up smoking again.

Oil   So? You smoke at parties.

Antler   But it's different. He's quiet. He looks . . . well . . . And I hate school. I hate it. I don't care about some revolution that happened eighty years ago. And there is no way I'm getting into uni with my grades and it's not like I have the money to move out and I don't have a job and I don't want to be like forty-five and still living with my mum.

Silence.

Oil   Is this all like . . . a hormone thing . . . or something?

Antler   I'm not on my period, Oil.

Oil   Ew. Gross. Look. Come down. And we can talk about it. I'm getting a right sore neck looking up at you and soon you won't be able to see where the branches are. Come down. It's just getting dangerous.

Antler   Good. Let it get dangerous.

Oil   You got a death wish?

Antler   No. But at least something would change. It's just grey. Look at all that grey.

—   And Antler felt a twinge in a muscle just left of her heart

—   As she looked out at the greyness

—   And she knew it wasn't about that stuff

—   Not really.

—   Go on then.

—   Tell him.

Antler   That's not really why I'm here. It's just . . .

Oil   Spit it out.

Antler   I learnt a word the other day. In English. She was going on about some old book about something and she said – it was about people being apathetic . . . It was about apathy.

Oil   Oh yeah. What does that mean then?

Antler   It's people not caring. People not wanting to care about anything.

Oil   Can you tell me how you sitting up a tree is you not caring?

Antler   No. That's not the point. After she said the word, I saw it everywhere and I can't stop seeing and feeling it everywhere. And I don't think that's right. People not caring. It's frustrating . . . it's . . . hard . . . It's . . .

Oil   Are you gonna start going on about starving kids?

Antler   Stop trying to make it small. This isn't small. These thoughts aren't small.

Oil   Look. Sort all that stuff out when we're out of high school. Keep it small. It's like a survival thing. Just got to keep that kinda thing in the back of your mind until you can actually do something about it.

Antler   What? Like everyone else around us?

Oil   You're not exactly volunteering, are you?

Antler   No. It's not that!

—   Antler grabs her chest.

—   And tears fill her eyes but none of them drop

—   She didn't like the world much

—   And she didn't know what do with that feeling

—   Didn't know where to put it

Oil   Look. Don't get all wrapped up in it. You can save the world another day. Just come down. Yeah?

Antler   But that's it, isn't it? I can't change the world and I definitely can't save it. I can't do nothing.

Silence.

—   The two friends look at each other

—   Oil started biting his nail again

—   And Antler felt like her lungs might burst

—   It's been years since they fought

—   They might only been feet away but they felt also worlds away

Oil   What about your sister?

—   Antler felt a double twang of guilt and sadness

Antler   I can't come down

—   I mean, she wanted to come down

—   She wanted to find her sister

—   And shout at her

—   Tell her off

—   And then hug her

—   The way that big sisters do

—   But she didn't

—   She was sitting there, in that tree

—   Wishing for something better

—   Wanting something bigger

—   One foot

—   Then the next

—   Antler looks out at the grey, her eyes wet with wanting

—   Oil looks at his friend and tastes blood in his mouth

—   Skin paces up the hill, looking for wolves, ready to jump

—   Blister walks two steps behind, uncertain of this change of sides

—   Finn touches her lips, thinking of the kiss, wondering how she felt

—   Crystal feels the power in her feet, in her hands

—   Desk suddenly turns on [his] feet. Suddenly aware that [he's] sent a pack of animals to roar at a girl up a tree . . . what has [he] done?

Crystal   Oil! You seen –

Oil   Crystal! Look, your sister won't get down.

Antler   You're alright? You're okay!

Crystal   I've been looking for you! I've been worried sick, I've been . . . what are you doing?

Oil   She won't get down

Antler   I was worried, I could see Blister coming after you. Did he hurt you?

Crystal   How did you know about Blister? What else did you see? Did you see me?

Antler   I could see him chasing you.

Crystal   And you didn't come help?

Antler   I mean . . .

Oil   She isn't coming down. She doesn't like the world.

Antler   So what happened with Blister? Why was he so mad?

Crystal   Hold the phone! What was that about the world?

—   Antler was lost again

—   Someone new to describe everything to

—   And somehow with these people who she was closest to

—   She found it hardest

—   She found it hardest to explain that ache

—   The ache in her chest, in her skull

Crystal   Is this about those sad adverts on the TV? I told you not to watch them any more.

Oil   I've already asked that – it's not about the sad adverts.

Crystal   Is it about school? Home?

Oil   No, it's not about that either. But also kinda everything.

Crystal   You can't be that upset – we're having a roast for dinner, oh and Mum says you're to get washing-up liquid.

Oil   Maybe it would help just not paying attention to what the TV is saying, yeah? Just like forgetting about all of it.

Crystal   This better not be a joke. 'Cause it isn't funny. I can't believe I spent all afternoon looking for you and you've just been stuck up here. You know what, Antler, I don't even care. I'm going home with or without. Oil, you coming?

Oil *looks at* **Crystal**. *He is tempted. He is turning on his feet.*

Crystal   Coming?

Antler   Just stop it!

— And in her head it was

— Images of screeching cars

— And flags in the air

— And police throwing gas canisters

— And homeless people

— And exam results

— And earthquakes

— Flooding

— Forests on fire

— Delayed buses

— Milk prices

— The age of consent

— Exams

— Pounds

— Euros

— Holidays with just friends

— Saving up for a flat

— Saving up for a car

— News broadcasters

— Trashy magazines

— Size zero

— Kissing boys

— Not kissing boys

— Not getting pregnant before you're twenty

— Turning off lights when you leave the room

— And recycling

Antler   Recycling!

Oil   What?

Crystal   You're kidding me. Now I really am going.

Antler   No. It's not that. But it is that. It's not that simple. There is nothing simple about these thoughts, there is nothing simple about me, or you, or this place, this town, this country. And people try to tell you it's easy. Simple. But really it's just that no one cares. No one cares enough to see what it's really like. How *hard* everything is. Because it's hard. It's hard knowing that you can't fix anything. You can't do nothing about anything. It's hard. And no one cares.

Silence.

Crystal   I care.

Antler   You care more about the shape of your eyebrows than you do about what's happening in the world.

Crystal   That's just mean.

Oil   Why should we care?

Antler   Because it's ours as well.

This is what we'll get. This. Their mess. And I don't want it, Oil. I don't want any of it.

Silence.

— With that, silence falls on the trio

— It's painful to see the world

— Oil understood that now

— It's painful to see what the world really is.

Oil   Well, hiding up a tree isn't the best way to . . . fix it.

Antler   Then what do you propose?

Oil   I've got no interest in proposing anything. Voting?

Antler   Do you think that does anything?

Crystal (*sarcastic*)   Oh sure. It's not nearly as useful as hiding up a tree.

— Minutes away Finn turns on her heels

— She knows that she's got to see that girl again

— Minutes away Skin and Blister march up closer to the tree

— Seeking out something to stir up, seeking out something.

— Minutes away Desk runs towards the tree

— Wanting to make sure no trouble was caused

Antler   Then what else? I can't think of anything else to do.

Crystal   You're acting like a right idiot. You haven't even got a decent reason. I'm gone, I'm so gone.

Antler   You're the reason. Crystal! You're the reason I'm up here!

Crystal   It's my fault? Why is it my fault?

Antler   I didn't want to tell you because I didn't want to upset you, but . . .

—   And just like that, everything changed again

Finn   Crystal!

Crystal   Finn? What are you doing . . .

Finn   I needed to talk to you, about what happened –

Oil   What you doing, knowing this loser? She's pals with Blister.

Crystal   She isn't like that. She . . . helped . . . me earlier.

Oil   Leopard can't change its stripes.

Antler   Spots. Leopards have spots.

Finn   I didn't mean anything earlier. Like, sorry about your phone and that. Blister was just joking

Oil   Wasn't very funny.

Blister   I thought it was pretty hilarious.

Skin   Don't mind us, we've got a bit of business needed with our friend here.

Oil   Thought you weren't friends with these guys any more.

Blister   No one said anything about friends.

Skin   I did. I said friend.

Blister   Oh.

Crystal   Just leave us alone.

Skin   Oh, we'll go, all in good time.

Oil   You just the sidekick, Blister?

Blister   You kidding? I'm still the boss around here.

Oil   Doesn't look like it

Skin   None of us have any bosses, not any more.

Blister   Oi. Skin. Watch your mouth.

Finn   Look, I'm sorry for before. I'm sorry. I was out of line.

Crystal   What are you saying, Finn?

Finn   Look, I've got some money at home. I'll buy you smokes for the rest of the week.

—   Crystal felt the knot of disappointment

—   Blister felt sweat in his palms

—   And Skin just glared at Finn

—   And I have no idea what is going to happen

Blister   I think that's fair, Skin. I could do with a smoke. We've all had a stressful day.

Skin   I don't. I don't think that's a good offer. I'm not soft like you, Blister.

Blister   Soft?

Finn   Look, Skin, what happened before, it didn't mean nothing.

—   With that Skin reaches down

—   She picks up the branch that Desk had snapped off

—   From up above Antler can see

Antler   Watch!

Skin *swings the branch near* **Finn**.

Finn   You planning on putting that down?

Skin   Are you planning on staying still for me?

She aims at **Finn**.

Crystal   What are you doing?!

Skin   Don't come near me!

Blister   This isn't funny. You could mess her up with that.

Skin   That's the point

Finn   Look, Skin. I didn't mean nothing. I'm sorry. Alright. No need to do nothing drastic.

Skin   I know you like to kiss girls. I was doing you a favour, keeping it private. But then today . . . when I saw you run off with her . . . I think . . . well, why don't I just show you what I think about that.

She steps forward. The branch in her arms. Ready to swing.

—   Now Finn sees the dried blood on Skin's shoes

—   She thinks about that three-legged dog

—   Thinks about what its head looked like after the rock

Finn   Stop! I'm sorry. Okay? I'm sorry. I didn't mean nothing. I kissed a girl. Okay? But I don't know . . . like . . . I'm just . . .

Skin   Do me a favour and stand still. Will you?

Crystal   We kissed. Alright? Didn't mean nothing. Just a kiss. No need to give someone a decking just for a kiss.

Blister   Just put it down, Skin. You hit her with that, you'll get done. You don't want that. Trust me, my brother got put in a unit. And she isn't worth it. She isn't worth it.

—   A tear creeps out of Blister's eye but he quickly wipes it away

—   Oil is pretty sure his heart has stopped

—   And Finn just stares into Skin's eyes

Desk   Don't hurt her! I won't let you hurt her.

—   Out of nowhere Desk rushes up to Skin

—   [He] tries to grab the branch

—   They tug back and forth

— Skin pushes [him] off

Skin   Enough! I oughta smash in all your skulls just for being cowards. Look at you. You don't have the guts to fight. You don't have the guts to do nothing about this, me. Scared of a stupid branch?! Bunch of cowards. Don't even know how to fight. You'll get nowhere if you don't know how to fight. You're just a bunch . . . of kids. Stupid kids, the lot of you.

She throws the branch on the ground.

— They stand there.

— In silence.

— Looking less like kids and more like adults by the minute.

Silence.

Crystal   I'd rather be a coward than just plain stupid

*She quickly picks up the branch. She points it at **Skin**, who barely finches.*

Blister   Oi! Don't talk to her like that.

— Skin looks at Blister

— Relieved to have the responsibility of words taken away from her

— Blister steps in the middle

He pushes the branch down.

— No one is getting hurt today, he thinks

— No one is getting hurt

— I don't know about you but I'm relieved

— Shhh!

Desk   What has been happening here?!

Silence.

Antler   We're just trying not to fuck it up.

—   One by one they turn and look at the girl in the tree

Antler   You're wrong. It isn't about fighting, not in that way. I mean look at everyone around us. All the power in the world and they don't care about nothing, don't fight for anything. We aren't being cowards by not fighting.

—   It's just about choosing what to fight for.

—   Antler realised that now

—   She did want to fight

—   But she wanted to fight for something better than this

Antler   Because when I fight I want it to be for more than you holding a branch up to some girl because she kissed another girl. Them kissing . . .what does it matter? If they're happy – that's a good thing. I don't want to fight that. Skin, you're fighting something pointless, something that doesn't need fighting, and I've got better things to do with my time, better things to fight for, we all do.

Silence.

Skin   No need for the lecture.

Oil   Antler, it's time to come down . . . yeah?

Crystal   Hold on. What did you mean, I caused you going up there?

—   With deep dark breaths Antler sighs

—   Exhausting

—   Antler knew one thing

—   Change was exhausting

Antler   It was that text.

Crystal   Text?

Antler   You sent me that message

Crystal   What message?

Antler   I asked you if you wanted to go and see Gran this weekend or next and you said – 'I don't care either way and I don't need you to organise my life'. You typed that into your phone and sent it to me. In about thirty seconds. You said you didn't care. You said you didn't need me.

—   The group looks amongst themselves

—   No one is quite sure of her point

—   To be honest, I don't know her point but I sense she probably has one

Crystal   I mean, maybe it was a bit harsh but there is no need for all this. I just meant I'm free all weekend . . .

Antler   But you said you didn't care. You said you didn't need me. And I thought, if my own sister can say that. Then it really is messed up.

Crystal   But that's just what sisters do? That's just normal. You say stuff like that all the time.

Antler   No. I don't. I'm careful with my words.

Crystal   You're older.

Antler   Only by a year . . . It's apathy. It's everywhere. You said you didn't care. You said you didn't need me. I mean what can I do? How can I change any of this? If I can't get my own sister to care about me.

Crystal   Look. I'm sorry. I was in a bad mood.

Finn   I think you're reading too much into it.

Antler   No. It was like . . . what's that saying?

Blister   The straw that broke the camel's back.

The whole group turn and look at him.

What? I know stuff.

Antler   Exactly.

Oil   Is that why you stamped on your phone?

Antler   Texting seemed pointless. Facebook seemed pointless. Taking another stupid photo of my cat seemed pointless. It doesn't matter – does it? Any of that stuff.

—   It doesn't matter when there is better stuff to care about.

—   That's what she wanted to say

—   That there was bigger stuff to care about.

Antler   That stupid phone was just . . . just . . . a distraction.

—   It stopped her from seeing the world for what it really is.

—   It stopped everything.

—   She saw that now.

Desk   If you ask me, Antler. You're the one who cares least . . . what's that word?

Blister   Apathy . . .

The group turn and look at him again.

What? I was paying attention.

Desk   Apathy. Sounds like some weird disease. Us, down here, on the ground. We care. We've got no choice. Otherwise it's just . . . boring or pointless or whatever. You've got to care about something. Everyone knows that. And you're just up there. In that tree. It's one thing to count yourself out but it just seems stupid to count yourself out because others are counting themselves out.

Crystal   What?

Desk   She is doing the exact thing she hates other people doing.

Crystal   Oh. Right.

Desk   I don't know how you fix people not caring. I don't know how you get people to notice all the things that need fixing. Because it's everywhere, the stuff that needs fixing. All of us can name three things in thirty seconds that need fixing, but you aren't going to fix it by not being part of it.

Skin   Talk about sugar-coating something

Blister   Shut up, Skin.

Oil   What you were saying before? You're right. This is ours. All of this is ours. But we can't make it ours, like truly properly ours, unless we're in it. Can't fix anything by being above it.

— There are shifts you feel

— Somewhere under your ribcage

— Somewhere just left of your heart

— Something happens

— Like something changes

— And it will happen plenty of times over the years

— Even I know that

— It's like a breathlessness

— Yeah, it's best described as a breathlessness.

— And Antler felt that. As she sat in the tree. Looking down.

— Looking down at those people

— People who looked just as confused as she was

— It had been a hard autumn, she thought.

— The autumn of what came before, and what comes next.

Oil   Please, come down.

Crystal   I need you. I'm sorry I said I didn't. Like . . . I was wrong. Simple as. I care. I've always cared.

— And just like that. It all changes again.

— Just when you get a hold of something

— Just when you decide

— It changes

Antler   Alright.

— An exhale

— A breath taken

Antler   On one condition. You all gotta come up here first.

Oil   What?

Antler   It's the sun. It's setting. You can't see it from down there. Too close to the ground. But from up here. The reds and the yellows. It's beautiful.

— Antler looks at Blister and Skin

Antler   But first I think it's best you guys get gone now.

Crystal   You heard her.

— Blister and Skin look at the group

— Bunch of no ones

— Bunch of everyones

Blister   We know where we're not wanted. You coming?

— Finn shakes her head

Finn   Not this time.

Skin   Best we don't see you again, yeah?

Finn   Yeah.

— In silence the two march off

— They won't talk about what happened today

— Not ever

— But it changed them

— In the smallest of ways, it changed them

Antler   Look, I promise I'll get down, afterwards. Come on. See this.

—   And just like that

—   One by one they start climbing the tree

—   Helping each other.

—   Clambering upwards

Crystal   I don't think I like heights

Finn   You'll be alright.

—   Branch after branch

—   One foot above the other

—   The group settle in the branches of the tree

—   Like crows

—   Or pigeons

—   Or seagulls

—   Or robins

—   All perched in the branches

—   Watching the light change

—   Watching the sun dip below this big lump of rock

Oil   It's cool how the light changes

Antler   Desk! I can see your glove! Look! Over by there . . . oh no. It's just a crisp packet.

Finn   Everything looks so much smaller up here.

Crystal   What do they call it? Like, in a photo. We just learnt it in art. All the depth and that . . .

Antler   Perspective.

Crystal   Yeah. Perspective.

— And then in a single moment

— A spec of white falls from the sky

— Antler holds out her hand

— And catches it and it disappears

— Was that snow?

— Antler wasn't sure.

— But she did know. The sun would most likely rise again.

— Just as it would set again.

— It's amazing what you can see if you look.

Antler   Nature is pretty cool.

— As darkness and shadows fall on the group

— They all sit in silence

— Hold on to the branches a little tighter

— And they are still, if only for a moment.

— Antler smiles to herself as she wonders if the whole day was worth it

— If it was worth the battle

— Just so she could see this sunset

— And she concluded it probably was

— It was always worth seeing another sunset.

— She promised herself she'd look up more. So she didn't miss it.

— Perspective, after all, is everything.

— With that Desk broke the settled silence

Desk   Just one thought . . .

How are we going to get down?

Remote

BY STEF SMITH

*Notes on rehearsal and staging, drawn from a workshop
with the writer held at the National Theatre, October 2014.
Workshop led by Caroline Steinbeis and Richard Twyman,
with notes by Rachel Bagshaw and Audrey Sheffield*

Notes from the writer

Stef started from the central image of a girl climbing a tree in
protest. Apathy – or its absence – became really interesting to
her. In particular she wanted to challenge the idea that young
people are apathetic – she feels they have acute insight and
a lot of anger and energy that she wanted to give voice to.
She workshopped the play with young people in Paisley and
was really struck by their desire to change the world. She
explained, 'This is not just a play about apathy; there are so
many things that Antler is seeing in the world, and she's
frustrated because she doesn't know how to say something
about this. In an adults' world, she feels powerless.' Stef feels
that adolescents are really present and in the moment, so she
didn't want to write about the characters' back stories or
home lives as a focal point.

In the form of the play, Stef was interested in writing
something that used filmic techniques and that didn't have a
lead character to dominate. She describes the play as being
like one long moment, one breath, a rush of energy.

Nature and urban landscapes are really important in the play
too. She does not have an absolute vision of what a
production of one of her plays should look like; instead she
wants to see productions that she couldn't have imagined and
likes to write with this in prospect. She is really open to
different interpretations of the play.

Stef chose the title *Remote* for lots of reasons. First, it
juxtaposes the fact that the title has connotations of a
technical device (a TV remote) with its opening image of the
destruction of a similar device (a mobile phone), and then is

entirely set outside any technology – but thematically explores the idea of the remoteness of its characters, especially Antler, who chooses to be remote from the world. It is also about how it feels to be an adolescent and to feel remote from being either an adult or a child.

Stef went to a youth theatre herself as a teenager and really values its importance in her own development as an artist. She was really drawn to the opportunity of writing for Connections and of giving voices to young people.

Stef's advice to a company:

'I know it will be tough but I hope that you find that thrilling. It's hard but I know you can do it. Trust it. There will be no production like yours – have fun with it and make it your own!'

Approaching the play

Below are a number of exercises that focus on work that can be done with your cast early on in the rehearsal process. Facilitating director Richard Twyman explained that they are all designed to help your company get close to the material, to open up and create a vivid world of the play, and to help make the storytelling clear and the characters rich and specific.

IMAGE EXERCISE: PICTURING THE STORY

- Divide the group into pairs, A and B. B closes their eyes, while A is given three minutes to tell the story of *Remote* to their partner as best they can. Encourage B to visualise and picture the story A was telling them as much as possible.
- B should then describe back to A whatever images came to their mind from A's telling of the story. These images could be literal, surreal or abstract.

This is a useful exercise to refresh people's perspectives, hearing the same story that they have read themselves, but creating it visually through someone else's response to it, touched by their different perceptions, rhythms, atmosphere and so on. As a director, there can often be the sense that you need to know everything, especially working with young people, and this exercise allows you to hear what the group thinks of the play, to find out their interpretations.

The exercise can also help you think about the play from an audience's perspective – envisaging how this narrative might come across to those unfamiliar with it.

It is very beneficial to start thinking about the storytelling aspect of directing from an early stage, recognising the natural need to divide the play into key narrative events and to articulate the important beats of the story to the audience. Doing this with your group will help to ensure that everyone is telling the same story – that you are all in the same world.

- You could tell it as a condensed version, with a time limit of sixty seconds. You could re-create the narrative using ten freezes; recount it chorally, simultaneously as a group; going round in a circle, with each person telling one part of the story in chronological order.

VISUALISING THE PLAY THROUGH IMAGES

Facilitating director Caroline Steinbeis introduced an exercise to focus on the images in the play. She often works in this way to open up how she sees a play and what is perceived as important. It also helps to start to visualise the world of the play.

- Split the company into small groups and give each group five sheets of paper. Ask them to draw what they see as the five most important moments of the play. Find the images that define how they see the play and what they perceive as its focal points. Examples from the workshop included images of the tree, the smashed phone, the kiss and the idea of space in the park, the dog incident with Blister and Skin, the blood on the trainer, the pound coin being thrown from the tree, Desk's single glove on the ground and the final image of the characters in the tree watching the sunset.

These images can help you see the important elements in the play – what is shared in people's visions and also what is different. They open up options for how to make things work, looking at what is important and why you are attracted to a particular image can help to guide you in your choices for your production. They are a really useful way of sharing your vision of the play with your company, and creating a shared understanding. The images also help to show the play's universal location: it could be anywhere and that is part of its appeal.

Ordering the images and possibilities for design

Working as a whole group, place the images into their order of importance in the play (this is not necessarily the order they are seen or heard in). Look at each of these images in turn, asking questions of them and thinking about how they might impact on their vision of the play.

Alternatively, you could create the storyboard for the full play by laying the images in narrative order on the floor so you can clearly see the story of the play in a visual way. It might be useful to tape this extended storyboard together into one long piece.

Below are some of the images discussed in the workshop:

IMAGE ONE: THE SMASHED PHONE   This is the first strong image and is the opening of the play. You could look at different ways of staging this, from the naturalistic option of using a real phone through to just hearing the description. You could explore physical, abstract ways to present this, using projection or shadows. Caroline pointed out that this could introduce a very different aesthetic, so think carefully about what this might do to the space of the park.

IMAGE TWO: THE WIDE OPEN SPACE OF THE PARK   Think about how this could be created – perhaps via projections and images of park landscape, the use of the ensemble to create the space, or lighting? The space needs to be fluid and allow for flexibility as the play shifts locations so quickly. Try to keep it simple and allow for movement and space. Using your actors to create the park rather than lots of set and props feels more in keeping with the feel of the play.

IMAGE THREE: ANTLER IN THE TREE   This is a very important image to get right. It is the central image that Stef started with and forms the backbone of the play. Possible staging ideas could include a stepladder, a tower, a tree trunk or a more abstract, built tree with branches, a simple set of boxes which could be moved to create the tree and other locations. How might it be possible to create a sense of isolation without necessarily needing to see a naturalistic representation of a tree? If we listened to the play with our eyes closed, the characters are telling us where they are. (Think carefully about health and safety and that whatever you choose, it must be practical for actors to work on.)

IMAGE FOUR: DESK TALKING TO ANTLER   There is a sense of distance in this image: what do you need to ask of your actors in order to create this? How do they communicate in order to convey this to the audience? Antler can often not be heard even when she is shouting down. However you stage the tree, this is a vital part of your approach in performance and really helps to set up the feeling of isolation.

IMAGE FIVE: ANTLER'S HOUSE   The play returns to Antler's bedroom after we've been in the park and it is important that the design allows for this transition. The space needs to move between locations quickly and fluidly, therefore you might need to think about a less literal way of creating locations.

IMAGE SIX: THE DOG   This is only described, but is a vivid, disgusting image. It feels like it describes apathy and is a metaphor for the protest at the heart of the play. The dog is vulnerable and completely defenceless; what is described is extremely visceral. It engages the audience in how dangerous Blister and Skin might be and the possible dangers that lie ahead. This is the game-changer moment in the play. How might this image be used in the production – how do we see it? It could be done through physical means or perhaps through film. Or is the description in the language enough to bring it to life in the audience's imaginations?

IMAGE SIX: THE MOMENT OF SKIN GRABBING CRYSTAL AND BLISTER GIVING A CHINESE BURN   The play is very filmic in feel and thinking about these images of violence in close-up might be a useful way of looking at how to stage it. How can you create the feeling of close-up onstage: can you use the ensemble to draw the audience's attention somewhere, create a feeling of time slowing down? Think about how you focus the audience's gaze on what you want them to see.

IMAGE SEVEN: THE ROOTS OF THE TREE   Showing the tree with roots could be explored as a possible staging option and might open up ideas for how the tree might work. Could it be possible for the top of the tree to be on the floor, and for everyone else to be lower still than Antler?

IMAGE EIGHT: THE GLOVE   Work out what this glove represents. Could it tell a story about Desk's chaotic home life but how selfless he is towards the other characters? It gives us a human moment of insight into Desk's life. He is outside the hierarchy of the other young people in the play, and there is warmth in this thread of the story that isn't always present in other moments, where there is a lot of anger, fear and resentment. The glove provides an opportunity for Antler to connect with someone else's issues; it makes her see that she needs to come back into the real world.

IMAGE NINE: THE KISS   This is a vital moment in the story: a thunderbolt. It is a moment of tenderness in an often harsh world, and it needs to stay with the audience as an image.

IMAGE TEN: THE FINAL MOMENT OF THE GROUP IN THE TREE   You could explore playing with space and how we see the group. Why is the group going up the tree? What is their intention?

This exercise of finding the structure of these images can help to shape your design and concept for the production. The play is one long fluid movement, and finding the structure of these images will help to unlock key points and find a shape to your production. This is such a visual play and there is a poetic image in nearly every line. It can also help to refocus what you think is important to get across in the storytelling, which could lead to your asking yourself: 'What is the minimum I need, visually, to be able to direct this play?'

FREE-WRITING EXERCISE: WHAT MAKES YOU ANGRY?

Focusing on the theme of Antler's anger in the play, ask the company to free-write their thoughts following on from three prompts:

PROMPT I   'What makes you angry?'

The group should write continuously for two minutes, without censoring themselves. Encourage them to be specific, think about where you feel the anger, how it feels.

Then ask them to respond to:

PROMPT 2   'The last time I was angry I . . . '

Write without stopping for a further two minutes.

Lastly, ask them to write continuously for another two minutes about:

PROMPT 3   'Things you feel you can't say out loud in your world'

You could then ask individuals to fold their pieces of paper in half and place them in the middle of the room so they become anonymous. Invite someone to choose a piece of paper and read it out loud to the group. Ask them to read it again, making eye-contact with the audience, then again putting some 'heat' under it. The final time ask the reader to take three words from the text and use these to engage with the audience. You can repeat this with different performers. The task ends with everyone taking one of the pieces of folded-up paper and tearing it in small pieces into the bin.

This exercise is a highly effective way of asking your company to engage with their physical response to anger and protest. It asks them to connect with that feeling both as performers and audience, and identifies where it is in the body. Anger is so present in the body and provokes highly physical responses. The exercise also gives voice to the feelings of powerlessness in the play. It can be done by your actors based on their own experiences, or applied to the characters, depending on what feels appropriate for your company.

Further suggestions as to how to get your cast thinking and talking about Antler's anger:

You could ask them to draw Antler's anger. The group could transfer her anger into a tweet and compose a message. They could make voice recordings on their phones in response to the prompts as above (as an alternative to writing), and then listen back to them afterwards . . .

Events of the play

An event is a moment in a play that changes the world for the characters onstage. The main event is what the play is building towards; identifying this will help you to shape your production. An example of an event would be the kiss between Crystal and Finn, which changes the world for both characters. In the workshop, the group identified the main event of the play as the moment when all the characters come together at the tree – the moment that the play is building towards that brings the characters together in the same space for the first time.

Identifying the events will really help to shape the fluidity of the one long scene structure. They will create a shape to work from, and provide punctuation within the text. This will also help to create a plan for you to build your rehearsal process round, breaking the text into smaller, more manageable chunks that you can rehearse. Caroline suggested finding the large units on your own but then working with the company to find the events of the play. This will create a common language and enable you to solve the play together. The whole company can then share the challenges of the play and find solutions together.

FINDING THE EVENTS

It is important to note that there is no right and wrong when finding events, just whatever you feel is useful.

Read from the beginning of the play and pay attention to changes for the characters and in the atmosphere. It's worth spending some time on the opening so that you are clear about what you want your production to be as it will define your vision to the audience.

The group identified the following key events:

INCITING INCIDENT   The text Antler receives from Crystal about visiting Gran

This is the moment that begins the action of the whole play. If Antler did not receive this message, she would not begin her protest and the play would not take place.

Another incident takes place before the start of the play: Antler sending a text to Oil. What mood is she in when she leaves the house? This all useful background information to use in building a picture of Antler at the opening of the play.

EVENT ONE: ANTLER SMASHING HER PHONE   The intention starts on the line 'pulling out her phone'. This is the first time we hear from Antler and is important for connecting her with the audience. It is a vital image and ends Antler's connection with the real world. Think about what is important – is it the phone-smashing or the decision to do it? What is the recovery for Antler after she has done it? How does the ensemble drive the audience's focus? Is Antler talking to the audience, to herself, rand/or interacting with the ensemble? This all forms the basis of your vision for the play.

EVENT TWO: CHANGE OF LOCATION TO THE PARK   This starts on the line, 'I've got somewhere I need to be'. This is the first time we change location and needs to be used to define how you will do this. How do we change location? The use of the ensemble, set, lighting and sound will all help to define this. You might wish to clear the whole stage to create the space of the park.

EVENT THREE: ANTLER CLIMBING THE TREE   This begins with a change at the line, 'With one thought, she leaves something behind her', and then begins on the line, 'And then she reaches for the nearest branch'. This is a vital moment as it creates the tree and Antler's physical place for the rest of the play. The journey up the tree ends on the line, 'Then she finds a branch solid and strong'.

FINDING THE UNITS
The group identified the first three major units of the play as follows:

UNIT ONE: OPENING UP UNTIL ANTLER'S MANIFESTO   The ensemble drives this and shifts the focus from Antler to Oil at the end.

UNIT TWO: OIL AND THE NEW LOCATION OF THE PARK
This begins with a new location as we move to the other side of the park and meet Oil. There is a very different feel in this unit – the difference in energy between Antler and Oil, the tension between the characters. Antler not answering the phone changes the shape of the world.

UNIT THREE: CRYSTAL IN ANTLER'S BEDROOM   This begins with 'somewhere a girl knocks on a door' and encompasses the next part of the story with the introduction of Crystal.

GIVING EACH UNIT A TITLE

It can be really useful to give each unit/event a title, so that everyone involved in your group always knows what that scene is, and it heightens the clarity of storytelling to the audience. You could invite your company to come up with the following different types of title for a unit:

- Create one sentence that best and most simply sums up the narrative of that mini-scene.
- Find a title in one word for your unit that refers to the action that takes place.
- Come up with a title to describe the story within your section by relating it to the weather.
- Choose a Twitter-style hashtag that best relates to your unit.
- Inspired by Arthur Miller's habit of taping one sentence above his typewriter as a reference to himself to sum up the essence of his play, construct a sentence that encapsulates what a character within your mini-scene wants, with a 'but' in the middle – to identify the obstacles that they face.

This last title type really makes you think about the drama of the scene, and the obstacles present for each character. For example 'Antler wants to escape the world but . . . '

Here is an example of the various unit titles:

Unit one

- Antler cuts herself off from the world and climbs a tree
- Disconnect
- A dense haar (fog or haze – that Antler needs to get around to have clarity)
- #distance
- Antler wants to escape the world, but can only get above it

You can go through the whole play titling each mini-scene you've identified in one of these ways. When putting all these unit titles together you could get a clear sense of the story.

This process can be essential as a director, especially when you reach a certain stage in your rehearsals when more practical issues come up and take your attention. It helps to keep the play clear for you and your cast. You can do as much or little of this work with your group depending on the time that you have.

Language

Stef is happy for any mention of 'high school' to be changed to 'college', if that helps with any references to the ages of your characters and cast.

There are only a couple of swear words and it is felt that these are important and should not be changed.

The punctuation is used deliberately – the full stops are used to denote rhythm, particularly in the ensemble's lines. In general it means the full stop is the end of a thought and then a new thought begins. A line without a full stop is an extension of thought.

Characters and characterisation

If there is any confusion over the kiss between Crystal and Finn, and who kisses who, Stef thought it was Crystal who kissed Finn, but stated that it is completely open to interpretation.

The abstractness of the characters' names can be regarded as another indication of the openness of this world, and is for you to fill in as you and your group choose.

Antler and Crystal are in their mid- to late teens and are one year apart (as it says in the script).

However, the characters can be cast as younger, depending on your actors. Antler is very astute and mature for her age.

Killing the dog probably did change Blister. He is not very emotionally intelligent, and wouldn't question the impulse he might have to do something destructive – he'd just live in the aftermath of it.

Blister is distant and distances himself more as the play goes on.

Blister and Skin probably don't go out looking for trouble, they don't hunt people and things out, but if they do come across them they can't resist the urge and instinct to bully.

Towards the end of the play, Blister and Skin stay by the tree with Antler and the others for as long as they do, partly because they're looking for comfort, and see warmth in the group. However, they are still complete outsiders, and when they're asked to leave, they know they don't belong there.

With this play being set so much within the present, Stef is also very aware of how full teenagers' lives are outside this moment, and she strongly suggested that all the actors should think about what their characters' lives would be like at home.

CHARACTER EXERCISE

Caroline and Richard suggested a character exercise that can be completed in small groups or that actors can do on their own.

- Choose a character in the play and go through the text, underlining every fact about them. Here, a 'fact' refers to anything that is concretely said in the script.

It is always key to start from within the text, as this is the backbone of facts, which you can then use as a starting point for your imagination to fill in. With this in mind, ask actors to answer some specific questions. There are suggestions below as a starting point:

- Age.
- Full name.
- Clues in the text of physical characteristics.
- How do they feel about money and where does their money come from?
- Where do they live?
- Is there something they lack in life?
- Is there something they need right now?
- Do they have a secret?
- Do they have a problem?
- Do they have a memory?
- Is there something that they believe in?
- Do they have parents and, if they do, where are they?

Below is an example of this exercise using the character of
Antler:

Antler

AGE   Sixteen.

FULL NAME   Antler – there is a story behind her name but
we don't hear this in the play (so this is up to your company
to decide).

CLUES IN THE TEXT OF PHYSICAL CHARACTERISTICS
Quick, speedy, on edge.

HOW DO THEY FEEL ABOUT MONEY AND WHERE DOES
THEIR MONEY COME FROM?   She has more than a pound.

WHERE DO THEY LIVE?   At home with her parents and
sister Crystal.

IS THERE SOMETHING THEY LACK IN LIFE?   The power to
change anything, a sense of peace.

IS THERE SOMETHING THEY NEED RIGHT NOW?   She needs
to change the way things are.

DO THEY HAVE A SECRET?   She smokes at parties; how she
got her name; how much Crystal's text had hurt her.

DO THEY HAVE A PROBLEM?   Everything is a problem,
everything matters. School is a problem and others' apathy.
Her mum cries in the bathroom and her dad is smoking
again – are they getting divorced?

DO THEY HAVE A MEMORY?   Things seemed better when
she was young, gymnastics, playing in the park, Dad used to
smoke.

IS THERE SOMETHING THAT THEY BELIEVE IN?   She
believes something should be done. She wants to be an
activist but doesn't know how to do it. She is thinking about
what world she wants to grow up in and how she wants it to
be better than it is now.

DO THEY HAVE PARENTS AND, IF THEY DO, WHERE ARE
THEY?   Yes, at home with her.

The ensemble (chorus)

The play is written to be performed with an ensemble which can be flexible depending on the size of your company – it could be three or thirty actors depending on what you require. The ensemble is a vital aspect of the storytelling and you should think carefully about how you want to use it in your production. They can actively move the action – i.e. cue the story physically by prompting action – or remain purely as narrators. They can tell the truth and also not know all the answers. It is up to you how you wish to use them and the style that you are going for in your production.

The ensemble is a chorus – they know everyone and the inner workings of all the characters. They are talking to the audience: think about how they do this. Do they make eye-contact with them? Are they acting purely as narrators or do they drive the action in some way, e.g. working with Antler to tell her story? Usually a chorus is always right; however, in *Remote* they contradict each other and make changes to the detail of the story. Think carefully about how you want this to be seen by the audience. Also think about how you might use the ensemble to create the physical shape of the play – the space of the park or Blister's gang – and how the story could emerge from the bodies of the ensemble.

You can be really specific with who the ensemble is – or wide open. This will obviously have an impact on your costume and design choices as well as how the ensemble is used.

Stef advised the groups to avoid having the chorus speak entirely in unison throughout the whole play. Speaking in unison could be used by the groups at moments, but Stef suggested that they should be conscious of how this might affect the pace and clarity. Ultimately the chorus drives the play forward; Stef encouraged everyone to be mindful of the chorus not collapsing in on itself. To help with this, she suggested keeping it light and not allowing the delivery to get too slow, this will ensure the pace is always moving forwards, and will keep the audience engaged from the very start.

Rehearsal exercises

GAME: WINK

A circle game.

- The group is in pairs, creating two circles with one person standing in front of the other and all facing in. There needs to be one free person who is 'it' to start the game. The aim is for the free person to get someone to join him by winking at someone in the inner circle so they run to him and stand behind him. But their partner can stop them leaving by tapping them on the arms or back.

This game places everyone on the front foot and gets them active and engaged. This is a brilliant warm-up for this play as it is precisely this energy that your company needs – the play needs momentum and drive.

You could go to a park with your group and try to perform some scenes there, if possible. The quality of acting and speaking outside in an open environment might be really beneficial and enlightening to your process and the world of the play that you are creating together.

ACTING EXERCISE I

This exercise encourages a better quality of active listening and helps the pace.

- Divide the group into pairs. Choose a scene to read through aloud and to always repeat the other characters' last two words before speaking each of their own lines of dialogue.

- Next, play the scene again, but without the repetition.

ACTING EXERCISE 2

- Divide the company into groups of four, then split into two pairs; one pair acts as 'feeders' for the other pair. Choose a scene and ask the 'feeders' to feed the other pair their text, line by line, for them to speak as they hear the words.

Although actors may feel self-conscious when they first start doing this exercise, it can potentially be very liberating for them – having no scripts in their hands and feeling more and more free as the exercise continues.

The feeders can also experiment with overlapping their feeding lines, varying the rhythm and pace, and making it more playful.

Status

It might be useful to think about the status of each character and how this may change throughout the play. You could mark their status between one and ten for every scene.

- Ask the actors to get into a line according to the status of their character, with high status at one end and low status at the other. See how this changes at different points in the play.

Design

The play requires a fluid and flexible design that allows for the space to change. Think about what the story is that you are trying to tell and then make design choices that support this for the audience. Your design concept should match the style of the play and work within the space you have rather than against it. It could be possible to stage this entirely rooted in the poetry of the play, using the ensemble to create the locations through the language.

Consider the practical production challenge of the action of Antler climbing the tree. How could you attain literal, physical height for this moment?

Ideas from the workshop included: scaffolding, stage blocks, rope, human lift, other actors lowering themselves, balcony, raked stage with Antler at the furthest upstage point, climbing frame, a pile of something from the world of the play (litter, for example), use of projection, mirrors, balloons, a pile of filled bin-liners, beanbags, crates, puppet, lifeguard-type chair, climbing nets, cherry-picker, stilts, A-frame, trapeze.

It could also be interesting to explore how to create the tree without using physical height. The workshop group came up with a range of options: using the ensemble and props such as books with the pages moving in the breeze or ribbons; using a camera and projection, with the camera looking up at Antler somewhere onstage to create the illusion of height; Antler being in the audience.

It could be possible to create something that Antler moves with herself – such as ribbons – and that the ensemble helps to create around her. Or it might work to place the tree firmly in the centre of the space and for the action to take place around it.

You could also give your company the challenge of finding non-literal ways of representing height using no set at all.

Lighting and sound

As with the set design, think carefully about your vision of the play when deciding how to use lighting and sound. The lighting can really help to create a sense of space and the light and shade of the park, but again, keep it simple and work with what you have. The play has a filmic quality and lends itself well to sound. There could be exciting possibilities for how you might use sound to drive the story and change locations.

Casting

While there is some flexibility for gender within this play, Stef would prefer for the casting to be as written, allowing for Desk to be played by either a boy or a girl. The exception to this is within single-sex schools where the casting could be flexible to suit the company.

There are some interesting questions to play with in the casting of the play. It can question people's perception of gender; the relationship between Skin and Blister provides a different perspective on how young women are often seen, and the casting of Desk can allow for the audience to see a gentle male role model. Think about what story you would like to tell and how your casting can help to shape this.

The kiss

This is a vital moment in the play and is clearly written as a kiss between two female characters. Stef said the kiss should feel like a positive moment within the play and in many ways it should feel entirely normal to both characters. This idea is highlighted later when Antler states that she has better things to fight than 'some girl because she kissed another girl'. She is alluding to the fact that these two girls kissing is entirely normal and Skin is just being pathetic by picking on something that is in fact not a problem.

There is an acknowledgement that a kiss between two girls might be challenging for some companies and audiences. Be sensitive to this in the casting of Finn and Crystal and in rehearsals and staging of the moment, and be clear on the importance of the kiss in your vision of the play. Any moment of intimacy requires gentle handling, so make sure that you take your actors' concerns into consideration when rehearsing.

Suggested reference

YouTube: International Devising Theatre Company (for ideas about the staging of the tree through movement and physical theatre).

The Crazy Sexy Cool

Girls' Fan Club

By Sarah Solemani

What makes a 'fan' girl? Who are they? What do they want? Who are the band? What are they in it for? And at £200 a ticket, who is the band's fan base? Surely not girls aged nine to sixteen?

This riotous satire explores the teen politics of a 'friendship group' and the chaos and torment that can come with stardom at an early age. A play about desire, fantasy and worship with a hilarious and horrifying showdown finish.

Age suitability: 13+

Cast size:
11 main characters
with potential for ensemble

Sarah Solemani is an award-winning actress and writer. Her performance as Becky in the BAFTA Award-winning BBC sitcom *Him & Her* won her the Royal Television Society Award for Best Comedy Performance. Her drama *The Conversation*, in which she also starred, was produced by Working Title for the BBC. Her comedy *Aphrodite Fry*, in which she also starred, was produced by Ruby for SKY and was described by Metro as 'a British answer to *Girls*'. She is under commission to write original comedy with FX Studio in the US and has work in development with Kudos, Tiger Aspect and Working Title. As a playwright, her first play was produced by the National Youth Theatre, where she started acting. Since then, her plays have been perormed at the Soho Theatre, Lyric Hammersmith, Arcola, Southwark Playhouse, Old Vic, Theatre503 and the Public Theater, New York.

Characters

♫ Lyrics of a song are indicated thus. They can be sung, chanted or spoken in whichever way the company see fit. The company can decide whether to compose music, to add variation or keep the same throughout – it is open to interpretation and should play to the company's strengths.

The only props really needed are a towel, a brick and an empty foil takeaway box. Crowd sounds and light changes are all that are required to indicate a sense of the crowd, foreboding and change of place.

Scene One

Jasmine, **Prancheeta**, **Lou** and **Gloria** *are singing in unison. It's almost aggressive.*

Another girl, **Jess**, *watches them, standing apart from the group.*

Jasmine/Pracheeta/Lou/Gloria
♪ Baby baby baby. You are beautiful. You are mine. Beautiful face. Beautiful –

Jess
♪ Beautiful body –

The girls stop as **Jess** *joins in.*

Jess *stops singing.*

They stare at her.

When she's silent, they start singing again.

Jasmine/Pracheeta/Lou/Gloria
♪ Beautiful face beautiful body, you are mine –

Jess
♪ You are mine. You are mi –

The girls stop singing.

Jess *trails off.*

They stare at her.

Jess   Sorry.

They look at **Gloria** *to lead them.*

Gloria *(staring at* **Jess***)*   So?

Jess *doesn't know what to say.*

Gloria   You know all the words?

Jess   Yeah.

Gloria   All the words to all the songs?

Jess   Yeah. I think . . . Yeah.

Gloria   So?

Jess *is stuck.*

Prancheeta   The point is, it's about *more* than words.

Lou   *So* much more than words.

Prancheeta   I just said that.

Lou   Sorry.

Jasmine   It's what the words *represent*.

Jess   Oh. Yeah. Okay.

Gloria   It's how you *feel* when you're saying them that counts.

Jess   Yeah.

Pause. They stare at her, unimpressed.

Jasmine   So who's your favourite?

Jess   Sam Gamble.

The girls look at each other.

Jasmine (*murmurs loudly*)   Ob-vi-ous-ly.

Jess *looks uncomfortable. Silence.*

Prancheeta   Why are you even here?

Lou   Yeah, why are you even here?

Prancheeta *throws a look at* **Lou**.

Jasmine   We're not 'cool' or anything.

Gloria   People say things. People might have told you 'They're cool', 'They're sexy', 'They're crazy' –

Lou   'They're cool'.

Gloria   But we're not. Not *really*.

Prancheeta   We're just regular girls.

Lou   Regular girls, that's all we are.

Prancheeta (*to* **Lou**)   Oh my God.

Lou   What?

Prancheeta (*to the other girls*)   I mean, come on. Do you know what I mean?

Lou   What? What have I done? I haven't done anything?

Prancheeta   You know . . . It's just like getting ridiculous now.

Lou   I haven't done . . . what've I . . . ?

Prancheeta   Will you just stop copying me for once in your life?

Lou   I'm not –

Prancheeta   It's like I can't breathe! It's like . . . give me some space . . . like, stop doing everything I do . . . Even your hair . . . it's beyond, like . . .

Lou   I'm not . . . I wasn't . . . Don't be like that.

Prancheeta   Do you know what I mean though? *God.*

Jasmine   Come on, guys, we're in the middle of an interview.

Gloria   I think we're done.

Jasmine   Really?

Gloria   Aren't you done?

Jasmine *looks* **Jess** *up and down.*

Jasmine   Erm . . . I don't know.

Gloria   Prancheeta?

Prancheeta   What?

Gloria   Are you d –

Prancheeta   I don't even care any more I'm just like . . .
whatever . . . I just like I don't even care.

Gloria   Lou ? Are you done?

Lou   If you are. I am. Like, I can be.

Gloria   Okay.

She stares at **Jess**.

Jess   So am I in?

She looks at all the girls.

Gloria   It's not my decision.

Jess   Oh.

Gloria   So don't look at me. Because it's not up to me.
We're a group. We're a democracy. If it were just up to me . . .
If only I made the rules, that would make me a big . . .
bastard . . . so it's not up to me. It can't be.

Jess   Okay.

Jasmine   It's always a group decision. Whenever we take
a new member.

Jess   Sure.

Prancheeta   We do things together – like a collective.

Lou   It's like a collective.

Lou   I swear to God I had that thought too, I like literally
had that thought 'it's a collective' at the same time as you,
just . . .

Prancheeta   You can join. I think. That's what I think
anyway.

Jasmine   Really?

Gloria   *Really?*

Prancheeta   Yeah. I mean, you seem cool, you seem . . . fresh, you know . . . Fresh is good.

Lou   It's good. It is.

Jess   Wow. Thanks. Thanks so much.

Jasmine   Hang on. You haven't asked me.

Jess *looks at* **Jasmine**.

Jasmine   Ask me then. If you want an answer, you've gotta, like, ask.

Jess   Can I, Jasmine? Can I join?

Jasmine   Can you join the club?

Jess   Yeah

Jasmine   This club?

Jess   Yes please.

Jasmine   You wanna be a member of our club, our little club?

Jess   I'd really like to.

Jasmine   In that case . . . my answer is . . . Yeah. Okay.

Jess   Wow thanks. Thank you! Thank you so much.

Lou   I think you're really nice. Your head is a really good shape. And your ears are nice. I like the way they poke through your hair.

Jess   Really? I hate that.

Lou   I like it, it's kind of funny.

Jess   Thanks.

Gloria   Hello? I'm standing here. I do have an opinion.

They look at **Gloria**.

Gloria I've been standing here and none of you have even listened to a word I've said, it's like, what is wrong with everyone, am I completely invisible should I just go and lie down on the ground and die or something?

Lou Sorry, Gloria.

Jasmine Sorry.

Prancheeta Sorry.

Gloria Okay . . . okay, forget it. So. 'Should Jess be in the club?' It's difficult.

Jess I'd like to be.

Gloria Erm, yeah? I think we got that part.

Jess Sorry.

Gloria I think we're all clear on what you want. It's not all about you.

Jess Yeah, I know. Sorry.

Gloria Okay. My answer: 'Should Jess be in the club?'

She stares **Jess** *up and down.*

Gloria Should Jess be . . .

She walks over to her and walks round her in a circle.

Gloria In . . . the . . . club? The club? Club club. Club club club.

The others stare at her.

Gloria Answer is . . . mmm . . . Yyyyyeee . . . Noo.

Jasmine What?

Gloria No.

Lou Really?

Gloria No.

Jess   Oh.

Prancheeta   Gloria. Come on.

Gloria   No. Sorry. No way.

Jess   'No way'?

Gloria   No. *No* way. Not going to happen. Negative. Nooooo.

Jess   That's like, that just . . . Okay. Wow.

Jasmine   I thought she should be.

Gloria   Yeah, but you don't know what I know.

Lou   What do you know?

Gloria   Secrets. About *her*.

Jess *looks ashamed.*

Gloria   Where she's come from. What she's left behind.

Lou   What has she left behind?

Gloria *stares at* **Jess***.* **Lou** *gets excited and scared.*

Lou   Who the hell is she? Tell us, Gloria.

Prancheeta   Tell us, for God's sake.

Jasmine   She's faking. She doesn't know.

Gloria   I *do* know.

Jasmine   You're faking.

Gloria   She was expelled. From her last school. Weren't you?

Lou *gasps.*

Lou   Really?

Prancheeta   Were you? Were you expelled?

Jess *looks at them. Decides to be honest.*

Jess   I was, yeah.

Prancheeta   What for?

Lou   Oh my God, what the hell did you do I'm like freaking out.

Prancheeta   Okay, *God*, stop making such a drama out of everything, it's so annoying, do you know what I mean.

Jasmine   What did you do?

Jess   I was texting.

Gloria   Texting?

Jess   Yeah. I was texting someone.

Lou   Was it rude?

Prancheeta   Must have been, to be expelled.

Jasmine   Your boobs?

Prancheeta   Must have been ruder than that, if she got ex –

Jasmine   Okay. Your bum hole or something?

Jess   No. Not that.

Lou   It was rude though.

Jess   Not really. I was texting my mum saying I'd get the bus back.

Lou   Well then . . . why would they . . .

She looks to the others in confusion.

Gloria   Seems a bit harsh.

Prancheeta   Very harsh.

Jess   I shouldn't have been using the phone.

She looks at the other girls.

Because it had been confiscated.

Lou   Oh. Okay.

Jess   And because the school was closed.

Gloria (*suspicious*)   Yeah?

Jess   And I had broken in.

Gloria   You broke in to your school?

Jess   Yeah.

The girls look stunned.

I smashed a window with my design technology coursework. It was a bird house made of MDF.

The dynamic shifts between the other girls and **Jess**.

Jasmine   So you just . . . you just bashed in a window.

Jess   Yeah.

Lou   That's so cool.

Prancheeta   I think that's cool.

Jasmine   How did you know how to do it?

Jess (*shrugs*)   Practice. (*Off the girls' stares.*) I've lost my keys a couple of times when my parents were in Spain.

Jasmine   Your parents go to Spain without you?

Jess   Well, my mum and her boyfriend.

Prancheeta   What about your dad?

Jess   I don't know my dad.

Prancheeta   Why not?

Jess   He had problems with commitment.

Prancheeta   What kind of problems?

Jess   Is this still the interview?

Lou   It's cool not to know your dad. I think so anyway.

Jess   Thanks.

A beat. The girls seem taken back. Impressed.

Jasmine   I've never broken into anything.

Jess   It's not hard.

Lou   I wouldn't know what to do.

Jess   It's really easy. When you know how.

Prancheeta   Is it?

Jess   Yeah, I mean, if you want to I can show you how to break into places.

The girls look at each other.

Gloria   We don't need to be taught how to break into things. We're not like that. Are we?

The girls look at her.

I'm not, anyway.

Jasmine   This is a fan club, Jess. Do you know what that means?

Jess   We like the same band?

The girls sigh and look at each other.

Jasmine   Okay. Who is going to tell her?

Lou   I'll tell her.

Jasmine   I'll tell her.

Lou   Or you? You could tell her.

Jasmine   We don't just 'like' the same band. We're not like the other stupid clubs.

Prancheeta   It's not about singing or dancing to their songs, though we are the best at that.

Jasmine   Show her your spin, Lou.

Lou *spins.*

Jasmine   Now do it with the lyrics.

Lou
    ♫ Baby baby baby, you are beautiful you are mine.

She spins on the spot.

They look at **Jess** *for a reaction.*

Jess   Well done.

Lou   Thanks.

Jasmine   No one spins as well as Lou.

Jess   No.

Jasmine   But that's not all we do. We go waving.

Jess   Waving?

Jasmine   Yeah. Waving.

Gloria   We've waved at them seventeen times.

Jasmine   And they've waved back seventeen times.

The lights change.

The sound of a crowd roaring. The girls take their places in the crowd.

Lou   Come in, stay with us, don't get separated.

Prancheeta   We link arms sometimes, so we stay together. You can link my arm if you like.

Jess *goes into the line and she links arms.*

Jasmine   If people push into you, just step back like this and tread on them, like this.

She steps back onto an imaginary part of the crowd. Suddenly the roar of the crowd, screams of girls.

Jasmine   See. There they are! On the roof. See?

Shaz, Lee, Mark, Jon *appear on the roof of a hotel.*

Jess   Oh my God.

Jasmine   See?

Lou   Can you see them, Jess?

Jess   Oh my God.

Lou   We wave and wave and wave. We wave like this.

The girls wave frantically.

And we shout.

The girls shout their names − 'Shaz, Lee, Jon, Mark' − and 'We love you', 'Over here', 'Look at us', 'Please look at us'.

Jess   But where's . . . hang on, is that − ?

Sam *arrives on stage. The crowd go absolutely mental.*

Jasmine   There he is.

Prancheeta   Sam Gamble.

Gloria   Just look at him.

Lou   Oh wow.

The band sing and dance

> ♪ Baby baby you are beautiful you are mine
>   Beautiful face beautiful body
>   You are mine you are mine.

They wave at the girls, who are all screaming.

Prancheeta   I love him so much it makes me angry.

She roars with anger.

Jess   I can't see properly.

Sam *strolls around the roof, waving at people.*

Jess   I want to be closer.

Lou   We're the closest you can be.

Jess   We can get closer, can't we?

Arms linked with the girls, she tries to push through the crowd.

Gloria   Hey. Stop pushing. *Hey!*

Jess   Let's charge. Let's go forward.

Gloria   We can't. This is our place, we can't push in.

Jess   We can, come on.

Lou   Should we?

Gloria   No. We'll fall. Stop pushing.

Jess   Come on. We can get much closer than this. We can get to the front.

She charges forward and, because she's linked arms with the girls, they topple over.

The lights change. The girls get up.

Gloria   What the hell are you doing?

They all stare at **Jess**.

Gloria   I don't like the way you did that, you pushed me, I just stubbed my toe.

Jasmine   It would have been fun to be a bit closer.

Gloria   You're not even in the club yet, she's not even in the club yet, and she's behaving like that.

Jess   Sorry.

Prancheeta   What did you think would happen?

Jess   I don't know. I mean . . . it's just waving.

The girls look at each other.

If this is a fan club then it should have special fan club privileges. You should do things differently to the rest of the crowd.

Gloria   I don't even know what she's saying. I'm not even *hearing* her.

Jess   Why stand outside in the cold when you could be inside hanging out with the band.

Lou   Hanging out with the band? Hanging with the . . . I've never even thought about that.

Jess   Well, maybe you should.

Lou   What, *me?* Hanging *out?* With . . . the *band?*

Gradually the lights change. **Lou** *steps into the spotlight.*

Shaz *comes out of the bathroom and* **Lou** *hands him a towel.*

Lou   Hey Shaz, here's your towel.

Shaz   Oh hey, Lou.

Lou   How was your bath?

Shaz   It was great.

Lou   Temperature alright?

Shaz   Yeah, nice and hot.

Lou   That's how I like my baths. Nice and hot. Make the skin go red.

Shaz   Yeah.

Lou   Lavender?

Shaz   Tea tree.

They smile at each other.

Lou   Nice.

Shaz   Soothing.

They stare at each other.

Shaz   Can I sing for you?

Lou Of course! I'll get the others. Prancheeta! Jess! Jasmine!

Shaz   No, forget about them. Can I sing just for you?

Lou   Yeah, wow, I'd love that.

Shaz
♪ Lou, baby, Lou, baby you are beautiful
   You are beautiful, you are mine! Beautiful face,
   Beautiful body, you are mine, you are mine.

Lou   Thank you, but it's not true.

Shaz   It is. You are. And I've heard you have the best spins. Can we spin together?

Lou   Of course we can.

They spin together. They spin and spin and spin.

Shaz   You're very pretty you know. Can I touch you? I'll be gentle.

Lou   I don't think so.

Shaz   You should let me touch you.

Lou   No thanks. I better be going now. Bye.

Lights change. The girls laugh at **Lou**.

Prancheeta   'How was your bath?' That was the most pathetic, embarrassing –

Lou   What? What's wrong with that?

The other girls laugh.

Prancheeta (*scornful*)   You are in a room with Shaz from *the Band* and the *only* thing you talk about is the *temperature* of his *bath water*? Unbelievable, Lou. You really let yourself down there.

Lou   Don't say that.

Prancheeta   Bit shameful if you ask me.

Jasmine   As if you would be any better, Prancheeta.

Lou   Yeah. As *if*.

Prancheeta   Me?

Jasmine   Yeah. You'd be just as bad.

Gloria   Worse, if anything.

Prancheeta   I wouldn't. I'd be cool. I'd be natural.

Jess   Would you?

Prancheeta   Course.

Jess   Go on then.

Prancheeta   Fine.

The lights change. **Prancheeta** *is in a room with* **Sam**.

A moment, before she loses it completely and starts screaming.

Prancheeta   Oh my God. It's *Sam Gamble*. Oh my God, it's him.

Sam *stands with his hands out looking like a trapped animal.*

Sam   How did you get in here?

Prancheeta   Don't move! Stay exactly where you are. Oh my God. Oh my God.

She fiddles frantically with her phone.

Sam   I need to get to back to my bandmates. We have a performance.

Prancheeta (*panicked*)   My video isn't working!

Sam   But I'm here. I'm standing here.

Prancheeta   I'm missing everything. God's sake!

Sam *waits while she fiddles with her phone. This takes some time.*

Sam You're not missing anything. You're here and I'm here.

Prancheeta *stops and looks at him.*

Prancheeta (*deadly*) If I don't capture the moment it doesn't exist.

Sam We could just have a conversation, if you put the phone down.

Prancheeta No! Don't be dense. It won't mean anything that way, will it?

Sam In that case I've got to go.

Prancheeta Aha! I've got it. It's working. Thank *God*. Stay there. Stay right where you are.

With her phone still out in one hand, she uses her other to touch his face. She touches it, but the grip tightens and tightens. She talks into her phone.

Prancheeta Hi . . . This is Prancheeta and I'm . . . with . . . Guess who? Sam Gamble from the Band. Yes, it's true. And I'm actually touching his face.

Sam Okay. Oww.

Prancheeta *digs her nails into his face and tugs at his cheek.*

Prancheeta It feels just like any old face but it's not, it's Sam Gamble's.

Sam Oww!

Prancheeta *drags his face down. She drives her fingernails into his face then looks at her hand.*

Prancheeta Blood. Sam Gamble's blood.

She videos the blood with her hand. She looks at it. Then she tastes it.

Sam *screams.*

The lights change.

Prancheeta *finds herself with her fingers in her mouth. Slightly shocked, she slowly removes them and puts them by her side.*

Prancheeta   I must remember to get my phone fixed.

Lou   Okay, I'm freaking out now, things are getting weird. Did anyone notice that Shaz tried to touch me? Was that creepy to anyone or . . .

Prancheeta   I just made Sam Gamble bleed.

Gloria   Okay, Jess. Okay. I don't know how you did things at your last school before you got *expelled*, but we don't do things like this. We're not that kind of fan club.

Jess   We're just thinking out loud, Gloria. That's all. It's not a problem if you can't take it.

Gloria   I can take it.

Jess   Go on then. Your turn. If you can take it.

Gloria   No. Why should I? Who the hell do you think you –

Jasmine   I'll go. I know what to do. I know how to work it.

Prancheeta   How?

Lou   Careful, Jasmine.

Jasmine   Obvious. I'd have a show. *The Jasmine Show*. On television.

The lights change.

TV Voice   Now on . . . *The Jasmine Show* please welcome . . . The Band.

The Band – **Mark**, **Jon**, **Lee**, **Shaz** *and* **Sam** *– come onstage and do their song.*

♫ Baby baby baby, you are beautiful you are mine,
Beautiful face beautiful body
You are mine you are mine

They stop to applause. A TV presenter – **Jasmine** *– bounds on stage.*

Jasmine   It doesn't matter how many times we hear it, and we've heard it literally thousands of times, haven't we?

Mark   Yeah it's been played quite a bit, we're really chuffed.

Jasmine   But it just gets better. Guys, guys . . . The Band!

Audience screams.

I mean, you turn on the radio, the TV, open a newspaper, a magazine and – there you guys are. You are literally literally everywhere. The other day, this may be a bit intimate, but the other day, this is God's honest truth, I was on the toilet and I . . . I wiped myself and –

The audience laugh.

No listen, this is literally true, I wiped myself after I'd been, you know, after the toilet, and there you were. The Band on – loo roll. Wow. Guys. Your toilet paper range it's – it's really taken off, hasn't it?

Shaz   Yeah, we were totally chuffed we got that deal with Andrex, we're really fortunate not only to be in people's bedrooms and living rooms but also to be in their bathrooms too – that's quite amazing.

Mark   No one's managed that.

Jon   Not even the Beatles were in bathrooms.

Lee   Yeah, and we're really grateful for that. So thank you all our fans. Thank you.

More screams.

Jasmine   How do you . . . deal with everything you've achieved. Mark ?

Mark   Erm, God, yeah –

Jasmine   What's the biggest achievement?

Mark   Wow. Erm, I think, probably buying my nan a house.

Audience 'ahh's.

Mark   She lived in a tiny council house her whole life. She never had anything. She didn't have a microwave, she didn't have a flat-screen TV, didn't have a computer, she just hung out with her church friends. So to be able to buy all that for her – has been really amazing. Really amazing. Yeah, hardly leaves the house any more, she just presses the channels, I think there's nearly three hundred channels? And she just flicks through them but she never actually watches anything – she's crazy!

Audience laugh. **Jasmine** *laughs harder.*

Jasmine   Shaz. What's your biggest achievement?

Shaz   Has to be travelling the world. Me and Jon had a bet we could try a McChicken Sandwich in every country in the world. And we did. And you know what – they are all the same. It's true. Everywhere you go, McChicken Sandwich is the same. Apart from Israel – they don't serve cheese on the chickenburger because of religious reasons. So yeah, culturally, like, travelling the world – that was incredible.

Jasmine   Jon?

Jon   The clothes. Has to be. Free clothes!

Jasmine   Literally amazing. Lee?

Lee   We've met all the famous people. And they all know our names!

Mark   Tell 'em, tell 'em what you did.

Lee   Oh God. This man came up to me and was like 'LEE. LEE! My niece is a massive fan – can I get an autograph?' And I had no idea who he was. No idea at all. But I did the photo and afterwards they were like, 'You idiot – you total idiot – don't you realise who that was?'

Jasmine   This is such a funny story, Lee. Who was it?

Lee   That was . . . oh God, now I've forgotten again, who was he . . . ?

Mark   Which one? They've been so many.

Lee   Black guy, really really famous. The most famous black guy.

Jasmine   Not Obama?

Lee   No, not him. Second most famous black guy. Wears a hat. Religious.

Mark   Desmond Tutu!

Lee   That's it, Desmond Tutu. No idea who he was. Totally embarrassing.

Everyone laughs. **Jasmine** *laughs.*

Jasmine   Sam? Biggest achievement?

Sam   Nothing.

Jasmine   What?

Sam   Nothing.

Jasmine   Come again?

Sam   Nothing.

Jasmine   That's literally hilarious, but I'm going to push you for one thing. What do you feel most proud of?

Sam *shrugs. He looks at the other boys.*

Mark   Mate.

Jasmine *drops her TV presenter act and turns to the audience.*

Jasmine   Right, can we stop there? We can't use that. Let's go again. Also I think I have a hair stuck in my tooth. It's like . . . (*Fiddles with her mouth.*) stuck at the back of my – So, hello – *hair*? Can someone come? Or make-up? Which department is it? Not sure. Someone? *Hello?*

Silence.

The lights change.

Jasmine   Wow. I don't think working in television suits me.

Prancheeta   You were so annoying.

Jasmine   I was, wasn't I? God, I was really annoying.

Lou   Why was Sam Gamble being like that?

Gloria   Who cares? This is stupid. Let's go. Lou – let's go back to yours.

Lou *looks at* **Gloria**. **Lou** *looks at* **Jess**.

Jess   Do you want to go back to yours, Lou?

Lou *looks uncomfortable.*

Jess   Lou's fine here, Gloria. You go home if you want to. We don't mind.

Gloria *looks stuck.*

Lou   She doesn't like going home.

Gloria   Don't –

Lou   She doesn't like it.

Jess   What's wrong with home? Gloria, what's wrong with home?

Lights change.

Shaz, **Jon**, **Mark** *and* **Lee** *are sitting around a kitchen table, eating.*

Jon   Gloria. Your dinner's ready!

Mark   Your favourite! Chicken and potatoes.

Gloria   Coming!

She enters.

Shaz   You must be starving.

Gloria   I am. I had netball.

Lee   Easy on the salt.

Jon She's so good at sports, I can't believe you are my daughter.

Shaz We were terrible at sports, weren't we?

Gloria I'm nothing special.

Jon God, I love my daughter!

Gloria I love you, Jon.

Shaz My sweet darling.

Gloria I love you, Shaz. And you, Lee.

Lee My favourite Gloria. I love you with all my heart.

Gloria Hmm, this is delicious.

Lee Tell us what you will be, Gloria, when you're a grown-up and have left home.

Gloria An astronaut. I'm going to be the Christopher Columbus of space. I'm going to discover all the planets that no one realises are there. I'll discover them. And send humans up to live on them so everyone has all the space they need. And there'll be no more wars over land or resources because there'll be enough planets for everyone.

Lee Clever Gloria.

Shaz Special Gloria

Mark Good Gloria.

Jon Careful, here comes Sam, he's angry because of all our debts so don't say anything to upset him.

Sam *joins – we can tell he's angry.*

Gloria Hi, Sam.

Sam Let me eat in peace.

They eat.

What's that beeping?

Shaz   Put it away, Gloria.

Gloria   I thought it was on silent.

Jon   Turn it off, you know how Sam is about phones.

Gloria   I put it on silent, I did.

Mark   Don't make a scene, just turn it off. Sam doesn't like it at the dinner table.

Gloria   If I turn it off no one will be able to get hold of me.

Sam   Are you trying to ruin my dinner? Are you trying to wind me up?

Gloria   I'm sorry.

Sam   Give me your phone.

Gloria   Don't, Sam, please, don't.

Sam   Give it to me.

Gloria   I won't be able to get hold of my friends. I won't know what's going on. I'll be left out of everything.

Sam   I'm going to destroy it. Stamp on it. So you lose all your contacts and all your photos and all your messages. Especially the photos where you think you look pretty. Especially the messages that tell you you are loved.

Gloria   I need those photos. I need those messages. I need to know I look pretty, I need to know that I'm loved.

Sam   You're going to get it now, Gloria, you've pushed me too far.

Gloria   Don't! Please don't! Don't hit me! Don't touch me.

Sam   This is my house and I'm in charge. Do you understand?

Gloria   Yes. I'm sorry. Don't hit me. Don't get angry. Please.

The lights change.

Gloria *looks scared.*

They run to her.

Gloria   Can we stop now? I think we should stop.

Jasmine   No one will ever hurt you. Not while you're in the fan club.

Prancheeta   I'm glad I hurt him. I'm glad I tasted his blood.

Lou   This is getting really weird now.

Gloria   I'm shaking. I am. My mouth is dry.

Jess   Guys, can everyone get a grip?

Gloria   Easy for you to say. He didn't try and hit you.

Lou   Or touch you.

Prancheeta   Or try and make you turn off your phone?

Jasmine   Or ruin your TV show.

Gloria   Enough now. We can stop now, right?

Prancheeta   Jess hasn't been.

Jess   I haven't been.

Lou   Oh God, she hasn't been.

They stare at **Jess**.

Jess   It's my turn.

The girls look fearful.

Gloria   Well . . . what are you going to do?

They stare at **Jess**.

Jess   I'm going to fuck with everything.

She smiles.

And all of you are coming with me.

The lights change. The girls appear on the roof of the hotel. The roar of the crowd below.

Lou   Look how high we are!

Prancheeta   Look at them all.

Jasmine   Thousands! Tens of thousands!

Gloria   All that time spent worrying about how we look. You can't even see who anyone is from up here.

Jess (*bellowing*)
  ♫ Baby baby baby

The crowd sing back.

Crowd
  ♫ Baby baby baby

Jess (*under her breath*)   They're listening to us.

(*To crowd.*)
  ♫ You are mine. You are mine

The crowd sing back.

Crowd
  ♫ You are mine

Jess (*looks to other girls*)   Come on –

Lou   Hey-ey!

Crowd   Hey-ey!

Lou   Ho – oo!

Crowd   Ho – hoo!

Lou (*laughs*)   I've always wanted to do this! Faster – hey!

Crowd   Hey!

Lou   Ho!

Crowd   Ho!

Lou Hey ho hey ho!

Crowd Hey ho hey ho!

Lou Wow, amazing!

Crowd Wow, amazing!

Lou (*laughing*) They'll say anything! Go on, try it!

Prancheeta (*calling*) We love the Band!

Crowd (*chanting*) We love the Band!

Prancheeta Wow.

Jasmine Marry me, Sam Gamble!

Crowd Marry me, Sam Gamble!

Jess STICK YOUR DICK IN A PIG!

Crowd Stick your dick in a pig!

The girls look to each other.

Jess They're so stupid.

Lou That's us, normally.

Jess You are *all so stupid.*

The lights change. Menace in the air.

Gloria Don't do that. It's dangerous!

Jess Stand back!

She has picked up a brick.

Lou Holy moly! She's breaking in!

Jess Did you just say 'Holy moly'? You're killing me, Lou. Killing me!

She smashes the brick through a window

Gloria I mean, is anyone else like . . . do you know what I mean?

Jess   No, Gloria. Just shut up and follow me.

Gloria   I don't think she should be speaking to me like that.

Lou   I think I agree with Gloria.

Gloria   No one deserves to be told to shut up.

Jess   Shut up, *you* do.

Gloria (*angry*)   *You* shut up. You're the new girl so just watch yourself. New girl!

Jess   Shut up. Shut up. Shut up!

She climbs through the smashed window. She turns back and shouts to the crowd.

The Crazy Sexy Cool Girls have opened up their club. Everyone welcome. Whatever school you went to. However well you behaved. No more stupid interviews. No more stupid waving. I'm the leader now and the doors are open. Follow me!

The girls follow. The sense of a huge crowd surging forward.

Gloria   But the crowd are spilling in, they'll be a crush.

Lou   Don't question her, Gloria.

Jasmine   Shh. Be quiet. She'll get angry at you again.

The lights change. **Jess** *moves through the building with the other girls following.*

Jess (*calling out*)   The Crazy Sexy Cool Girls are in the building. You can't hide from us.

Sense of the girls roaming from room to room.

Jess
    ♫ Baby baby baby you are mine you are mine

The girls join in.

All
    ♫ Beautiful face, beautiful body

Jess   Ready or not, we're coming to get you!

The girls storm into a room. The Band are sitting cross-legged around one small foil container. Silence.

Stillness, as the girls register the boys for the first time. The girls stand over the Band, who look vulnerable around their single foil container.

Prancheeta   What are you doing?

Sam   We're eating a biryani.

Jon   Chicken.

Gloria   Seems a very small portion for all five of you.

Jon   We like to share.

Jess   Where's the booze? Where's the music? Where's Kate Moss?

The Band look at each other.

Lee   We don't really party.

Jon   Partying isn't our thing.

Sam   We tend to just come home after a show and have a biryani.

Jon   Chicken.

Shaz   Sometimes veg.

The girls look speechless.

Jasmine   Oh.

The Band carry on eating.

Just . . . thought it be like the music videos. Driving in cars with the roof down in the sunshine.

Lou   Jumping in the air with your tops off.

Prancheeta   Spraying beer out of your mouths in a man fountain.

Shaz   Nope. We don't really drink. Not in real life.

Lee   And none of us have a licence for a car, so . . .

The Band carry on eating.

The girls just stand there, at a loss.

Lou   Shall we just stand here and watch them eat, then?

The girls just stand there.

Jess   No, Lou. We haven't come all this way to stand here and watch them eat.

She walks over to the Band. She stamps on the foil container.

Now get up and sing.

The Band look at one another.

Sing your song.

The Band look ashamed.

We're your number-one fans. So sing for us. Right, girls?

The Fan Club look hesitant, before agreeing.

Lou/Gloria/Prancheeta   I wouldn't mind. / Yeah. / I'd like them to.

Sam   Actually –

He finishes his mouthful.

Will you pass the napkin, Shaz?

Shaz *passes the napkin.* **Sam** *wipes his mouth.*

Sam   Actually, today was my last day in the Band.

The girls stare at each other.

Lou   It can't be!

Prancheeta   What?

Sam   I'm leaving.

Prancheeta Why?

Sam To concentrate on my music.

Jasmine Why the hell would you want to do that?

Jon He's made his decision.

Lee We're in agreement.

Shaz It's been fun but it's time to move on to other things.

Mark Sorry we couldn't sing for you. You can buy a DVD.

Jess We don't want to buy a DVD. We've come all this way. Sing!

Sam We're sorry, but it's just not possible.

Mark I'm afraid we're going to have to ask you to leave now.

The girls stay rooted to the spot. A sudden crash. The sound of a crowd singing.

Crowd
  ♫ Baby baby you are beautiful you are beautiful
    You are mine

Jess The doors are open and the girls are pilling in.

Jon What?

Lee They can't be.

Shaz In here? We'll be crushed to death.

The crowd sings louder and more menacingly

Crowd
  ♫ Beautiful face beautiful body you are mine you are mine

Prancheeta I don't want to be crushed to death.

Jess Sing then. Sing!

Sam We're not contracted.

Jess   Fuck the contract!

Jon   We can't be in breach of contract. We'll get in trouble.

Jess   Get in trouble then! Why is everyone so *scared* of getting in trouble? If no one got in trouble nothing would *ever* happen! Sing!

The crowd grow louder and stronger and deeper

Crowd
♪ Baby baby baby you are mine you are mine

Lee   Look, we don't make the rules.

Shaz   If it were up to us, we would, but it's not up to us.

Mark   We get to decide very little, really.

Jon   It's management. It's all up to management.

Jess   Grab them. Quick, grab the Band and take them to the roof.

Lou   Grab them? *How?*

Jess *grabs* **Sam** *by the collar. She drags him to the door.*

Jess   Come on!

The light changes. The girls and the Band are all on the roof.

The crowd beneath them roar.

Crowd
♪ Baby baby baby you are beautiful
   You are mine you are beautiful

Jess   Stop struggling!

Prancheeta   Stop struggling, she said!

The girls throw the Band down. **Jess** *gestures to the crowd.*

Jess   Can you see how far the girls go?

Sam   Miles and miles and miles, yes.

The boys look over the edge.

Prancheeta   What's wrong with you? It's simple. *Sing!*

Sam   Okay, okay. We'll sing.

Mark   Don't, Sam. We'll get told off!

Lee   Careful, Sam, please.

Sam
♪ Baby baby baby you are beautiful

Jess   Say it like you mean it!

Sam (*hesitant*)
♪ You are beautiful you are mine

Prancheeta   I don't believe him.

Lou   Neither do I. Do it properly!

Sam   I'm trying. I am!

Jess   Sing it better. Do your spin!

Prancheeta   Sing it like you understand what it means, for God's sake.

Sam (*weak*)
♪ Beautiful face, beautiful –

But I don't understand what it means.

Gloria   They are *your* lyrics! You *have* to understand!

Lee   They're not our lyrics, we didn't write them.

Lou   But you have to know what the words *represent*? Love and life and fun and dreams and hope?

Mark   Not really.

Sam   I never got that. Sorry.

Jess   Then it's meaningless.

Sam   Yes, the songs are meaningless.

Gloria   Then you are meaningless.

Jess   Then it has to end.

Sam   No. Please, no . . .

Crowd
    ♪ Baby baby you are beautiful you are mine baby baby

The Band teeter on the edge of the roof. The Fan Club approach them.

Jess   After three –

Gloria   Really?

Jess   We have to.

Lou   We *have* to!

Jess   After three they're going down.

Lou   Oh my God.

Sam   It's not our fault, you know. It's the managem –

Jess   One. Two –

The sound of the crowd grows to an almighty roar.

Blackout

Very slowly, the sound of the crowd dies out.

Lights up.

Lying on their backs on the ground are the Band, their bodies all disjointed. Standing over them are **Jess**, **Prancheeta**, **Lou**, **Gloria** *and* **Jasmine**.

Prancheeta   Well . . . that's that, then.

Lou   That's that.

Prancheeta   I just said that.

Lou   Sorry.

They stare at their bodies.

Jasmine   His neck is all twisted.

Gloria   His spine has bent in on itself.

They stare.

Lou   Hang on.

*She goes over to where **Mark** is lying. She picks up his foot. Underneath is the crumpled foil container.*

Lou   It's still got some biryani in it.

She tries some.

Oh, it's not actually that bad.

She offers the others. They try a little bit.

Prancheeta   If I was in a band, I'd probably want to eat this after a performance. That or tuna pasta with Tabasco.

Lou *throws the empty foil container on to the ground. The girls stare at the bodies a little longer.*

Jess   Do you all hate me?

Will you slag me off behind my back?

Will you exclude me from things?

The girls stay staring at the bodies.

Their bones are all broken. They're bodies are all smashed. They'll probably never wave back again.

*They look at the Band on the ground. **Lou** goes over and lifts up **Shaz***'s arm. It flops back down limply.*

Lou   Yep. Extremely unlikely they'll wave back.

Gloria   We can still be a club though can't we. Can't we?

Jasmine   Can we?

Lou   How would that work, Gloria?

Jasmine   Not sure how that would work.

Lou   We could find another Sam Gamble.

Prancheeta   We could find another band.

Gloria   We don't even need a band. We don't even need songs.

Jess   She's right.

Gloria   We can just meet up. And think out loud.

Jess   Go places. Like we just did.

Lou   Go to all the places.

Prancheeta   It was scary at first. When I made him bleed.

Lou   And when he tried to touch me.

Jess   And who I became.

Prancheeta   But everything is scary at first. Until you've done it and then it's just something you've done.

Lou   We should do more things.

Gloria   You know what I think . . . ?

Prancheeta   Like what?

Jasmine   I liked the astronaut idea, Gloria. That was great.

Lou   Me too.

Prancheeta   Or the TV presenter, Jasmine. Why not?

Gloria   Or we could . . . become a band ourselves even. Maybe. *Say*.

Lou   But you don't sing.

Gloria   No. And you don't play guitar.

Lou   No.

Prancheeta   None of us play any instruments.

Gloria   No.

Pause. They all look at each other.

Jasmine   Although, if you think about it . . . Neither did they.

They look at each other.

Prancheeta   And I guess . . . we can always . . . *learn.*

Jess   I like that idea. That's a good idea. I'd love to be in a band.

The girls are silent.

If you'll have me?

The girls are silent.

Will you have me?

Gloria   Well. I mean . . .

Lou   It is a group decision.

Jasmine   At the end of the day . . . it's not just down to one person.

They all look at **Gloria**.

Gloria   Do you want to be in our band, Jess?

Jess   Yes, please.

They look at each other − they all smile.

Lights fade.

Curtain.

The Crazy Sexy Cool Girls' Fan Club

BY SARAH SOLEMANI

*Notes on rehearsal and staging drawn from a workshop
with the writer held at the National Theatre, October 2014.
Workshop led by Amy Hodge, with notes by Jacqui Honess-Martin.*

How the writer came to write the play

Sarah Solemani was inspired to write *Crazy Sexy Cool Girls' Fan
Club* after watching a documentary by Kathleen Hanna called
The Punk Singer. The documentary charted the feminist punk
movement which saw female artists move from fanzine
writers to performers. Sarah saw a contemporary resonance
to the strong fan culture surrounding pop groups such as One
Direction and wanted to write a play that explored what
would happen if that young, female fan base redirected the
significant time and energy of being a fan into creating
something themselves.

Approaching characters and characterisation

Some exercises were suggested to enable strong preparation
before beginning rehearsals so that directors were confident of
the material before exploring it with their young companies.

It could be useful for directors to complete the following pre-
rehearsal exercise in order to gain a strong understanding of
the individual characters in the play. It is a thorough and
time consuming task, but it is extremely useful to find the
different voices of each of the girls in the Fan Club and the
boys in the Band, allowing directors and actors to keep every
individual's journey alive throughout the play and to form a
strong foundation for each character.

CHARACTER EXERCISE I: 'I AM . . .'

Work on each character in turn and write down everything
she says as a simple list. So, for Lou:

- *So* much more than words.
- Sorry.

- Yeah, why are you even here?
- They're cool.
- Regular girls, that's all we are.
- What?
- What? What have I done? I haven't done anything?
- I haven't done . . . what've I . . . ?
- I'm not.
- If you are. I am. Like, I can be.
- It's a collective. I swear to God I had that thought too, I like literally had that thought, it's a collective at the same time as you just . . .
- It's good. It is.
- I think you're really nice. Your head is a really good shape. And your ears are nice, I like the way they poke through your hair.
- It like it, it's kind of funny.
- Sorry, Gloria.

And so on to the end of the play.

Reading through the list of lines gives you strong clues about Lou from the words she uses, what she repeats, how many questions she asks and the rhythm of what she says.

Then, take each of her lines individually and explore what the thought behind the line might be.

Express those thoughts as statements beginning, 'I am . . . ' and try to adhere to the rule that each statement should be a concrete idea that actors could play.

For example, the thought behind the line 'Regular girls, that's all we are' could be

- I am normal.
- I am part of a we.
- I am a follower.
- I am not sure of myself.
- I am strong as part of this group.

The thoughts behind the line 'What? What have I done . . .' could be:

- I am eager to please.
- I am keen to keep my place.
- I am not saying anything out of line.

Spend time analysing the difference between playable ideas and judgements of the character. Statements like 'I am lonely', 'I am insecure', 'I am naive' might be the conclusions that the audience watching the character would draw (or we as the reader may infer). However, they are not as useful to an actor. It is extremely challenging to try to play 'I am insecure'. 'I am eager to please' is more playable and accessible to an actor.

This exercise invites you to work from the inside out rather than imposing from the outside.

Working from the inside also means the thoughts behind the lines have the potential to be positive. For example, when Lou is with Shaz her line 'Of course! I'll get the others' could suggest:

- I am uncomfortable on my own.
- I am in need of support.
- I am not worthy.

But it could also suggest:

- I am a good friend.
- I am empowered as part of a group.
- I am excited to share this with my friends.

The discipline of the exercise is not to jump on conclusions or make judgements but to construct an understanding of the architecture of a character's thoughts. This architecture will have depth and breadth if it has been built from what is in the text.

You could either do this exercise alone pre-rehearsal or together with your company, perhaps in pairs working on a character each. Statements can then be shared and discussed.

Here are some examples of the thoughts behind lines that were discussed in the workshop.

PRANCHEETA

- I am knowledgeable.
- I am someone.
- I am sure.
- I am seeking reassurance.
- I am being undermined.
- I am not being heard.

JESS

- I am important.
- I am not afraid.
- I am trying my best.
- I am willing to conform.
- I am worthy.
- I am the best.
- I am better than you.
- I am hungry for power.
- I am not ashamed.

GLORIA

- I am a leader.
- I am the boss.
- I am the decision-maker.
- I am in control.
- I am intelligent.

JASMINE

- I am knowledgeable.
- I am important.
- I am not being listened to.
- I am proud.

Take note of contradictory statements as you move through the play, particularly with complex characters like Jess, and recognise that 'I am . . .' statements fundamentally shift as the character changes.

Once you have a list of statements for a character right through to the end of play, the next stage of this exercise is to distil your long list of 'I am . . .' statements into three or four that you feel encompass them all. For Lou these could be:

- I am eager to please.
- I am strong as part of a group.
- I am someone.

These statements give the director and the actor playing Lou a strong foundation of character to work from.

It is important that you work through to the end of the play before drawing up these final, summary statements as the character may change significantly through the action of the play. For instance, Lou shouting a call-and-response from the roof of the building to the crowd is not something we could see her doing in the first scene. Writing out the 'I am . . .' statements for the whole play will help you to see the key moments where she grows in confidence and strength, and so to chart her overall journey.

The three or four statements are not intended to give you a specific note for each line, but should provide ways to guide actors to make strong character decisions supported by the text, which may link up to larger themes or functions that your production wants to explore.

OBSERVATION! Arriving at this foundation requires detailed and thorough work that takes a lot of time.

The Band

Completing the 'I am' exercise will raise some interesting questions for you to explore in rehearsals. In particular, an important question to address is: who are the Band? How might you approach them?

Does the Band and its individual members only exist as the girls' projections or do they have integrity as characters on their own?

Think about the Band and its members in terms of how they serve the girls' stories, or (to express this slightly differently) think about their dramatic function.

Here is a useful exercise that could help arrive at this understanding:

• Once you have completed the lists of 'I am' for each character, use those statements to make another list of statements beginning 'The Band is . . . ' from each of the girls' perspectives.

The difference in how each of the girls see the Band, what they represent to them, is not only useful in understanding the girls' devotion to them, but should also reveal what impact they are having on the girls in each scene, how this changes and develops, and what you think that impact is in the play as a whole.

Having an idea of this function will also guide the answer to what kind of band they are, the truth you want to articulate about boy bands in your production and how that might express itself in how you individualise each band member.

The 'I am' statements for Sam Gamble seem to reveal a through line. He doesn't like who he is being asked to be in every scene:

• I am not into this.
• I am not comfortable with the role you are putting me in.

This could eventually lead to:

• I am breaking free.

However, his scenes could also be read as a very personal reaction to the girl in question:

• I am not interested in Jasmine.

And this is where an understanding of the Band's function will help you to make choices.

These character exercises can be quite 'heady' or intellectual to do in a rehearsal room with your company, but there might be ways to put the actors on their feet to explore some of the statements or explorations practically.

Form and structure

The play is a combination of fantasy or imagined scenes and reality, and the group were keen to discuss the implications of this in production.

Amy Hodge, the facilitating director, suggested that there is no correct answer to how this challenge in form should be tackled but instead offered tools to understand and break down the structure of the play so that you are empowered to make choices.

You could break the play down into scenes and make titles for those scenes. The titles should encompass the essential action and be playable.

You could read the play aloud with your company until you reach what you think is the end of the first scene. You could decide this together. In the workshop, the group decided the first, long scene ended at the lighting shift when the girls went to wave.

Various titles for this scene were discussed including: 'The Cool Girls Interview Jess', 'Getting to Know the Fan Club', 'Jess's Secret is Revealed'.

Suggestions for the titles of the second scene included: 'The Rules of Waving are Tested by Jess' and 'The Group's Fantasy of the Hysteria of Waving is Broken by Jess'.

The task would then be to divide the whole play into scenes and give each scene a title. Write these up alongside one another or put them on Post-it notes. This gives you a blueprint of the essential action of the play and lets you see the function of each scene. This is the scaffolding of the play.

You could then experiment with putting the imaginary and reality scenes in different colours so you can see the rhythm of how the play moves between the two.

It was suggested that 'Is this scene real?' is not a useful question to bring into the rehearsal room. Every scene has a reality for each character. Once you understand the function and essential action of each scene, you can enjoy the shifts in tone and atmosphere between reality and fantasy and be playful in how you realise them in your production.

Themes

It could be a useful exercise for the company to brainstorm the themes of the play on a large piece of paper in the form of a spider diagram.

Here is what the workshop group came up with:

- Imagination.
- Identity.
- Metaphor for growing up.
- Self-discovery.
- Belonging.
- Obsession.
- Group hysteria.
- Acceptance.
- Desire.
- Tribes.
- Culture of celebrity.
- Success.
- Sexualisation of young girls.
- Feminism.
- Technology.
- Fantasy and reality.
- Building relationships.
- Fears.
- Passivity to action.

You could then distil these themes down to three headings that encompass most of the words on the page and which you feel are most important and interesting to you and your company. The workshop group's themes were:

IDENTITY AND SELF-DISCOVERY

CELEBRITY-ISM

FEMINISM AND FANTASY VS REALITY

This is an excellent exercise to do in rehearsals. It gives the whole company ownership of the material and of the story they are trying to tell, and means that you can find a shared language to talk about themes like feminism or sexualisation of young girls in a way that resonates with the lives of your young people. It may also be an opportunity to introduce and discuss some big themes and ideas to a group and give the actors ownership of those themes. This is also important for creating an ensemble and a shared understanding of issues surrounding gender in a company where there will be a clear divide between girls and boys through rehearsals and performance.

You could extend this work by enabling improvisations around these themes, or setting research tasks as homework.

Style and technique: comedy

A question was raised about how appropriate it was to bring some of the themes into the rehearsal room for a comedy. Exploring difficult and political themes through comedy is a strong tradition; there is no need to shy away from an exploration of some of the deeper subject matter simply because we are then asking an audience to laugh at it. Good comedy comes from truth and careful, specific observations. Finding what these are for your cast and your production will need exploration and analysis.

The comedy of the play is in the rhythm and pace of the language. Pay attention to these rhythms and pace and much of the work is done for you.

All the same, the attention you would usually pay to character and theme is still appropriate. Good comedy comes from detail and specificity. Ground the characters in reality so that when you move to larger comedy moments, they are specific and rooted in the text.

Production, staging and design

Amy introduced the idea of the design triangle – a triangle with the words SPACE, AUDIENCE and PERFORMER at its three points.

When thinking about your design it is useful to approach it from the slightly wider perspective of these three key relationships before moving to detailed specifics about props, for instance.

AUDIENCE AND SPACE   Where is the audience in the space? What relationship does the audience have with the performers in the space? How might you use these relationships to help the function of the crowd scenes?

A minimal aesthetic is suggested in the text and the group discussed ideas for moving from a very realistic understanding of the space, which may still be needed by the performers, to an aesthetic where you are only using the absolute minimum necessary to make something clear.

The quick changes, particularly between imagined and realistic scenes, could be achieved in many ways, not just through set and lighting changes. You can break an atmosphere by moving through the space differently, by breaking the rhythm or tone.

The ending of the play could present a challenge in staging as the girls rush through the house and eventually push the Band off the roof. The group discussed possible meanings behind the ending: they are dead to them; they have their own identity; death to false idols; destruction of fantasy; triumph of feminism and friendship; reality conquers fantasy; the active choice to stop.

The group concluded that pushing the Band off the roof is a metaphor for choice. This choice could be expressed in any number of ways as the scene slowly slips back to the girls' reality. However, the image of the broken boys' bodies is important to the meaning of the text in the final scene.

You could decide that the frenzy and desperate search before arriving at that choice is the key thing to communicate to an audience in the final scenes rather than the specificity of geographical locations the girls run through as they search the house.

Casting: how to use the ensemble

One of the strengths of this text is the potential to use a large ensemble. The crowd are the mob, the masses, the fans, the concert-goers and possibly other girls in the group.

There is the potential for cross-casting and all-female productions; to make the most of talented female performers in the Band; tripling or doubling up on the playing of parts; and also the potential to use the audience to make the crowds.

Sound and music

Sarah was keen to emphasise that you should play to the strengths of your group when thinking about the potential for music. Music videos, playing live, lip-synching and shouting the words are all absolutely acceptable. The lyrics are deliberately banal to reflect a key theme about pop culture. Sarah intended the audience to experience the repetition of the meaningless lyrics in the script but encourages you to be creative in how you reflect this.

Sarah was also keen to emphasise that the beat at the end of the play should be triumphant. She was excited to see how different productions would articulate that.

Participating Companies

ACS Cobham International School
Act Youth Theatre
Alnwick Playhouse Youth Theatre
Ariel Drama Academy
Artsdepot
BA2 Theatre Company
Backwell School
Bacstage
Badenoch and Strathspey Youth
    Theatre
Barbara Priestman Academy
Barnwell
Barton Court Grammar School
Bay House School and Sixth Form
Bedford Free School
Berzerk Productions
Best Theatre Arts
Bingley Grammar School
Bishop Gore School Performing
    Arts Company/Bishop Gore
    School Swansea
Bishops High School
Black Box Theatre Company
Blatchington Mill School
Bloxham School
Bodens Performing Arts
Borders Youth Theatre
Bradley Stoke Community School
Brannel Theatre Company
Brewery Youth Theatre
Bristol Grammar School
Brit MT Collective
British International School Riyadh
Bromsgrove School
Burnage Academy For Boys
Burnt Mill Drama Company
Buxton Opera House Young
    Company
BYT Benenden Youth Theatre
Calderdale Theatre School
Camberley Youth Theatre

Canons High School
Carney Academy
Castle Youth Theatre Company
Cavendish School
Chapter 4 (Mansfield Palace Youth
    Theatre)
Chase High School
Cheltenham Youth Theatre
Chichester College
Chichester Festival Youth Theatre
Chickenshed's Youth Theatre
Churchill Theatre Connections
    Company
City of Westminster College
Clapton Girls' Academy
Class Act Drama Academy
Core Actors
Craft Works
Cranbrook School
Crescent Arts Youth Theatre
Curve Young Company
Drama Lab
Drayton Manor High School
Duckegg Acting School
Dudley College
Dumfries Youth Theatre
East Berkshire College
Easy Street Theatre Company
Eden Court Young Company
Epping Forest College
Fallibroome Academy
First Floor
Flying High Theatre Company
Found in the Forest Youth Theatre
Fowey River Academy
Further Stages Theatre Company
Grand Opera House Youth
    Theatre
Great Glen Youth Theatre
Greenfields School Theatre
    Company

Gresham's School
Groundlings Theatre Company
Gulbenkian Youth Theatre
Halesowen College
Headington School
Helenswood Academy
Hellesdon High School
Hemsworth Arts and Community
    Academy
High Tunstall College of Science
High-Jinks Creative Drama
HMTP
Hugh Baird Players
Hunterhouse College
Immediate Theatre
In Translation at Chobham
    Academy
Indelible Arts Youth Theatre
Inspire Academy
Interact Youth Theatre
Intrepid YPC
Invergordon Youth Theatre
Invicta Grammar School
Ipswich High School
Isle of Skye Youth Theatre
IV3 Youth Theatre
Jada Young Company
JCG Youth Theatre
Jigsaw Youth Theatre Company
John Cabot Academy
Key Youth Theatre
Kidz R Us at St Ives Theatre
Kildare Youth Theatre
King Edward VI Five Ways School
King's Company
King's Theatre Company
Kings Youth Theatre
Kingsley School Community
    Youth Theatre Company
Kirk Hallam Community Academy
Lady Manners School
Lincoln Minster School
Lincoln Young Company
Llanelli Youth Theatre

Lochaber Youth Theatre
Lost Youth Theatre Company
Lostleters
Lowry Young Actors Company B
Lsc Expressive Arts
Lyceum Youth Theatre
Lyme Youth Theatre
Lymm High School
Lytchett Minster School
M.A.D Youth Theatre
Macrobert Young Company
Mark Rutherford School
Marlowe Youth Theatre
Mercury Theatre Colchester
Montage Theatre Arts
Morepies
Morpeth School
New College, Swindon
New Vic Youth Theatre
Newquay Tretherras School
New Vic
NHSG Drama
North Durham Academy
North Lanarkshire Youth Theatre
North Norfolk Partners
Northampton High School
Norwich School
Norwich Theatre Royal Youth
    Company
Odd Productions/Galashiels
    Academy
Old Buckenham High School
Oldswinford Hospital School
Orange Tree Theatre Young
    Company
Ormiston Sudbury Academy
Oslo International School
P & S Youth Company
PACE Youth Theatre
Pangbourne College
Patrician Youth Centre
Peploe-Williams Academy
Perfect Circle Youth Theatre
Perpich Center For Arts Education

Pool Academy
Purplecoat Productions
QE School
Queens Theatre Hornchurch
Ratzcool
Reactivate
Red Productions
Ricards Lodge High School
Rising Stars Youth Theatre
Riverfront Youth Theatre
Rokeby School
Rotherham College of Arts and
    Technology
Royal & Derngate Youth Theatre
Sacred Heart High School
Saffron Walden County High
    School
Salisbury Playhouse BTEC
Scarborough Youth Theatre
Sgioba Drama Oigridh Inbhir Nis
Shadow Syndicate
Sheffield People's Theatre
Shenfield High School
Shenley Academy
Sherborne Girls School
Sherman Theatre
Shetland Youth Theatre
Shotton Hall Theatre School
Soho Additional Company
Something Wicked This Way
    Comes
South London Theatre Youth
    Group
South West College
Southfields Academy
Spid Theatre Company
Spotlight UK
Springs Youth Company
St Brendan's Sixth Form College
St Francis College
St Ives Youth Theatre
St John's School
St Joseph's Theatre Company
St Marylebone C of E School

St Mary's Catholic College
St Monica's Theatre Company
St Saviour's & St Olave's School
St Wilfrids
Stagecoach Cambridge and
    Cambourne
Stagecoach East Kilbride
Stagecoach Southgate
Stagecoach York
Step on Stage Productions
Stephen Joseph Youth Theatre
Stockton Riverside College
Stopsley High School
Strode's College
Suffolk New College Performing
    Arts
Sundial Student Theatre Company
Surbiton High School
Take 2 Youth Theatre
The Actors Centre Theatre
    Company
The Arts Hub
The Astor Players
The Blue Coat School
The City Academy Hackney
The Customs House Youth Theatre
The Drama Studio
The Fiat Lux Theatre Company
The Garage Theatre Company
The Hastings Academy Drama
    Students
The John Roan
The King's School
The Lowry Young Actors
    Company Addison School
The Nelson Thomy
The Petchey
The Regis School Theatre Company
The Roses Big Company
The Savi Churchill School
The Wirtors Company
The Y Company
The Yal Stratford East
Th

Thomas Tallis School
Thurso High School
Tomorrow's Talent
Tower Drama
Trapdoor Performing Arts
Trent Repertory Company
Tyne Valley Youth Theatre
University of Worcester Youth
    Theatre
Urock Youth Company
Uxbridge College Performing Arts
Vivace Theatre School
VWNC Theatre Company
Warwick Arts Centre Connections
    Company
Warwick School

Watermans Theatre
Wellington School
West London Free School
Wester Hailes Education Centre
What
Winstanley College
Winterhill School
Woodbridge Theatre Company
Woolwich Polytechnic School
Worthing College
Yew Tree Youth Theatre
Young and Unique
Young Dramatic Arts Theatre
    Company
Ysgol Aberconwy
YT2

For a complete listing of Bloomsbury
Methuen Drama titles, visit:

www.bloomsbury.com/drama

Follow us on Twitter and keep up to date
with our news and publications

@MethuenDrama